Laboratory Techniques Series

LABORATORY TECHNIQUES
IN
BOTANY

U.S.A.:	Butterworth Inc. Washington, D.C., 20014: 7300 Pearl Street
England:	Butterworth & Co. (Publishers) Ltd. London: 88 Kingsway, W.C.2
Australia:	Butterworth & Co. (Australia) Ltd. Sydney: 20 Loftus Street Melbourne: 473 Bourke Street Brisbane: 240 Queen Street
Canada:	Butterworth & Co. (Canada) Ltd. Toronto: 1367 Danforth Avenue, 6
New Zealand:	Butterworth & Co. (New Zealand) Ltd. Wellington: 49/51 Ballance Street Auckland: 35 High Street
South Africa:	Butterworth & Co. (South Africa) Ltd. Durban: 33/35 Beach Grove

LABORATORY TECHNIQUES
IN
BOTANY

M. J. PURVIS, R.H.S.

Department of Spectroscopy and Chemical Physics, Battersea College of Technology (Proposed University of Surrey)

D. C. COLLIER and D. WALLS, A.I.S.T.

Botany Department, University College London

With a Foreword by
D. LEWIS, D.Sc., F.R.S.

Quain Professor of Botany, University College London

SECOND EDITION

WASHINGTON
BUTTERWORTHS
1966

First edition 1964

Second edition 1966

Suggested U.D.C. number: 581.08

©

Butterworth & Co. (Publishers) Ltd.

1966

Printed in Great Britain at the Saint Ann's Press
Park Road, Altrincham

FOREWORD

The scientific study of plants, animals and micro-organisms has produced, in the last few decades, a basic unity in the structure, biochemistry and heredity of living organisms. This unity has been achieved partly by hypothesis and theory, and partly by the application of an ever increasing battery of instruments and techniques used in experiments. It was the technique of radioactive isotopes applied to bacteriophage which proved conclusively for the first time that the hereditary material is deoxyribonucleic acid. Many other important and far reaching discoveries can be traced to the use of new techniques. Chromatography, centrifugation, electron microscopy and the 'squash' technique for the study of chromosomes are but a few which have been indispensable for the development of whole new fields of research. The present-day biologist, whether he works on plants or animals, must not only be aware of all the current thought and literature but of all the techniques that are available to him. Several books on histological and cytological techniques are available; there are whole books devoted to chromatography but there are few books which cover a variety of techniques used by biologists. The authors, M. J. Purvis, D. C. Collier and D. Walls, are technicians. They are fully aware of the importance of the instruments and techniques which they use, both in teaching and research. Their book, which is a record of their first-hand experience, should be a useful source of information for technicians, students and staff in schools, universities and research institutes. 96078

D. LEWIS

v

CONTENTS

vii

ACKNOWLEDGEMENTS

The idea of this book was conceived by Mr. G. Wasley of the Wright–Fleming Institute.

The authors wish to express their appreciation to Mr. P. Bell, Dr. W. G. Chaloner, Professor L. Fowden, Professor D. Lewis, Miss K. Luck, Mr. J. Mackey, Dr. I. Morris, Dr. P. W. Roberts, Mr. W. E. E. Smith, Mr. P. J. Syrett, Dr. D. J. B. White and the staff of the Herbarium (British Museum) for their help and advice on technical problems.

The authors are indebted to Dr. K. Taylor for writing Chapter 17 and to Mr. R. Brinsden for taking the photographs. They also wish to thank Professor D. Lewis, Mr. P. J. Syrett and Dr. D. J. B. White for reading parts of the manuscript.

ACKNOWLEDGEMENTS FOR SECOND EDITION

In addition to the above mentioned, the authors wish to express their appreciation to Mr. A. W. Robards, Mr. V. B. Salmon, Mr. H. Tristram, the staff of the Jodrell Laboratory, Kew, and the many reviewers of the first edition.

The authors are indebted to Dr. I. Morris for writing Chapter 18.

CHAPTER 1

GENERAL LABORATORY APPARATUS AND TECHNIQUES

General information will be given in this chapter on apparatus and solvents in common use. For greater detail regarding the makes and workings of the apparatus, information can be obtained from the manufacturers concerned or from literature quoted in the reference list.

BUNSEN BURNERS

These are common and well known pieces of laboratory equipment. They can be of two basic types: gas or electric.

The gas bunsen is the more common and a variety of types have been produced to meet the requirements of different fields of work.

Details of the ordinary gas bunsen are shown in *Figure 1*. The bunsen is lit by closing the air-hole, turning on the gas supply and applying a light source. A yellow luminous flame will be produced. By turning the sleeve of the bunsen so that the two air-holes correspond, or partly correspond, air is allowed to be drawn into the tube. This produces a hotter blue flame and, when the maximum amount of air is available, a characteristic roaring noise is heard, i.e. a 'roaring flame'. Occasionally when the gas is turned down, particularly with the air-hole open, a popping sound is heard which generally means that the bunsen is 'burning-back', the gas being alight at the gas jet instead of at the top of the bunsen tube. Usually this can be remedied by turning the gas full on and tapping the rubber tubing sharply with the side of the hand. If this is not successful the bunsen must be turned out and relighted.

It is dangerous to use a bunsen when it is burning-back as the production of carbon monoxide can be lethal in badly ventilated places.

On rare occasions the gas jet of the bunsen may become blocked. It should be cleaned with a piece of fine wire or better still one of the prickers recommended by the manufacturers of portable camping stoves.

A*

It is important to adjust the bunsen flame to luminous when it is to be left alight and not in use, as a quiet blue flame is difficult to see in some lighting conditions, especially strong sunlight.

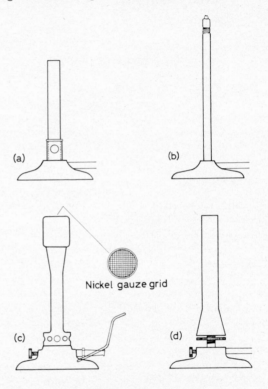

(a)

(b)

Nickel gauze grid

(c)

(d)

Figure 1. (a) *Standard bunsen burner;* (b) *Batswing burner;* (c) *Meker burner;* (d) *Teclu burner*

Fish-tail Burner

This bunsen gives a wide flame and is useful for heating reduction and ignition tubes. The smaller type is often used to heat glass tubing or glass rod prior to bending. It is possible to obtain a fish-tail adaptation to fit a standard bunsen burner. The adaptation can be either screwed on to a threaded bunsen barrel or pushed on to an unthreaded one.

Batswing Burner

This is also used for bending glass tubing and glass rod. The stem

2

tube is normally longer and thinner in this type of bunsen than in any other. There is no air-hole.

Micro Bunsen

This is very useful for heating preparations on slides where only a small flame is required. In many cases it has superseded the spirit lamp.

Pilot Jet Bunsen

By means of a lever situated at the base of the bunsen, the main flame can be extinguished leaving only a pilot jet alight. When the lever is moved to the 'on' position the main flame is relighted.

It is an ideal bunsen for use in a confined space, such as an inoculating chamber, as only the pilot flame need be alight between operations, which helps to prevent overheating of the area.

A later development is the Therma Spina with a spring-loaded plunger which can be locked in the 'on' position, instead of a lever.

Meker Burner

This is a specialized bunsen used for heating crucibles. It consists of a tapered tube surmounted by a nickel grid or gauze, and has a number of air-holes instead of a simple sleeve as in an ordinary bunsen.

The burner produces a large, low, hot flame.

Teclu Burner

This has a larger diameter tube than the ordinary bunsen burner and the air adjustment consists of an open ended fixed cone covered with a washer which can be screwed up or down to decrease or increase the air supply.

Electric Bunsen

An electric bunsen is a useful, supplementary piece of laboratory equipment. It can be used where a gas supply is not available and, in most cases, can do the work of a conventional gas bunsen, although by comparison it takes longer to achieve a working temperature. It is clean in operation and the temperature of the element can be fully regulated. The working temperature of the element is approximately 900°C.

A cowl is supplied with the bunsen to direct the heat away from the hand but this may be removed whenever a flat surface is required, for example to support a pipe clay triangle and a crucible.

BALANCES

Manufacturers of balances will supply catalogues and literature to interested people. Detailed information regarding loads, tolerances, etc. can be obtained from these sources.

Owing to the limited uses and high costs of some balances it is important to consider for what purpose a balance will be used before purchasing.

Balances can be divided into two major groups—undamped and damped.

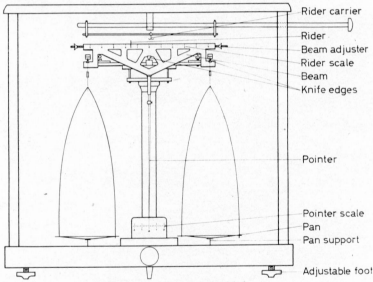

Rider carrier
Rider
Beam adjuster
Rider scale
Beam
Knife edges

Pointer

Pointer scale
Pan
Pan support
Adjustable foot

Figure 2. A general chemical balance

Undamped Balances

The common types of balances in this group are: field, triple-beam and general chemical. The majority of them are manual in operation.

The field balance—This is capable of weighing quantities of material up to 3 kg, with a fair degree of accuracy but it is not accurate enough to enable small amounts of material of less than 10 g to be weighed precisely. These field balances are naturally of robust construction and rather simple in design.

4

The triple-beam balance—This is another form of simple balance that can cover a range of loads with a reasonable degree of accuracy. It is normally capable of weighing to a maximum load of 2 kg and is fairly accurate to a single decimal place. This balance is occasionally used as a field balance.

The general chemical balance—This is very similar to the diagram in *Figure 2*. It may or may not have a rider scale and the final reading is the sum total of the weights on the scale pan, plus the rider reading, plus the reading from the graduated scale along which the pointer swings. A good, undamped balance of this type is capable of weighing to three or four places of decimals with reasonable accuracy. An old chemical balance is useful when speed and not accuracy is required. Most laboratories having one of these balances term it a 'rough' balance.

Damped Balances

A balance is damped to enable the balance pan(s) to come to rest quickly without affecting its accuracy.

These balances are generally semi-automatic or fully automatic in operation which enables fast and reproducible results to be obtained even by unskilled workers. Owing to the high accuracy and precision required during their manufacture, the cost of such balances is correspondingly high.

The majority of modern damped balances have a beam lowering device to prevent damage to the delicate knife edges. However, the beam should still be set free in as gentle a manner as possible.

Cased single and double pan balances—These are of a better quality than general chemical balances and are normally semi-automatic in operation. Accuracy can be as high as five or six decimal places with a maximum load of 20 g. Those with a maximum load of 100–200 g weigh to three or four decimal places. Some models have a taring device.

Top pan balances—These are single pan balances which are normally damped magnetically. The pan is exposed and not housed in a glass-fronted cabinet. As the pan is situated on the top of the instrument it may be subjected to air currents but protective shields are available for most models. Top pan balances are useful for weighing unwieldy objects such as twigs, leaves, potted plants, etc. and for the rapid weighing of liquids, powders, and crystalline substances.

Those with low maximum weights, e.g. 80 g, are accurate to four decimal places. Other models, capable of weighing 5 or 6 kg, are accurate to only one or two decimal places.

Examples of these types of balances are the Sartorious Kilomat, the Sauter Toppan and the Mettler.

Two interesting features of these balances are a taring device and a slow-moving loading scale. The taring device enables the weight of the container to be counter-balanced leaving the weighing scale still set at zero, thus allowing rapid and accurate continuous weighing. The use of the slow-moving loading scale facilitates the weighing of liquids, powders or crystals which is normally a tedious business. Whilst watching the slow scale, either large amounts or a cautious stream of a substance can be added until near the end point. Then, whilst observing the accurate scale, the final additions by small amounts, can take place.

The torsion balance—This works on the principle that a weight applied to the end of a beam will twist a piece of torsion wire along its horizontal axis. The piece of wire is fixed at right angles to the beam. The beam tip acts as a pointer to a calibrated scale. Although originally designed to test the surface tension of liquids a wide variety of models are now available. They have maximum weighing capacities ranging from 0·01 g to more than 2 kg. Although extremely robust in design they are very sensitive to air currents. Their most common use is for repetitive weighing of samples, etc.

The Torbal analytical balance is a very neat torsion balance and as such has no knife edges to damage. It is capable of weighing to a maximum of 160 g with a taring device to 20 g. For a single pan cased balance it is of a very robust design and accurate to the fourth decimal place. The weights are automatically added by rotation of a series of dials on the front face of the casing. The addition of the weights is continued until the pointer registers the null point, which is the precise zero of the balance and is determined by a galvano-meter coupled to the beam. The needle is at the central position when at the null point. The balance is no more sensitive to air currents than a normal analytical balance. The balance beam must be locked before and after operations.

Electric balance—This is a new concept of weighing, where the weight of the sample is compensated by an electric current. A good example is the Cahn electro-balance which is a very rugged machine immune to vibration, temperature, levelling, air currents, etc. It is a self-contained unit weighing approximately 12 lb and fully portable.

The small weighing chamber can be detached from the main unit and used, by remote control via four electrical connections, in a variety of places, for example a radio-active area, cold room or even in an oven at 121°C. Its main disadvantage is a limited maximum sample weight range of only 175 mg to 2·5 g. The cost of certain models may be prohibitively high for some laboratories.

The upkeep of a balance is quite simple and straightforward.

Undamped Balances

These need to be dusted regularly and spillage on either of the scale pans should be removed immediately by brushing with a good quality camel-hair brush. Adjustments need only be made to level the apparatus by raising or lowering the adjustable feet. Normally a spirit level or plumb-line is provided to check a true level position.

To adjust the balance of the pans, the two small weights, one on each end of the balance beam, should be screwed in or out. When correctly adjusted, the pointer should swing along the graduated scale and come to rest at the zero position.

Damped Balances

Servicing of these should be performed by the manufacturer's service department or by a qualified person. On no account should they be interfered with by unqualified people. It is necessary to dust the balance case regularly and to keep the scale pans clean, but any further adjustments should be left to the expert.

The sensitive balance should be positioned in a part of the laboratory that has the least amount of vibration. The position can be determined by placing a dish of mercury in various parts of the room and the area causing the least disturbance will show the best position for the balance. It is important to remember that mercury vapour is dangerous when it exceeds 100 mg of vapour per m^3.

Special tables can be purchased which consist of a platform mounted in such a manner as to make it steady and vibration free. The relative humidity of a balance room should be about 65 per cent.

Using a balance is easy if a few golden rules are observed.

1. Balance weights must be kept clean, and when not in use placed in the box provided. They must not be handled with the fingers but

with forceps. Good quality accurate weights should be handled with bone or plastic-faced forceps.

2. Only weights must be placed on the right-hand scale pan. The balance case should be closed whenever weights or materials are not being transferred to or from the balance. There should be no additions to, or removals from the balance pans while they are free swinging. For top pan balances, additions can be made while the pan is 'free'.

3. A spatula should be selected which is a suitable size for the amount of substance to be weighed.

4. Deliquescent substances must be weighed in a stoppered weighing bottle. The type with the stopper fitting on the outside of the bottle is preferable.

5. All glassware used in weighing must be clean. If very accurate work is required the glassware, after cleaning, should be polished with an 'anti-static' cloth to prevent the attraction of dust, etc.

6. Any spilt chemicals must be removed from the scale pans or balance floor immediately.

7. The balance must be 'set free' gently and returned 'to rest' in a similar fashion. Rough handling of a balance quickly damages the delicate knife edges, resulting in a loss of accuracy.

8. When rough weighing on filter papers, a paper of the same size and grade must be placed on both the scale pans and balanced by adjustment or by the addition of weights. Filter paper should not be used for accurate weighing.

9. For accurate weighing, the balance, substance to be weighed, weights and weighing bottle must be at the same temperature, pressure and humidity. This is known as equilibrating and is achieved by placing the articles inside the balance case for 20 min before weighing, the balance side doors being left slightly open to allow circulation of air.

10. Liquids are weighed in stoppered bottles and the introduction or removal of amounts of liquid accomplished by using a fine capillary pipette and teat.

CENTRIFUGES

A centrifuge is used to separate two or more substances which have different densities, generally particles in suspension. There are two terms used in the technique with which one has to be familiar. They are supernatant and precipitate. After separation, the substance at the bottom of the tube is regarded as the precipitate. The solution remaining, in which the precipitate was suspended, is the supernatant.

The separation, or settling rate, is increased artificially by induced centrifugal force in the centrifuge. The rate of settling of spherical particles can be deduced from Stokes' law.

$$r = \frac{2a^2g(dp - dm)}{9\eta}$$

where r=rate of settling in cm/sec.
       a=radius of spherical particles in cm.
       dp=density of spherical particles.
       dm=density of suspension medium.
       η=viscosity of suspension medium.
       g=Gravity (at Greenwich)=981·188 cm/sec².

The settling rate is increased by:

1. Having larger particles.
2. Having a suspension with a lower viscosity.
3. Decreasing the density of the suspension medium.
4. Increasing the force of gravity. This can be artificially produced in a centrifuge, and the actual g created is measured as the Relative Centrifugal Force (R.C.F.). The R.C.F. can be obtained from either of the following formulae:

    (a) R.C.F. (in g)=$1·118 \times 10^{-5} \times R \times N^2$
    (b) R.C.F. (in g)=$0·0000284 \times R \times N^2$

where, in (a) R=radius of centrifuge in cm and,
     in (b) R=radius of centrifuge in in.
            N=revolutions per minute (r.p.m.).

The radius is measured from the centre of the shaft to the extreme tip of the centrifuge tube when it is in position and at the speed required.

The type of centrifuge that is required depends upon a number of different factors. The most obvious of these is the actual R.C.F. required, for example yeasts need a minimum R.C.F. value of 1,000 g, precipitated proteins 15,000–20,000 g and viruses 50,000–150,000 g in order to effect equivalent sedimentation in a reasonably short time.

Temperature is important, particularly in enzyme work where a rise in temperature above approximately 4°C is likely to denature the majority of enzymes. Therefore a refrigerated centrifuge is required.

The maximum capacity of a centrifuge is another factor to bear in mind. It would be a tedious operation to centrifuge a large volume of material in a small capacity machine. There are machines available which have maximum capacities in excess of 4 litres but these generally have low maximum R.C.F. values. Where a high R.C.F. value is required it is essential to use a machine which has a continuous flow system, e.g. a Sharples centrifuge. Some of the standard machines have special adaptors and rotors to enable continuous flow centrifugation to take place.

9

Centrifuge Heads (Rotors)

Centrifuge heads are available in three basic types, fixed-angle, swing-out or continuous flow.

Fixed-angle heads have the advantage that the tubes are enclosed in a streamlined head which reduces air resistance and therefore also reduces the tendency of a rise in temperature of the tubes. As the head revolves, the particles are forced against the side of the tubes and they then slide down to the bottom. This results in a slightly faster settling rate than with a swing-out head used under similar conditions. One disadvantage is that, when the supernatant is removed, the precipitate in the tubes is occasionally disturbed. When speeds over 15,000 r.p.m. are obtained, even these streamlined heads offer quite a high resistance with the subsequent rise in temperature. Therefore in most high speed centrifuges the head spins in a vacuum thus reducing the air resistance. As a further aid the machine can be refrigerated.

Swing-out heads have pivoted buckets to hold the tubes. As the speed of the head increases, the tubes swing nearer the horizontal position but owing to the non-streamlined shape, the air resistance is high with a resulting rise in temperature. The heads of some models can be fitted with wind shields thus converting the head into a streamlined form and preventing increases in temperature due to air resistance. Very high speed swing-out heads have an integral shield allowing the maximum R.C.F. values to be obtained, e.g. 300,000 g at 60,000 r.p.m.

The continuous flow rotor which can be fitted to certain centrifuges enables large volumes of suspension to be separated. The precipitate is collected in tubes or by deposition on the side of a collection vessel. The supernatant is then led away and collected in a vessel outside the centrifuge.

Centrifuge Containers

The type of container in which a substance is centrifuged depends on the volume of material, the R.C.F. value required, the chemical nature of the material and to a lesser extent whether a swing-out or a fixed-angle head is to be employed.

Standard centrifuge tubes are available in capacities from $1\cdot0$ ml to 150 ml. They are made in a variety of substances, for example, glass, polypropylene, polyethylene, polycarbonate, Teflon, stainless steel, etc. These substances have various properties and it is advisable to obtain data from the manufacturers in order to determine the most suitable material. For general work below 3,000 g glass is usually the most suitable material. It is transparent, normally autoclavable and is resistant to most chemicals but it is fragile. Polypropylene is suitable for R.C.F. values to 300,000 g. It has variable opacity and is auto-clavable at 15 lb./in.^{2} for 30 min. It is also shatterproof but not so chemically resistant as glass. It is probably the most widely used material for centrifuge containers. Polycarbonate is transparent, autoclavable at 15 lb./in.^{2} for 30 min, resistant to a wide range of chemicals, and strong enough to stand R.C.F. values of 360,000 g. However, it is more expensive than polypropylene and glass.

Caps are available to fit most sizes of tubes and should always be used in vacuum centrifuges. High speed machines should generally have caps with an expanding gasket (see *Figure 3*), although those tubes used in swing-out heads of the ultracentrifuges are an exception to this as sealing facilities are integral with the buckets.

Centrifugation of large amounts up to 1,250 ml necessitates the use of bottles. These are available in most of the materials from which tubes are manufactured. Again caps are required for vacuum work.

Non-refrigerated, Non-vacuum Centrifuges

This group ranges from the micro-centrifuges to centrifuges having maximum capacities of approximately 3 litres. By selected use of heads, a wide range of tube and bottle sizes can be accommodated giving R.C.F. values to 5,000 g. Some manufacturers have 'super-speed' attachments and by the use of these it is possible to boost the speeds to 20,000 r.p.m. giving an R.C.F. of 18,000 g but special high speed heads are required.

Not all of this group have the head spinning in a protective bowl although mesh guards are generally available.

Some manufacturers within this group are: Baird and Tatlock (the microcentrifuge), Griffin Christ, Lourdes, M.S.E. and Servall.

Refrigerated, Non-vacuum Centrifuges

These centrifuges can be broadly classified into two types; the large capacity machine and the medium speed models. The former have maximum capacities of about 6 litres with R.C.F. values to 6,000 g. A number of different heads are available in both the swing-out and fixed-angle forms. As in the previous section 'superspeed' attachments can be fitted to some models.

The medium speed machines have maximum speeds in the order of 18,000 r.p.m. with the highest R.C.F. value at approximately 40,000 g. Some machines can be fitted with a continuous flow rotor which greatly increases the scope of the machine.

11

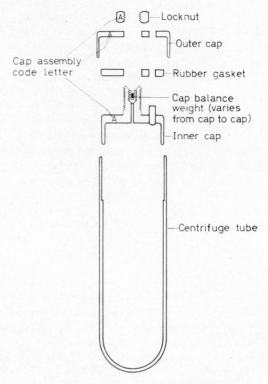

Figure 3. A high speed centrifuge cap assembly (M.S.E.)

Most models have manual speed control, automatic timers and a method of pre-selecting the bowl temperature, the control of which is in the order of $\pm 1°C$ of the pre-selected temperature. However, the head must be at the required temperature before using the centrifuge.

Safety-wise, some measure of armour plate is provided. Electrical cut-outs protect the circuitry of the machine.

Some of the manufacturers are Griffin Christ, Lourdes, M.S.E. and Servall.

Refrigerated Vacuum Centrifuges

This group comprises very high speed machines giving correspondingly high R.C.F. values, for example 300,000 *g*.

Machines of this type are produced by Griffin Christ, Lourdes, M.S.E., Servall and Spinco to name just a few.

The highest R.C.F. values are generally obtained with a stream-lined swing-out head holding small capacity tubes. All tubes should be sealed or capped. With the very high R.C.F. obtained by these machines, a great deal of strain is imposed on the heads. It is therefore of great importance to treat the heads with care and to follow the manufacturers instructions with regard to their upkeep. Even when given care and proper treatment, heads which run at maximum speeds are liable to fracture after a period of time. To prevent this, most manufacturers insist on a log book being kept which records the head number, the date, the time run at a selected speed, the speed and the operator's name. After so many hours or so many years the heads are either replaced by part exchange or are down graded, i.e. their maximum speed is reduced by a set factor.

Speeds are usually pre-selected, as are temperature and time. Once the conditions have been set, the majority of machines are automatic. The settings can be locked to ensure that the required conditions are not altered by other personnel.

Safety systems in the form of electrical cut-outs, armour plate, etc. are provided. It is essential to pre-cool the head when low temperatures are required.

OPERATION OF LOW SPEED MACHINES

(1) Place the tubes in the buckets, checking that the rubber cushions are in place. The buckets, plus the tubes, must be weighed and balanced accurately in pairs against each other, water being added to the bucket, not the tube, to achieve this balance.

(2) Place the balanced tubes diametrically opposite each other in the centrifuge. If uneven numbers of tubes are used, a further tube must be weighed to counter-balance the odd tube. Check that any plugs will not be forced down the tubes. This can be prevented if the cotton wool is splayed-out, folded back over the tube and secured with an elastic band. Also check that the plugs will not foul the protective lid or cover.

(3) Check that the variable resistance is at zero and then switch-on. Slowly increase the speed, pausing frequently to allow the speed to stabilize. When the required revolutions are reached, timing of the operation can begin.

(4) The resistance switch or lever should be returned to the zero position after the centrifuge has been switched off.

Note—The centrifuge must be allowed to come to rest automatically, not by removing the lid and slowing by hand; this procedure is not only dangerous, but it is likely to disturb the precipitate which, if delicate, will go into suspension again.

(5) When using any centrifuge it is most important to follow the manufacturer's instructions explicitly.

13

(6) Maintenance of simple centrifuges can be carried out according to the maker's instructions. All centrifuges are best serviced by skilled engineers.

OPERATION OF HIGH SPEED MACHINES

(1) Switch on the mains supply to the machine and select the required temperature.

(2) Carefully balance the tubes in pairs, by making additions to or subtractions from the tubes. The specific gravity of the suspension should not normally exceed 1·2; if a high sp.gr. is encountered the top speed of the machine must be reduced proportionately. If an odd number of tubes are being used, it is necessary to balance a further tube using a solution of similar specific gravity to that of the suspension being centrifuged.

The Griffin Christ centrifuges employ a self-centring spindle, thus the need for accurate balancing of the pairs of tubes is avoided; the machine will tolerate 'out of balance' of approximately 1 per cent, generally the tubes need only be filled to a similar level in order to keep within this tolerance.

(3) Fit the caps carefully, ensuring that they are seated correctly and then tighten to ensure an air-tight seal.

(4) Place the balanced tubes diametrically opposite in the head which has been maintained at the required temperature. Fit the lid to the head and secure firmly.

(5) Place the head carefully in the machine ensuring that it is correctly located on the spindle.

(6) Close the lid, on some machines this is automatically controlled by the start switch.

(7) Select the required speed, set the time, the break mechanism if needed and check that all indicators are functioning correctly then start the machine.

(8) When the pre-selected time is completed the machine will automatically stop and allow the head to come to rest. Open the lid (if not already open due to the automatic control) and remove the head using two hands and place on to rubber strips attached to a suitable board.

(9) Remove the lid from the head and then remove the tubes carefully. Release and remove the caps and very carefully decant the supernatant.

(10) When all centrifugation is completed, switch off the mains supply to the machine. When the refrigerated bowl has achieved the ambient temperature, remove any condensation by wiping with a dry cloth.

CARE OF HIGH SPEED CENTRIFUGES

Heads

After use, the heads must be washed in hot water to which a little detergent has been added. The sockets should be well brushed, taking care not to damage the protective coating. After washing, the head must be rinsed well with water with a final rinsing in distilled water.

It is placed upside down on the rubber faced storage board and allowed to drain dry. When completely dry, a coating of silicone polish is recommended to help resist attack by salts, etc. especially in the case of anodized heads.

When the head is not in use it should be stored upside down on a storage board at a suitable temperature.

Caps

Between each operation, the caps should be carefully wiped with clean tissue to remove debris from the previous material centrifuged. After use, they must be taken apart and thoroughly washed and rinsed with a final rinse in distilled water before drying. When dry, they should be reassembled carefully, ensuring that all the parts of one cap have the same code letter. If the parts are not coded, then the components of the caps are interchangeable. The rubber gasket has the leading edge chamfered to facilitate entry into the centrifuge tube. An exploded diagram of an M.S.E. cap is shown in *Figure 3*.

Tubes

Tubes and bottles should be cleansed in the normal way, bearing in mind that some materials vary in their properties towards solvents, etc.

It pays to mark each batch of tubes in some way so that the age can be ascertained. Then if a breakage occurs due to prolonged use, it would be advisable to use tubes of that batch at a lower R.C.F. than usual.

MICROSCOPES

A vast range of microscopes have been produced to help the geologist, bacteriologist, crystallographer, photographer, etc.

The ultimate magnification of a microscope is dependent on the wavelength of the type of light used as an illuminant. The wavelength of light limits the separation of two adjacent points. If two points are closer together than half the wavelength of light, they cannot be seen as separate points, therefore a certain amount of detail is lost. It is this factor that limits the worthwhile magnification. Any magnification that increases the size of the object beyond the limits of the wavelength of light used is known as *empty* magnification.

The microscopist must be familiar with a number of definitions and their applications.

The total magnification of a microscope can be calculated roughly by the following formula:

$$\text{Magnification} = \frac{\text{Magnification of eye-piece} \times \text{mechanical tube length}}{\text{Focal length of objective}}$$

The objective forms a real enlarged image of the object known as the primary image and the eye-piece converts this image to an enlarged virtual image known as the secondary image which is then recorded by the eye. The primary image is dependent on the ratio of the size of the image to the size of the object, or the ratio of the distance of the image from the objective to the distance between the object and the objective. For approximate magnification, the optical tube length can be taken as equal to the mechanical tube length.

Optical tube length—This is defined as the distance between the rear principal plane of the objective lens system and the plane of the image formed in the upper part of the draw tube. This distance will vary with each lens used and, in order to assist calculation many, manufacturers inscribe lenses with their primary magnification.

Mechanical tube length—This is the distance between the eye lens of the eye-piece and the base of the nose-piece (the point where the objective fits into the objective carrier). This distance is fixed, usually at 160 mm but, if the microscope has an adjustable tube length, by means of a draw tube, then this distance must be pre-set before using the microscope. The majority of the lenses are calculated to produce their best results at this tube length.

Focal length—This can be found inscribed on the side of the objective. This distance is calculated by the manufacturer and approximates the working distance of the objective. Thus, the magnification of a 16 mm (^{2}/$_3$ in.) objective with a $\times 10$ eye-piece at a tube length of 160 mm is:

$$\frac{160}{16} \times 10 = 100$$

The magnification of the eye-piece is inscribed on the lens mount.

The objective lenses must have a number of important qualities apart from the ability to magnify an object, such as brightness, resolution, and definition. These factors are dependent, to some extent, on the numerical aperture (N.A.) of a lens.

16

Numerical aperture—This is the ratio of the diameter to the focal length of the lens. The German microscopist Abbé evolved the mathematical formula used today to denote the N.A.

$$N.A. = n \sin u$$

where n is the refractive index of the medium between the object and the objective and $2u$ is the angle subtended from a point in the centre of the object to the extremes in diameter of the front lens of the objective. The maximum angle that $2u$ can equal is 180 degrees— when the lens is touching the object. Thus the maximum reading for $\sin u$ is $\sin 90° = 1$ and the maximum N.A. that any lens can have is $1 \times$ refractive index (which for air is approximately $1 \cdot 0$ and

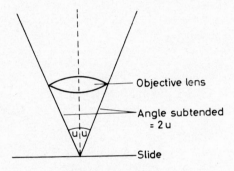

Figure 4. Diagram demonstrating numerical aperture

for oil immersion liquid is approximately $1 \cdot 5$). Generally speaking of two lenses with the same focal length, but of different N.A., the lens with the higher N.A. will produce a brighter and better image. A larger diameter lens will allow the entry of more light. The depth of focus, which is the depth of the object that is in focus at the same time, becomes less with an increase in N.A. The N.A. also affects the final resolution of a microscope.

The resolving power—This is the ability of a microscope lens to separate two adjacent points, and it is this power that limits the amount of detail that a lens can show. Resolution must not be confused with magnification. As mentioned previously, the former is dependent on the type of light source used as an illuminant and it is thought that two points closer together than half the wavelength of the light used cannot be resolved. With ordinary light the maximum useful magnification is 1,000 diameters for a student type microscope and 1,450 diameters for a research microscope. It is possible, by using high-power oculars, to boost the magnification beyond these figures but as a result the precise focus of the object is lost, i.e. a loss of resolution. Green light will slightly increase the resolution of a lens. Ultra-violet light has a much shorter wavelength than white light and can increase the resolution by a factor of 2 or 3. The electron microscope uses a beam of electrons instead of white light and these electrons have a wavelength of about $1/100,000$ of that of white light. The resolution of an electron microscope is about 100 times better than that of an ordinary microscope. The definition that can be obtained with a microscope is limited by optical faults in the lens. These faults are known as aberrations and the two commonest are spherical and chromatic aberrations.

Spherical aberrations—These are caused by the light rays at the edge of the lens being refracted more than the rays from the centre of the lens. This means that the meeting point of all the rays is not just one point but two or three, resulting in a distorted image.

Chromatic aberrations—These are caused by the lens material splitting the white light rays into the different coloured rays of the spectrum. Due to the different wavelengths of the colours, some colours are refracted more than others. Again the rays do not all meet at one point and this results in a blurred image having a coloured fringe.

By using different combinations of optical glass, the majority of lens aberrations can be corrected. With high power lenses the field of view, as seen through the microscope, might not be in complete focus; this is known as curvature of field. This means that the centre of the field and the edge are not both in focus at the same time. This fault is quite common and can be partially corrected by using compensating eye-pieces.

Objectives

As mentioned previously, it is not possible to produce a good quality lens from only one type of glass. The perfection and also the cost of a lens depends on the number of components and the types of glass used in its construction. The construction of a lens is a very skilful job and many calculations must be made before a lens is put on the market. The lens components are usually mounted in some form of balsam, so their immersion in substances likely to dissolve the balsam should be avoided.

Achromatic objectives—These are constructed so that the wavelengths of two colours are corrected and brought to a common focus, the intermediate colours being almost eliminated, although a faint coloured halo may be noticed. They are generally designed for use with green light. They are suitable for the majority of routine work, students' use, and even for some aspects of research. For photography and critical research work a better quality lens is required.

Apochromatic objectives—These are almost perfect lenses which are very costly to manufacture and should be treated with great care. They are corrected for three colours and nearly all lens aberrations are eliminated. The numerical aperture of this type of objective is usually larger than an equivalent achromatic lens. A good apochromatic oil immersion lens should have an N.A. of about 1·4.

Fluorite lenses—These are intermediate between the achromatic and apochromatic lenses. The use of fluorite in the construction of a lens helps to produce a high class lens at a slightly lower cost, although the final result is not quite so good as the apochromatic objective.

It is important to note that the fluorite and the apochromatic lens will only produce the best results when used in conjunction with compensating eyepieces, to prevent curvature of field.

Eye-pieces (Oculars)

The eye-pieces in general use are the Huyghenian, the compensating and the wide field eye-piece.

The Huyghenian eye-piece—This has two plano-convex lenses and between these is a circular field diaphragm. The diaphragm is situated at the point of focus of the upper, or eye lens and is used to restrict the field of view. The lower, or field lens collects all the possible light transmitted through the objective and focuses the image in the diaphragm. The image is then magnified by the eye lens to produce the final virtual image. Both the eye and field lenses are simple in design. There are two other types of ordinary eye-pieces, the 'Kellner' and the 'Ramsden'. They differ from the Huyghenian in that the field diaphragm is beneath the field lens. They are usually used for measuring the size of the object by means of a calibrated scale placed on the diaphragm.

The compensating eye-piece—This is similar in design to the Huyghenian in that the field diaphragm is situated between the eye and field lenses, but one or both of the lenses are compound in structure. It was designed to correct the slight chromatic aberrations present in the majority of very high power objectives and also to compensate for the slight curvature of field obtained when using these objectives.

The use of this type of eye-piece is recommended for all high power work irrespective of the type of objective in use.

The wide-field eye-piece—This eye-piece is based on the Huyghenian type but as its name implies it is modified to give a wide field. Its use is largely determined by personal preference.

The Mirror

Where the light source is not an integral part of the microscope, the mirror reflects the light so that the rays are projected through the condenser to the object on the stage. The plain side of the mirror should always be used in conjunction with a condenser.

Condensers

A condenser should always be used when magnifications of more than 20–40 (depending upon the microscope) diameters are required. The normal condenser found on most microscopes is the 'Abbé' condenser which consists of two, or possibly three lenses which concentrate the rays of light on to the object on the stage. At the bottom of the condenser there is an iris diaphragm which can be partially closed to cut out marginal rays of light and so provide more critical illumination. Although the Abbé condenser is not optically correct, it is good enough for all but the most critical work. The aplanatic type of condenser is designed to be used with light of one colour only. It produces quite a good image of the light source. The apochromatic type is almost as efficient as an objective and nearly as costly. It will only give the best results when correctly centred and operated according to the manufacturer's instructions. There are two special condensers that must be mentioned and these are the dark-ground and the phase contrast types. These will be covered under the special techniques in microscopy (see page 26, 27).

Lighting

There are three types of light source available for use with an ordinary microscope. Lighting for special microscopy will be covered in the appropriate section.

Natural light—Daylight can be used if it is bright enough but this is bluer than that obtained from an artificial source. It is often said that the concave side of the mirror should be used with natural light in conjunction with a condenser; this is not the case and the concave mirror should only be used when there is no condenser.

Low intensity light—This can be obtained from an opal or a pearl tungsten filament bulb. The bulb is normally fitted into a simple housing which has an aperture to allow the light to reach the microscope. Again the plain side of the mirror should be used in conjunction with the condenser.

High intensity light—This can be obtained from a low voltage, high wattage bulb regulated by a variable resistance or rheostat.

The *Köhler* type of illumination is commonly used. A low voltage, high wattage bulb with a filament is used as the light source. As the latter is so small, a lens mounted on the lamp unit is used to enlarge the beam of light. The lens is fitted with a variable iris diaphragm. Facilities for using filters are usually arranged between the lamp lens and the microscope mirror. Better results may be obtained if the filter holders are between the lens and the bulb, but this is not advised for gelatine filters as they are liable to melt due to the heat produced by the bulb. Modern microscopes may have a built-in light source which, if fully aligned, is ready for immediate use.

Mechanical Stages

The more expensive microscopes have a mechanical stage as an integral part of the instrument. For the majority of microscopes without this type of stage, a detachable stage may be fitted. This type of stage is fitted with vernier scales along both the east-west and north-south traverses. The scale is used to mark the position of the slide so that the required area can easily be located and examined at a later date. The left slide clip is usually marked and a similar mark made on the vernier scale. This is so that the slide clip can be placed in the same position each time. Unless the left clip is in the same position the vernier scales cannot be used to locate a previously marked slide position.

If Petri dishes are to be examined microscopically, a stage having removable clips is essential. Alternatively a special holder may be used[1].

Eye-piece Micrometer

Although special eye-pieces having a micrometer scale as an integral part of their construction may be purchased they are not absolutely essential. A micrometer scale, which is inscribed on a glass disc, can be inserted into an ordinary Huyghenian eye-piece. This disc is placed on the field diaphragm. The latter must be adjusted to bring the scale into focus. The divisions of the eye-piece scale are arbitrary and, to convert these units to absolute measurement, the scale is calibrated against a slide, or stage micrometer. (This is a glass slide having a scale 1 mm in length subdivided into 100 equal parts.)

To calibrate the eye-piece scale, the slide micrometer is focused and the eye-piece scale superimposed upon the slide scale. The ratio of the two scales can then be calibrated and noted for future reference. When a different objective, or a different tube length is used the scales must be re-calibrated.

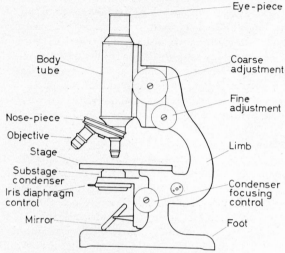

Figure 5. Diagram of a standard microscope

TYPES OF MICROSCOPE

Figure 5 shows a standard microscope labelled to show its component parts. During recent years, the design of research microscopes has changed radically and many models now have a built-in light source. Even student types are becoming more streamlined in appearance with changes in the method of focusing involving the stage as the movable part and not the objectives. Gillett and Sibert Ltd. produce a student microscope which may be built up into a research model, as all parts are interchangeable and a binocular head is fitted easily (*Figure 6*). Apart from being used as a research microscope, the conference microscope (also made by Gillett and Sibert) can be fitted with a prism projecting head, a viewing head or with photographic attachments. Coarse and fine stage focusing are both carried out by the movement of a single knob.

The monocular microscope is of the basic type and is fitted with only one eye-piece. However, both eyes should be kept open when using any monocular microscope.

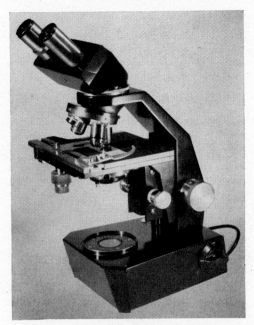

Figure 6. The Lablynx research microscope
(By courtesy of Gillett and Sibert Ltd.)

The binocular microscope is used with both eyes. The light rays coming from the objective are split by a prism so that half the light is transmitted to each eye. It is not advisable to use eye-pieces stronger than ×10 unless a high intensity light source is used.

The stereo microscope (*Figure 7*) has matched pairs of objectives and is binocular in design. The two objectives allow the eyes to function normally and so produce a three-dimensional image. They are not used for magnification of more than 150 diameters as, above this, resolution and definition are lost. They are more often called plate or dissecting microscopes and are generally used for micro-dissection, pure culture techniques and manipulative work.

A METHOD FOR SETTING-UP A MICROSCOPE HAVING AN EXTERNAL LIGHT SOURCE

(1) Place the light source in line with the microscope and about 6–8 in. (for an opal type bulb), or 10–15 in. (for a high intensity light) from the plain side of the mirror. Place a well stained slide on the stage, positioned so that the object is above the centre of the condenser.

(2) Click the low power objective (16 mm) into position. Rack up the substage condenser until it is 1–2 mm below the lower surface of the slide.

(3) Adjust the mirror so that the field is evenly illuminated. Lower the objective and focus on to the object.

(4) Remove the eye-piece, almost close the substage iris diaphragm and observe the illuminated field and the sharply defined iris diaphragm in the back of the objective. If the objective does not appear evenly illuminated, adjust the mirror until the field is even. If the iris diaphragm appears off-centre, the condenser must be centred by adjusting the centring screws. Replace the eye-piece.

(5) Adjust the condenser up or down until the lamp filament or the lamp iris diaphragm is in focus with the object on the slide. The condenser is then slightly racked down until the image of the filament, etc., is lost and even lighting is obtained.

(6) Adjust the lamp and substage iris diaphragms to cut down glare.

(7) If the light is too bright a rheostat must be used to reduce the power of the light source. Alternatively a ground glass screen is placed in the filter carrier of the lamp. It is unlikely that an opal or a pearl bulb will give too strong a light.

For more detailed information on set-up for different types of lighting, conditions, etc., the reader is advised to take advantage of the literature cited in the bibliography.

CARE AND CLEANING OF MICROSCOPES

Apart from routine dusting and occasional greasing, a microscope does not need much attention. Optical faults or mechanical troubles should be attended to by a skilled microscope mechanic. The mirror and lenses can be dusted with a warm fine camel-hair brush and finally polished with lens tissue. Care should be taken not to get finger marks on the cleaned glass.

The microscope stand and stage should be regularly dusted with the brush. Occasionally a speck of dust is apparent in the optical system and rotation of the eye-piece will determine whether the dust is on the objective lens or eye-piece; if on the eye-piece then the dust will also rotate. On no account should the prism housing of a binocular microscope be taken to pieces as it requires very accurate reassembly. The coarse and fine adjustments and the slides of the mechanical stage should be lightly greased according to the maker's instructions; vaseline may be used if the correct grease is not available.

Adjustments for a slipping body-tube or for backlash in any of the moving parts vary with different makes and it is advised that the manufacturer's instructions should be followed to correct these faults.

When not in use, the microscope should either be covered, pre-

Figure 7. A stereoscopic microscope
(By courtesy of W. Watson and Sons Limited)

ferably with a polythene sheet or bag, or returned to the microscope case. The microscope is a delicate instrument and should be treated with care and respect.

OIL IMMERSION

It is an established fact that refraction occurs when light rays travel from one medium to another of a different density.

When an objective is used which has a small lens and a high N.A. the amount of light it can pass is small in comparison with the lower power objectives. If light is refracted during its passage from the slide to the objective then a large amount of light is lost. If a transparent substance (having an R.I. similar to that of the glass slide) is placed between the objective and the slide, there is no loss of light due to refraction or total internal reflection.

Oil immersion lenses are designed for use with an oil having the same refractive index as the glass of the slide. As the working distance of higher power objectives is very small, great care must be taken to ensure that the objective is not racked through or even down on to the cover glass. Some of the modern objectives have a spring-loaded lens mount as a safety device.

A drop of good quality immersion oil, preferably a non-drying oil or cedar-wood oil, is placed on the slide immediately above the spot on the specimen which is to be examined. The objective is lowered until it just touches the oil which will then appear to 'light-up'. By looking sideways at the slide, the objective is carefully lowered further until almost touching the cover glass (only practice and experience can really help towards this work.) While looking through the eye-piece, the objective is then raised slowly until the object is in focus. For very high quality work it is advisable to place oil between the condenser and the slide. After use, the oil should be carefully removed from the condenser and objective lenses. The slide should be cleaned if it is to be kept for future reference. This is done with a lens tissue lightly soaked in carbon tetrachloride or xylene. On no account should the oil be allowed to dry or harden on the lenses. If this occurs, then only patient gentle wiping with lens tissue and solvent will remove the oil.

The lenses must never be immersed in xylene or similar solvents of balsam.

DARK-GROUND MICROSCOPY

A special condenser is required for this technique, although for 'rough' work the standard condenser can be adapted.

The condenser is designed so that light rays converge on the object in the form of an annular cone, the apex of which is in the plane of the object. Direct rays of light must not reach the objective and so any objective having an N.A. of more than $1\cdot0$ should have a funnel-stop positioned behind the lens to reduce the N.A. The thickness of the slide is important and the condensers are designed for use with a particular thickness of slide (see maker's instructions). Immersion oil is placed between the condenser and the lower surface of the slide. The mirror is adjusted to give an evenly illuminated field. With a low power objective, the slide should be focused upon and the condenser adjusted by means of the graduated ring until the circle of light becomes as small as possible. Changing to higher power objectives may require adjustments to the iris diaphragm or to the mirror.

The objects on the slide appear as white outlines against a dark background. This method is very useful for the identification of spirochaete bacteria.

The ordinary condenser can be adapted by placing a circle of black paper or a patch stop beneath it so that only the marginal light rays can reach the object. This method is only successful when using low power objectives.

PHASE CONTRAST MICROSCOPY

Special equipment is required for this work and is listed below:

1. A special condenser which has a circular plate carrying a number of annuli. These annuli are formed from an opaque glass disc having a ring of clear glass to allow the passage of light rays. The annuli have different diameters and are specific for a certain objective.
2. Phase objectives. These are similar to ordinary objectives but have a phase plate consisting of a transparent glass disc which has a groove etched in a circle. The depth of the latter is such that the light passing through it differs by a quarter of a wavelength from the rest of the disc. The phase plate is inserted in the back focal plane of the objective lens. Each objective has its own specific phase plate.
3. A focusing telescope which is placed into the eye-piece tube in order to correct the alignment of the condenser and phase annuli.

The microscope is set up as for normal work. The slide is placed on the stage and a low power phase objective focused on to the specimen. The correct annulus for the objective is rotated into position and the normal eye-piece replaced by the telescope. Through the telescope will be seen two rings, one brighter than the other. This brighter ring must be exactly superimposed on the other one and this is accomplished by adjusting the condenser by means of the centring screws provided. To obtain even illumination, the condenser might need up or down adjustment.

Briefly the principle is that the cone of light from the substage annulus passes through the preparation and any light rays passing through the object on the slide will be diffracted. The direct light rays pass through the objective phase plate and are retarded by one-quarter of a wave length. The diffracted light passes through the rest of the phase plate and is not retarded. Therefore there is a phase difference between the object and the remainder of the slide and this can be seen as various shades of grey.

The method can be used with either a monocular or binocular microscope.

The Watson Microscope Company have a slightly different system in that the substage annuli are separate plates, the appropriate plate for the objective is fitted to the condenser lens of the light source. It is used in conjunction with their standard condenser.

Some microscopes are fitted with a variable condenser which takes the place of the annuli plates or discs. The annulus within the condenser is variable to suit each objective.

FLUORESCENT MICROSCOPY

The resolution of a microscope can be increased by the use of light of a shorter wavelength. Ultra-violet (u.v.) light has a very short wavelength and, as such, is invisible to the eye. Some materials fluoresce when in contact with u.v. light and certain fluorescent dyes can be used to 'stain' the specimen.

Ordinary glass is capable of absorbing the short wave light rays and therefore the condenser lenses are made of quartz glass. Preferably the slides and cover glasses should also be made of special glass.

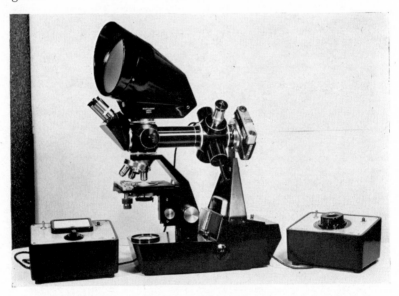

Figure 8. Conference microscope complete with camera attachment and viewing head
(By courtesy of Gillett & Sibert Ltd.)

The introduction of the iodine-quartz lamp has greatly simplified the technique of fluorescent microscopy. This lamp emits a range of wavelengths which can be selected by the use of a number of special filters. Special precautions do not have to be taken. The working life of the lamp is some 25 hours at maximum light intensity. However, by intelligent use of the voltage control, the life can be expected to exceed 100 hours. The lamp is suitable for general microscopy and when it is run at the correct voltage (12 volts for Gillett and Sibert microscopes) is perfectly correct with regard to colour and as such is immediately available for good quality colour photography.

The Gillett and Sibert Conference Microscope (*Figure 8*) is fitted with an iodine-quartz lamp and is designed for all types of microscopy.

The other method for producing ultra-violet light for use in fluorescent microscopy is to employ a mercury vapour lamp. The light rays are passed through a Wood's glass filter. This produces other light rays which must be removed by another filter, for example, a 4 per cent ammoniacal copper sulphate solution. The Wood's glass filter is placed nearest the light source and the copper sulphate solution between this and the microscope condenser. The slide can be observed in the normal way by using a special glass filter placed over the eye-piece to prevent the harmful u.v. rays from entering the eye. Photomicrography is used to record observations of fluorescent specimens and is absolutely essential when using dyes that have a very short fluorescent life which is often as short as a few minutes.

Examples of fluorescent dyes are: acridine orange, auramine, thioflavine S, thiazol yellow G, fuchsin, and primulin. They are used as very dilute solutions.

It should be noted that many oils fluoresce, including immersion oil. A substitute for immersion oil is pure non-fluorescent liquid paraffin or sandal-wood oil.

THE POLARIZING MICROSCOPE

The polarizing microscope utilizes the fact that, when a ray of normal light passes through a crystal, it is divided into two separate rays which are polarized at right angles to one another and have different velocities. The crystal is thus acting as though it had two refractive indices and is, therefore, termed birefringent. Substances with more than one refractive index are described as being optically anisotropic, as opposed to optically isotropic materials which exhibit one refractive index only.

The botanist generally requires to examine crystalline material at a considerably higher magnification than would a geologist. For this reason a polarizing microscope in a botanical laboratory should be a precision instrument, thus enabling the necessary fine alignments to be made.

A polarizing microscope is basically identical with a normal light microscope but the following modifications are necessary. There should be a mechanical stage capable of being rotated through 360°

with calibration in degrees and facility for clamping it in any desired position. A polarizing material (in most modern microscopes this is a piece of Polaroid film) is placed in the light path below the object, usually as an attachment to the substage condenser; this Polaroid filter is known as the polarizer. A second piece of polarizing material, the analyser, is arranged in the light path above the objective. It can usually be moved in or out of position by means of a knob on the side of the draw tube. Either the polarizer and/or analyser should be capable of being rotated.

It is necessary to align the light path accurately through the microscope before use. When the light passes through the polarizer, only rays vibrating in one direction are allowed through and the emergent light is said to be plane polarized. If the analyser is orientated so that it will allow light which is vibrating in the plane of polarization of the polarizer to pass through, then the eye-piece field will appear bright. If, however, the direction of light transmission from the analyser is at right angles to the plane of polarization of the polarizer then the field will be dark and the Polaroids are said to be crossed. When a crystalline material is placed between the polarizer and the analyser in the crossed position the incident rays will be refracted as described above. These rays, on emerging from the crystal, may then have a component vibrating in the plane of transmission of the analyser. Such rays will, of course, pass through the analyser and will appear bright against the dark background in the eye-piece field.

Two commonly encountered plant materials which may be studied with the polarizing microscope are starch and cellulose, the latter being the basic material of the majority of plant cell walls.

By suitable adaptation of the technique outlined above, precise quantitative data can be obtained on the orientation of cellulose molecules within plant cell walls. Such techniques have been used particularly in the study of algal cell walls and those of woody angiosperms and gymnosperms.

THE ELECTRON MICROSCOPE

The electron microscope (*Figure 9*) is constructed to provide a greater degree of magnification than is possible with a light microscope.

Instead of a light source, a beam of electrons is emitted from the cathode in an electron gun and these electrons are focused by passing through electro-magnetic or electro-static fields in a similar manner to the way a beam of light can be focused by a convex lens. A high vacuum is maintained in the instrument to prevent the electrons

30

from colliding with molecules of gas and thus scattering. The beam of electrons is bent as it passes through either the electro-magnetic or the electro-static 'lenses' and is focused on a fluorescent screen. The image is projected on to this screen and it can be recorded either by photographing from the latter or by exposing a photographic plate directly to the electron beam.

Figure. 9 A Siemens electron microscope (Elmiskop I)
(By courtesy of W. Wykeham and Company Limited)

Most electron microscopes are large pieces of apparatus but it has been possible to reduce the size in the electro-static models. In addition to the microscope and its complicated electrical apparatus, pumps are necessary to maintain the high vacuum which is required.

FUME CUPBOARDS

Fume cupboards should always be used when dealing with sub-stances which give off harmful vapours. It is very important that these substances are not used openly in the laboratory.

It is equally important to switch on the extraction unit before using the fume cupboard. The front should be left open a few inches when the extraction system is operating, in order to allow adequate air flow.

For radioactive materials, the transparent windows should be constructed of lead glass and the interior surfaces should be of a replaceable nature in order to prevent contamination by background radiations.

REFRIGERATORS

Refrigeration is an artificial method of maintaining low temperatures and can be achieved by either of two systems, using absorption or compression units.

Absorption Unit

This unit can be powered either by gas or electricity and the running cost is quite low. It is silent in operation and reasonably trouble-free. By comparison, an absorption unit is not so efficient as a compression unit in producing low temperatures quickly, especially in refrigerators which have capacities of more than 6 ft^3.

Compression Unit

This is operated by electricity and is the most common unit in industrial use. As it incorporates a motor and a compressor, a certain amount of vibration may be experienced, particularly when the motor 'cuts-in' under thermostatic control. The majority of com-pressor units are sealed systems. This means that damaged or defective units must generally be replaced entire and not in part.

MAINTENANCE

The refrigerator should be kept clean and tidy and periodically a check should be made to ensure that all unwanted items have been removed.

The refrigerator must be defrosted at least fortnightly. This con-sists of switching off the unit and allowing the ice, which has formed round the ice-box, to melt. The water is collected in the drip tray provided and is discarded. At the same time the water in the ice trays should be replaced with fresh drinking water. After defrosting, the trays and ice-box should be wiped with a dry cloth and the unit switched on again. Ice should not be chipped off from around the ice-box, as serious and expensive damage may easily result.

USE

It is important to pack a refrigerator as sparsely as possible in order to allow adequate air circulation. This is essential just under the ice-box, which is the coldest part of the refrigerator. If too much is packed in this position, it will seriously affect the correct functioning of the thermostat.

To prevent evaporation, as much of the material as possible should be wrapped in polythene sheets or placed in polythene bags.

DEEP FREEZERS

Deep freezers are cabinets which are capable of maintaining a sub-zero temperature by thermostatically controlled compression units. The rules applicable to refrigerators also apply to deep freezers with the exception of defrosting, as deep freezers do not have an ice-box or a drip tray. To defrost, the material is removed and placed in another deep freezer and the unit is then switched off. The cabinet is left until all the ice has melted and the resulting water is removed with swabs. Defrosting is generally required only once or twice a year dependant upon the amount of material stored in the cabinet.

COLD ROOMS

For some aspects of laboratory work it is necessary to work in a room which has a controlled low temperature. These rooms, which may function below zero centigrade, pose particular problems: water supplies may freeze solid unless they are protected by electrically heated lagging. Special electrical fittings are required to prevent shocks due to condensation. These fittings must also be fitted to *all* apparatus which is used in the cold room. Door locks of a special type must be fitted which prevent the lock freezing. It is essential to fit every cold room with an alarm system which can be used in an emergency to summon aid.

The method of cooling is by a compression unit coupled to a fan which re-circulates the cold air, the temperature being thermostatically controlled. These units normally defrost themselves and this operation is generally indicated by the fan stopping.

It is quite common to find a cold room being used as a general store but this should not be tolerated unless the material in question must be stored at a low temperature and that refrigerator space is not available.

One golden rule in a cold room is to clear up after each day's work and thus leave the bench space clear so that someone else can use the room.

Columns of the Sephadex and cellulose type are easily stored in Terry clips attached to battens fixed to the wall of the room.

MAINTENANCE

Apart from periodic cleaning and the removal of unwanted material, the only maintenance which is required is the service of the cooling unit and this should be performed by a refrigeration engineer.

INCUBATORS

In order that experiments can be performed under controlled and repeatable conditions, cultures need to be grown at specific and controlled temperatures.

These conditions can be obtained by using an incubator which can be heated by gas, electricity or oil. The incubator is thermostatically controlled at the optimum temperature of the organism. The thermostats are normally of the expanding capsule type for gas and oil heated incubators or of the bi-metallic kind for electrically heated incubators; capsules can also be used for the control of electric incubators.

The electric thermostat may be of the Sunvic type which has a bi-metallic coiled rod inserted into the incubator. When the required temperature is attained, the metal expands and makes an electrical contact which in turn breaks contact from the mains supply via a hot-wire relay. The reverse occurs when the temperature drops.

The capsules contain substances that vaporize at a specific temperature. When this temperature is reached, the gas formation causes the capsule to expand and a short rod, resting on the capsule, is pushed either against a diaphragm which reduces the gas pressure or restricts the oil flow thus causing a drop in temperature, or against a bar thus breaking electrical contact.

The majority of modern incubators have a jacket of water as a means of holding a temperature and this also acts as an insulator from the room temperature.

Occasionally, a temperature is required which is below the ambient room temperature. This may be obtained by allowing cold water to trickle through the water jacket; the thermostat is then set for the temperature required. Some incubators have a separate water-cooling system consisting of continuous pipes inset into the water jacket. Cold mains water is allowed to circulate through these pipes thus cooling the water in the jacket, which in turn reduces the temperature in the incubator.

Petri dishes of solid media can be placed in the incubator in an inverted manner to stop excessive condensation forming in the lid of the dish. This rule does not hold good with all incubators and only trial and error can ascertain the correct way of incubating the dishes.

The incubators should be periodically swabbed-down with a 3 per cent lysol solution to disinfect the interior and 24 hours should elapse before use in order to allow the disinfectant fumes to evaporate.

To prevent evaporation of water from medium during incubation, a basin or dish of water may be placed in the bottom of the incubator to raise the humidity of the air.

FILTER PUMPS

Filter pumps can be constructed of glass, plastic or metal and they rely on water pressure to suck air from a vessel and so produce a vacuum.

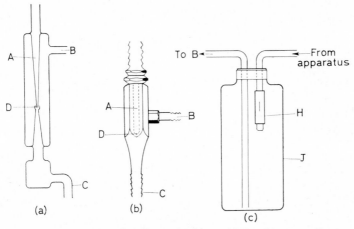

Figure 10. (a) *Glass filter pump;* (b) *metal pump;* (c) *trap vessel*

The mains water flows through tube A (*see Figure 10a and b*) and the pressure is increased by the restriction orifice at D. The water emitted from D is in the form of a narrow high-pressured stream which passes through C to waste. The force of water through D sucks air through the side arm B which is connected to the apparatus requiring the vacuum. The air is then forced by the water pressure to waste. A trap should be inserted between the pump and the apparatus to prevent water being sucked back into the latter if the water pressure fluctuates. The trap (*Figure 10c*) consists of a polythene or glass vessel of at least 500 ml capacity, fitted with a non-return valve such as a bunsen valve. This valve, H, is quite simple and is made of a piece of rubber tubing blocked at one end with a glass rod. The open end is connected to a short length of bent glass tubing which leads to the apparatus. The rubber tubing has a $^3/_8$ in. slit in one side. A positive pressure inside the tubing will cause the slit to open. Similarly a positive pressure outside the tube, in the trap vessel, will force the slit shut. When the apparatus is *in vacuo*, there is a negative pressure in the trap vessel, J. Any sudden reduction in water pressure through the pump will cause some water to be sucked back into the trap, thus producing a positive pressure in the vessel. This pressure closes the slit in the rubber tubing and prevents any water entering the apparatus. The metal pump can be purchased (from Edwards High Vacuum Ltd.) with a non-return valve as an integral part of the side arm; this eliminates the need for a trap. However, it appears in practice that the integral non-return valve is not fully efficient when slight fluctuations of water pressure occur.

The maintenance needed for this type of pump is virtually nil. Apart from changing the tubing in the trap when signs of perishing are noticed and keeping the pump clean there is nothing that should need attention. A pressure of 20 mm Hg can be obtained. The rubber tubing should be thick-walled and of large bore to prevent collapse when under negative pressure.

An all-glass pump should be used when evacuating corrosive vapours.

VACUUM PUMPS

Pumps of the Speedivac type (made by Edwards High Vacuum Ltd.) fall into this category. These pumps are capable of obtaining pressures as low as 10^{-4} mm Hg when used in an air-tight and degassed system. A degassed system is one that has had all the gas removed from it by being under slight negative pressure until bubbling has ceased.

A trap should be used with these pumps, particularly when condensable vapours are likely to be encountered. The trap should take the form of a U-tube immersed in ice to condense any vapours before they reach the pump unit. Specialized traps should be used for corrosive vapours and manufacturers will supply useful literature on the subject.

Short, large-bore, thick-walled tubing should be used for all connections to obtain a good pumping speed and a low vacuum.

Strain on the pump motor can be obviated by rotating the pump pulley in the correct direction and then switching on the motor. Care must be taken to prevent trapping fingers. Maintenance of these pumps consists of keeping the vacuum oil at the correct level, checking the connections regularly and an occasional lubrication of the pump motor.

VACUUM GAUGES

There are many types of gauge available for measuring the effective vacuum of a system, and of these the McLeod and Pirani gauges are manufactured by Edwards High Vacuum Ltd.

McLeod Gauge

This is an all glass piece of apparatus which uses a small quantity of mercury as an indicator. The reading is taken by comparing the height of a column of mercury with a calibrated scale incorporated behind the column. The gauge is turned through 90 degrees before use to nullify the previous reading.

The gauge can be coupled to the vacuum system either by rubber pressure tubing or by a metal tube. It is manufactured in pressure ranges from 10 to 10^{-6} mm Hg.

Pirani Gauge

This gauge is electrical in operation and relies upon the variation in resistance of a filament due to changes of gas pressure in the vacuum system. The measurement is read directly from the calibrated scale of a milliameter.

The gauge is available in a pressure range of $10-10^{-4}$ mm Hg.

HOT AND COLD BATHS

Hot baths of various kinds are used for heating partially immersed flasks, tubes, beakers, etc., when the direct use of a bunsen flame is dangerous or when a reasonably constant temperature is required to be maintained. In addition, cold baths are frequently required. The type of bath media employed is governed by the range of temperature required.

Water baths are useful for temperatures up to 100°C. Most of them are electrically heated and can be thermostatically controlled. Some are fitted with a constant level device. More refined models have stirrers incorporated, while others are fitted with a small centrifugal pump to enable the water to be circulated through an external closed system. A lid provided with some models prevents undue evaporation when the bath is used above 40°C.

If the bath is required at a temperature slightly below ambient, a cooling coil is needed. In theory, water baths can be used from a temperature slightly below ambient to 100°C. It is, however, advisable to use a light oil (as supplied by Hopkin & Williams) for temperatures above 80°C. When using oil, temperatures in excess of 100°C can be obtained *if the temperature range of the tank allows for this event.*

Temperatures far below ambient can be obtained using a refrigerated tank with temperature ranges down to −30°C. Water and ethylene glycol mixture should be used for temperatures down to −15°C. Odourless kerosene is recommended for temperatures from −15°C to −30°C. A safety cut-out *must* be employed in case of thermostat failure if kerosene is used because of its low flash point (65°C).

For temperatures below 6°C a lid must always be used to cover the tank.

A Tecam fluidized bath, as manufactured by Techne (Cambridge) Ltd., is useful for temperatures from ambient up to 600°C.

Apart from the proprietary baths mentioned the need for a small bath capable of producing reasonably steady, if not constant, heat often arises. The bath itself can be a Pyrex glass beaker, a small metal pan, a Dewar vacuum vessel or a shallow metal tray, etc. The bath media will vary according to the temperature range required. Table 1 gives a list of the various bath media plus their respective temperatures. It should be noted that it is necessary to use either a bunsen burner or an electric element as the initial heat source for the heated baths.

TABLE 1

Type of bath	Heat source	Temperature range
Sand bath (Shallow dish holding sand)	Bunsen burner	0 to 360°C
Oil bath (liquid paraffin)	Bunsen burner	0 to 360°C
Water bath	Bunsen burner or electric element	0 to 100°C
Water and ice	—	2 to 3°C
Water and ice and salt	—	0° to −21°C
Methylated spirits and solid CO_2	—	0° to −72°C
Liquid nitrogen	—	−196°C

Great care must be taken when handling solid CO_2 and liquid nitrogen. The former can cause serious 'burns', which are in fact a form of frostbite, if held too firmly in the bare hand. If asbestos gloves are not available for protection, a pair of forceps should be used to handle the solid CO_2. Freezing mixtures using solid CO_2 should be prepared and used in wide-necked Dewar vacuum vessels.

Liquid nitrogen must also be treated with caution, because of its extremely low temperature. On *no* account must the fingers be immersed in the liquid nitrogen. Care must be taken when transferring it from a large vacuum storage vessel to avoid undue spilling and splashing on the hands. Because of the rapid evaporation, even in a Dewar vacuum vessel, on no account must a cork or lid be used or an explosion will occur.

HOT PLATES AND ELECTRIC MANTLES

Hot plates should be of the enclosed element variety controlled either with a low, medium and high switch, or a non-stepped switch giving a wider choice of temperatures, ranging on both models from approximately 100°C to 450°C. A further model having a much lower temperature range is manufactured specifically for drying microscope slides.

Thermostatically controlled hot plates are available for use where temperature maintenance is required to within $\pm 5°C$.

Some models are fitted with a magnetic stirrer, which can be used independently if required.

Insulated electric mantles can be used for heating round-bottomed flasks. Several models are available from the large single mantle type to the smaller multi-mantle variety. Special models are made for use with pear-shaped flasks and beakers. Temperatures up to 600°C can be reached, but of course the appropriate vessel would be used if the temperature required is higher than the melting point of glass.

Electrically heated insulated tape can be obtained for lagging apparatus. It can be bought in various lengths according to requirement.

When purchasing electrical equipment for the laboratory, models which have a thermal cut-out should be obtained whenever possible.

GAS CYLINDERS

Various gases are used in a botanical laboratory. Generally it is not necessary to use medical quality gas. Before gas cylinders are used a cylinder head complete with gauge must be attached. Non-flammable gases are provided with a valve which has a right-handed thread, and flammable gases have a left-handed thread. Thus, cylinder heads made with the requisite screw-thread must be used with the appropriate cylinders. On no account must the cylinder valves be greased. Commonsense precautions, such as not smoking, should be carried out when using flammable gases. After use, not only should the tap on the cylinder head be closed, but the valve of the cylinder should be closed tightly. Cylinders should never be used without being placed in a proper stand. A list is given below of the colour coding for the cylinders containing the gases which the botanical worker is likely to use.

TABLE 2

Gas	Commercial Colour Code
Oxygen*	Black
Nitrogen	Grey body, black shoulder
Oxygen free nitrogen	Grey body, black shoulder with white spot superimposed
Carbon dioxide†	Black
CO_2+nitrogen	Grey body, green band, black shoulder
CO_2+air	Grey body, green band+appropriate lettering
Hydrogen	Red
Methane	Red+appropriate lettering

*Although oxygen supports combustion it is not regarded as a flammable gas.
† Medical grade is usually grey body.

LIQUID CHLORINE CYLINDERS

Liquid chlorine cylinders can be obtained from I.C.I. ($3\frac{1}{2}$ lb. and 10 lb.). They are coloured yellow and deliver gaseous chlorine. When in use the cylinder must be clamped in an *upright* position.

The cylinder must be stored in a *dry* well-ventilated building and direct radiation from any heat source must be avoided. Care must be taken when handling liquid chlorine cylinders so that agitation of the contents is kept to a minimum.

A comprehensive instruction card and a first-aid card dealing specifically with the hazards met with by operators using chlorine should be obtained from I.C.I. Both cards should be displayed prominently in close proximity to the place in which the cylinder is to be used.

pH

pH is the measurement of the acidity or alkalinity of an aqueous solution.

A solution will dissociate to a greater or lesser extent to produce positive and negative ions. Hydrochloric acid will dissociate to form positive hydrogen ions and negative chlorine ions.

$$HCl \rightleftharpoons H^+ + Cl^-$$

Sodium hydroxide dissociates to form positive sodium ions and negative hydroxyl ions.

$$NaOH \rightleftharpoons Na^+ + OH^-$$

In order to measure pH, there must be a standard with which to compare other substances. This standard is pure water.

$$H_2O \rightleftharpoons H^+ + OH^-$$

Pure water dissociates to produce an equal number of hydrogen and hydroxyl ions, but the degree of dissociation is quite small, therefore the amount of un-ionized water will be fairly constant.

It has been determined that at 22°C the concentration of both hydrogen and hydroxyl ions in pure water is 10^{-7} gram-ions/l. of each. The product of the concentration of H^+ and OH^- ions is therefore

$$10^{-7} \times 10^{-7} = 10^{-14}$$

This figure (10^{-14}) is the equilibrium constant K_w; for any increase in the number of hydrogen ions there must be a corresponding decrease in the number of hydroxyl ions, or vice versa, in order to maintain the equilibrium constant at 10^{-14}.

pH is the negative logarithm to base 10 of the hydrogen ion concentration.

$$pH = -\log_{10} [H]^+ = \log \frac{1}{[H]^+}$$

Therefore the pH of pure water is

$$\log \frac{1}{10^{-7}} = 7$$

The range from 0 to 7 denotes the acid range, from 7 to 14 the alkaline range and number 7 is the middle or neutral point. It is important to note that pH values are given as the logarithmic indices and that the scale is reciprocal to the hydrogen ion concentration.

When an acid is added to water, the acid dissociates and hydrogen ions are liberated. The greater the amount of acid added, the higher the concentration of the hydrogen ions and therefore the lower the pH value.

Similarly, when a base (or alkali) is added to water, the base dissociates liberating hydroxyl ions. The higher the concentration of a base, the greater the number of free hydroxyl ions and because of the equilibrium constant, the lower the number of hydrogen ions, resulting in a higher pH value.

Unfortunately, not all acids or bases fully dissociate when concentrated. Those that do are termed strong acids or bases and, logically, those that do not are termed weak acids or bases. Hydrochloric, sulphuric, picric and trichloroacetic are examples of strong acids. Sodium and potassium hydroxides are examples of strong alkalis. Acetic, uric, boric and carbonic acid are a few of the weak acids, while sodium bicarbonate, borax, calcium carbonate and ammonium hydroxide are examples of weak bases.

COLORIMETRIC MEASUREMENT OF pH

This can be effected by any of the following methods:
1. Indicator solutions or papers—approximate only.
2. Capillators and comparators—more accurate than papers or solutions but not as accurate as a pH meter.

Indicator Solutions

Acids and bases partially dissociate, in aqueous solution, into ions. This may be expressed as an equation thus:

$$HA \rightleftharpoons H^+ + A^-$$

where HA is an acid in its undissociated form. When the pH of the solution is such that there are equal quantities of undissociated molecules and dissociated ions present then:

$$\frac{H^+ \times A^-}{HA} = K_a$$

where K_a is the dissociation constant. The pK_a is simply the negative logarithm of the dissociation constant. In this form pK_a may be compared numerically with pH, i.e. at this point the $pK_a = pH$.

Indicators are weak acids or bases and as such each one has its own pK_a. They undergo a colour change when the hydrogen ion concentration is altered. The undissociated molecule will give the acid colour while the dissociated ions will give the alkaline colour. Since the reaction is reversible the addition of any substance which alters the hydrogen ion concentration, will alter the pH of the indicator one way or another on either side of its pK_a point, and so effect the colour change. At the pK_a point the colouration should be therefore an exact mixture of the acid colour and alkaline colour. When using indicators to determine the pH of a solution, the choice should be made of an indicator whose pK_a is close to the suspected pH of the solution. This will give a more accurate determination than if the suspected pH is at either end of the scale given for a particular indicator.

There is a universal indicator solution which gives a gradual colour change from pink to mauve throughout the pH range from

4 to 11. Table 3 shows the colour changes of some common indicator solutions.

It is important to note that indicator solutions changing colour at pH 7·0 will only do so correctly when the acid and alkali are of the same type.

Indicator papers are pieces of absorbent paper impregnated with indicator solution and dried. The colour change is compared with the appropriate chart.

To determine an approximate pH—A sample of the liquid having the unknown pH is withdrawn and one or two drops of universal indicator solution are added. The colour change is compared with the colour chart provided. Alternatively, a pH paper corresponding to the probable range, is dipped in the sample and again the colour change is compared with the correct colour chart. A specific indicator is then used to determine the actual pH (see Table 3).

TABLE 3

Indicator	pH range	pKa	Colour change
Cresol-red (acid range)	0·2– 2·8	—	Red–yellow
Thymol-blue (acid range)	1·2– 2·8	1·65	Red–yellow
Bromo-phenol-blue	2·8– 4·6	3·85	Yellow–blue
*Methyl-orange	3·0– 4·4	3·46	Red–orange/yellow
Bromo-cresol-green	3·6– 5·2	4·66	Yellow–blue
Methyl-red	4·3– 6·1	5·00	Red–yellow
Thymol-red	4·4– 6·2	—	Red–yellow
Chloro-phenol-red	4·6– 7·0	6·00	Yellow–red
Bromo-cresol-purple	5·2– 6·8	6·12	Yellow–purple
Bromo-thymol-blue	6·0– 7·6	7·10	Yellow–blue
Phenol-red	6·8– 8·4	7·81	Yellow–red
Cresol-red	7·2– 8·8	8·3	Yellow–red
Thymol-blue (alkaline range	8·0– 9·6	8·9	Yellow–blue
Phenolphthalein	8·3–10·0	9·7	Colourless–red
Universal indicator	4·0–11·0	—	Pink–mauve via yellow, green and blue

* When used for acid/base titrations methyl orange tends to give an indeterminate end-point. Screened methyl orange will give a much sharper end-point. Screened methyl orange can be made as follows:
1 g methyl orange and 1·4 g xylene cyanol FF are dissolved in 1 l. of distilled water. The colour change using this indicator will be red–grey–green.
pH 3·0   pKa 3·46   pH 4·4

B.D.H. Capillators

Each capillator set contains a number of colour standards. These standards consist of hard glass capillary tubes which are filled with buffered indicator solution and sealed. The capillary tubes are fixed on a card, each card covering a different colour range for a particular indicator and marked with pH values. Also in the capillator case there is a set of indicator solutions in small bottles and a number of capillary tubes marked at a certain level. Rubber teats and small watch glasses are also included. When using a capillator, it is necessary to obtain a rough estimate of the pH of the sample solution by using the universal indicator solution or paper. A capillary tube is then filled to the graduation mark with the sample solution and emptied into one of the small watch glasses. Another capillary tube is filled to the graduation mark with the appropriate indicator (determined from the rough estimate by the universal indicator) and emptied into the watch glass with the sample solution. These equal quantities of sample solution and indicator are mixed together. A capillary tube is then half filled and held against the standard card to match the colour and so obtain the pH value.

Lovibond Comparators

A number of coloured filters standardized to different pH factors for a known indicator solution and two hard glass tubes are provided.

The two tubes are filled to the graduation mark with the solution to be tested. One tube is left as a blank and to the other tube is added the correct amount of the appropriate indicator. This information can be obtained from the instruction sheets provided. The tubes are placed in the comparator and the blank tube is viewed through a filter. The disc holding the filters is rotated until the colours, as seen through the two viewing ports, are the same.

This form of pH measurement is useful when the sample is slightly coloured.

ELECTRICAL MEASUREMENT OF pH

For the electrical determination of pH, three essential components are necessary; a set of electrodes, a solution of known pH and a meter to register the pH value.

Electrodes—Two electrodes are required, an anode or reference electrode and a cathode or glass electrode. These are fitted into a holder which slides up and down a retort stand. Between samples, the electrodes should be rinsed with distilled H_2O and carefully blotted dry with a tissue.

Some manufacturers' catalogues of pH electrodes contain very useful information on the types, their care and use.

Reference electrode—This electrode generally consists of a mercury and calomel element in contact with a saturated solution of potassium chloride which acts as a bridge between the sample solution and the calomel element. The saturated potassium chloride is allowed to make contact with the sample by a controlled leak via a ground glass sleeve or a ceramic plug. When this electrode is not being used, it must be placed in a solution of saturated potassium chloride. The level of potassium chloride within the electrode should be maintained at more than half the height of the glass barrel. When the electrode is in use, the level of potassium chloride must be above that of the solution under test.

Glass electrode—The cathode comprises a reservoir partly filled with $N/10$ hydrochloric acid in contact with a silver chloride coated silver wire. The reservoir terminates in a special glass tip, generally in the shape of a bulb. When the tip is in contact with an aqueous solution containing hydrogen ions, a potential is induced which is relative to the concentration of hydrogen ions. This potential is then measured on a pH meter.

These cathodes are manufactured in a number of different types and may operate accurately only within a particular temperature range. It is therefore very important to choose an electrode which is suitable to the work in hand.

When the glass electrode is not being used it should be immersed in distilled water. If a pad of cotton wool is placed in the bottom of the container, damage to the glass bulb can be prevented.

New electrodes should be immersed in $N/10$ hydrochloric acid for at least 24 hours before they are used. This should also be carried out if an electrode has been allowed to dry out.

Combined electrodes—It is possible to obtain the reference and glass electrodes in a single combined form with the advantage of a compact unit which is useful when measuring small volumes of sample.

Standard pH Solutions

A buffer solution of known pH value is required to standardize a pH meter before use. For highly accurate work it is essential to standardize with a buffer of similar pH to the expected pH of the solution under test. For general work only two buffers are required, an acid standard, e.g. pH 4·0 and an alkali standard, e.g. pH 9·0. These can be prepared as follows:

pH 4·0 Potassium hydrogen phthalate. (According to B.S. 1647: 1950) 0·05 M potassium hydrogen phthalate prepared with fresh distilled water gives a true pH of 4·0 at 15°C, 4·005 at 25°C and 4·026 at 38°C.

pH 9·0 Sodium *tetra* borate (borax). (According to B.S. 1647:

1950) 0·05 M $Na_2B_4O_7$. 10 H_2O (Mol. wt. 381·43) gives a true pH of 9·18 at 25°C and 9·07 at 38°C.

Most manufacturers of pH meters will supply standard buffers in tablet form.

pH Meters

A pH meter works on the principle that a solution containing dissociated ions is capable of passing an electric current. In other words the solution is an electrolyte and, logically, the more ions in solution, the greater the capacity of that solution for passing an electric current. Negative or hydroxyl ions will be attracted by the anode or reference electrode; and the positive or hydrogen ions will be attracted by the cathode or glass electrode. pH meters can be either battery operated or mains powered.

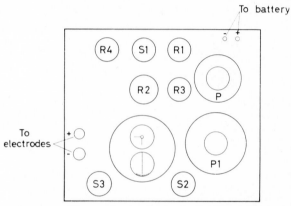

Figure 11. Diagram showing the top of a Cambridge pH meter

Battery operated—Different makes of pH meter will vary slightly in the method of operation but a sheet of instructions is normally provided by the manufacturers. However, the schedule will be similar to that of the Cambridge pH meter as shown below (*see Figure 11*).

(1) Adjust the galvanometer needle to zero. Connect the electrodes.
(2) Connect the battery. Set R2 to the temperature of the electrode system. Set S1 to pH.
(3) Press S2 and operate R1 to balance the galvanometer. Release S2.
(4) Place the electrodes in the buffer solution. Set P and P1 to the pH of this buffer.
(5) Press S3 and operate R3 to balance the galvanometer. Release S3.
(6) Operate R4 to balance the galvanometer.
(7) Remove the electrodes from the buffer solution and wash in distilled water. Place the electrodes in the unknown solution.

(8) Press S3 and balance the galvanometer by adjusting P to the approximate pH and then by adjusting P1 for a final reading.

(9) Switch off the unit.

(10) Disconnect the reference electrode and place in appropriate solution (saturated potassium chloride for a Calomel electrode).

(11) Disconnect the glass electrode and place in distilled water.

(12) Disconnect the battery.

The batteries which are used must be in a good state of charge to prevent fluctuation of the current.

Mains operated—These meters are extremely simple to use, are accurate, fast and give highly reproducible results.

The scale registers the pH from 0 to 14 at full scale deflection and normally it has an anti-parallax mirror. Some of the more expensive meters have an expanded scale converting their full scale deflection from 0–14 to any two consecutive pH values, i.e. full scale deflection reads 0–2, 1–3, 6–8 pH, etc. which enables even greater accuracy. The accuracy of these meters is in order of 0·02 pH with the scale readable to 0·05 pH on the normal scale or 0·003 pH on an expanded scale. If a continuous recording on paper is required, it is normally possible to plug a recorder into the instrument.

Where different temperatures are encountered it is sometimes possible to fit a compensating thermometer which, when it is used in conjunction with the electrodes, provides automatic correction of the pH reading. Other instruments have a correction dial, which is adjusted to the temperature of the test solution.

The method of use will be similar to the E.I.L. schedule below.

(1) Ensure that the machine is at 'check' position and that the glass electrode is still connected to the meter.

(2) Connect the reference electrode.

(3) Switch on.

(4) Wash and blot the electrodes.

(5) Immerse the electrodes in the standard buffer.

(6) Switch to 'pH' and adjust the 'set buffer' to the pH of the standard.

(7) Return to the 'check' position and remove the electrodes, wash and blot.

(8) Immerse the electrodes into the test solution.

(9) Switch to 'pH' position and record the pH measurement.

(10) Return to the 'check' position, remove the electrodes, wash and blot.

(11) Disconnect the reference electrode and place it in saturated potassium chloride.

(12) Place the glass electrode in distilled water.

(13) Switch off.

BUFFER SOLUTIONS

These are solutions which resist changes in pH when acids or alkalis are added. Generally they consist of a solution of a weak acid with its sodium salt.

The amount of acid or alkali that any one buffer can resist is known as its buffering capacity.

Buffer solutions are required to standardize pH meters and are used in volumetric analysis, media, enzymology or any other situation where the pH of a solution needs to be constant.

Figure 12. An expanded scale pH meter
(By courtesy of Beckman Instruments Ltd.)

COLORIMETERS

There are times when volumetric or gravimetric analysis is impracticable for one reason or another and, where minute traces of a substance are involved, these methods will prove tedious and not very accurate. If, however, a chemical is added to a solution of a sample being analysed which will react with it to produce a colouration, then this colour can be compared with a standard colour and a relation formed between the two. This is the basic concept of colorimetric analysis. In the past, the comparison between standard colours and the colour produced in the sample solution has been made by visual means. Nessler tubes, being parallel-sided and of equal size in diameter, are filled to the graduation mark with the coloured solutions, placed in a rack with a white base and viewed longitudinally from above. The depth of colour may be clearly seen and comparisons made. However, human error caused by poor eyesight or colour blindness may render this method unsatisfactory. The introduction of an optical instrument improved upon the use of Nessler tubes. Such an instrument is the Klett colorimeter[2], where the sample and the standard are placed in two cylinders fitted with plungers. Light is reflected up through the cylinders. These are racked up and down individually. The rays from the cylinders pass through a compound prism to reach a common field and are viewed with a microscope eye-piece. The field is divided by a thin line. When the two halves of the field are identical colorimetrically, the depth of the solutions may be measured by means of the vernier scales on the instrument.

Although the Klett colorimeter is a more elaborate apparatus, human error still has to be taken into consideration.

Nowadays, these two visual methods have been superseded by the use of photo-electric colorimeters. The principle used here is that of the light absorption of coloured liquids. If measured in the light of a complementary colour, the relative concentrations of the coloured solutions may be read in terms of optical density. Colorimeters are made in a variety of patterns and with various refinements. Basically they consist of a light source, a silica or quartz cell to hold the solution and a photocell which will generate sufficient current to be recorded by a galvanometer. Coloured glass filters may be inserted between the light source and the cell in order to provide light of the required complementary colour and, therefore, of a specific wavelength. An alternative arrangement is to have a rotating disc of filters built into the apparatus. Measurements taken at lower wavelengths may be made using ultra-violet light. Thus colorimeters may be divided into three types: (*a*) visual colorimeters; (*b*) photo-electric absorptiometers and (*c*) spectrophotometers.

The visual types have been described previously. With regard to photo-electric absorptiometers and spectrophotometers a brief description of the models available is given below.

ABSORPTIOMETERS

All photo-electric absorptiometers have one photocell but a few models are provided with two balanced photocells which compensate for voltage variations from the light source. A tungsten filament lamp supplies the continuous light source, the wavelength of which may be selected by the use of coloured filters fitted into a slot provided on the machine. Some machines are supplied with a shutter which may be closed to protect the photocell when the optical cells are being changed over. Absorptiometers having one photocell are usually

Figure 13. An EEL colorimeter
(By courtesy of Evans Electroselenium Ltd.)

constructed so that a direct reading is possible, either by means of a deflecting needle or by a reflecting galvanometer. This type of galvanometer projects a light spot with a line index on to a calibrated scale.

The general method of use is to place the sample solution in one optical cell and the solvent used for the solution in another to act as a blank. This blank cell should be placed in the machine so that it is positioned between the light source and the photocell as shown in the following pattern:

Light source—filter—cell—photocell—galvanometer—meter scale. The requisite filter should be placed in position.

The aperture, in which the optical cell is placed, should be closed by the lid or cap supplied with the instrument in order to exclude stray light. The electric current should now be turned on and the instrument adjusted. This is done by turning the knob or dial which will open or close a shutter and increase or decrease the amount of light passing through. The effect of this is to deflect the needle or light spot on the calibrated scale. When the instrument is properly adjusted the needle or light spot should rest on the zero point of the scale. The optical cell containing the solvent (which is often water) should now be changed for one containing the coloured solution to be tested and the reading on the scale noted. The coloured solution should now be removed, the blank cell replaced and it should be checked that the meter reading is back to zero. A series of readings can be taken one after another if required. The zero adjustment should be checked between each reading. If the instrument is provided with an extra shutter to completely exclude the light from the photocell, this should be used while changing the optical cells. It is standard practice when measuring the concentration of substance in solution, to plot a calibration curve using a series of solutions of known strength. It is a simple matter to find the concentration of a solution of unknown strength if its optical density, as measured on the instrument, is compared with the prepared calibration curve.

Alternatively, if one standard solution of known concentration is measured, then that of the unknown solution may be expressed by the equation

$$C_1 = \frac{C_2 \times e_1}{e_2}$$

where C_1 = concentration of the test solution.
C_2 = concentration of standard.
e_1 = reading of test solution.
e_2 = reading of standard.

Absorptiometers may be used to determine the degree of turbidity of a solution, since a turbid solution will also absorb light in a similar way to a coloured solution.

A short list of absorptiometers and where they can be obtained from is given here.

The first model has been found to be a compact instrument, eminently suitable for student use.

The EEL Portable Colorimeter
Evans Electroselenium Ltd.,
St. Andrews Works,
Halstead, Essex

The Biochem Absorptiometer
The Spekker Absorptiometer

Hilger & Watts,
St. Pancras Way,
London

Spectrophotometers

Spectrophotometers work on the same principle as absorptio-meters but they enable measurements to be taken at shorter wave-lengths as well as in the visible region of the spectrum. They are slightly more complex in design, having a monochromator placed in line with the photocell. The sensitivity of the instrument is very much more than that of the absorptiometers previously mentioned. Some spectrophotometers are extremely expensive and are only likely to be found in a research laboratory. A few of the models available and the manufacturers are listed below. The first two are useful for the visible region of the spectrum.

The Diffraction Grating Spectrophotometer
The Unicam SP600 Spectrophotometer

Unicam Instruments (Cambridge) Ltd.,
Arbury Works,
Cambridge

The Uvispek Photo-electric Spectrophotometer

Hilger & Watts,
St Pancras Way
London

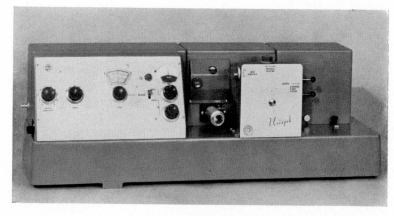

Figure 14. Uvispek spectrophotometer
(By courtesy of Hilger & Watts)

Fluorimeters

Some substances emit the light they absorb, that is to say they fluoresce. This fluorescence may be measured in an instrument called a fluorimeter. Substances to be measured should be in solution and the solvents which are used must be free from any particles of matter which will cause fluorescence.

Full instructions for the use of all the instruments described in this section are supplied by the manufacturers.

THERMOREGULATORS FOR CONSTANT TEMPERATURE TANKS

Toluene-mercury thermoregulators are made of glass in several patterns, two of which are shown in *Figure 15 a and b*. The ring or bulb (A) at the bottom of the regulator is almost filled with toluene, while the vertical tube (B) and the remaining space in the ring or bulb are filled up with clean mercury. The reservoir (C) above the tap should be one-third full of mercury and the trough (D) at the top of the vertical tube, should hold mercury also. A capillary tube (E) is attached to the vertical tube in the centre of the trough. Two platinum or tungsten wires are mounted in a stopper of Perspex which is placed in the neck of the regulator. The central wire extends down into the capillary tube and is adjusted by means of an adjusting screw. The second wire dips just below the surface of the mercury in the outer trough. A lead and 2-amp plug are connected to the two wires. The plug is placed in a socket on the control panel between the Sunvic control and a small neon lamp. The thermoregulator is immersed in the tank until the ring or bulb is well covered. It should be held rigidly by a clamp and copper wire. The tap of the regulator is opened, the Perspex stopper placed in position but the 2-amp plug is not yet connected. The heating elements are switched to *High* until the requisite temperature has been reached, then switched to *Off* position and the column of mercury is forced up the capillary tube until it contacts the wire. This may be done by applying pressure to the top of the mercury reservoir, above the tap, with a moistened thumb. The pressure is maintained until the tap has been closed with the other hand. The 2-amp plug is now connected and the elements turned to *Low*. When the central needle contacts the mercury, the circuit is completed and the hot wire switch of the Sunvic control comes into operation, switching off the electric elements. As the temperature drops fractionally, the mercury will also drop as it and the toluene contract, thus breaking the circuit. The hot wire switch will bring the heating elements into operation again and so the temperature will be maintained. When the elements are heating, the small neon lamp will light up. When the elements are off the neon lamp will go off too.

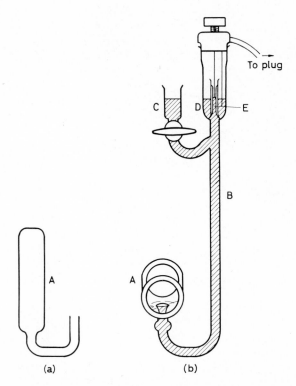

Figure 15. Toluene-mercury thermoregulator: (a) *bulb extension;*
(b) *complete thermoregulator—ring type*

Several models of sealed thermoregulators are available which are gradually replacing the toluene-mercury type. The sealed models are virtually trouble-free and are usually robust as they have metal jackets. Unlike toluene-mercury thermoregulators, they do not need cleaning as in the following section.

N.B. The thermoregulator should never be adjusted with the 2-amp plug in position.

CLEANING AND FILLING OF THE THERMOREGULATOR

Cleaning

The mercury in the thermoregulator becomes dirty after a while, particularly that which is in contact with the air. This condition must be rectified if the temperature is to be controlled accurately. The exposed surfaces may be partially cleaned without dismantling the entire apparatus. The electric current should be disconnected and, using a damp piece of filter paper (15 cm dia.) folded into a spill, the mercury in the trough and in the reservoir can be cleaned with a stirring motion. The capillary tube may be cleaned with a minute wisp of moistened cotton wool wrapped round an inoculating needle.

If, however, the temperature cannot be regulated properly, i.e. the neon lamp does not flick on and off frequently, indicating adequate temperature control, and the partial cleaning procedure fails to correct this fault, more drastic action must be taken.

First the electrical circuit should be checked, by-passing the thermoregulator. If this is found to be correct the regulator must be completely dismantled and cleaned in the following manner.

(1) Remove the thermoregulator from the tank, take out the stopper, open the tap and turn it upside down over a large beaker. The mercury will fall into the beaker under its own weight.

(2) Remove the toluene by holding the regulator bulb or ring under hot running water. (Toluene expands and contracts rapidly. It is this physical property which is used to facilitate emptying and filling the regulator.) As the toluene expands, it will be forced out of the top of the regulator.

(3) Wash the regulator with water by reversing stage (2) in the following way. Fill the reservoir with water and shut the tap. Heat the ring or bulb under hot running water for a minute or two and transfer quickly to cold running water, opening the tap simultaneously. Swill the water, taken in in this way, round the inside of the regulator, then remove it by the heating procedure again. Repeat the washing, then repeat the procedure using a little chromic acid cleaning liquid. Wash the regulator several times with water after the acid wash and finally rinse with acetone.

(4) Place in a drying oven at 100°C for 24 hours or more.

If a regulator is broken it must be emptied, cleaned and dried in the manner described before being repaired.

Refilling

For this procedure re-distilled toluene is required, also a quantity of clean mercury and two good quality corks, one to fit the main mouth of the regulator and one for the mouth of the reservoir.

(1) Fill the regulator completely with re-distilled toluene, in a similar manner to stage (3) of the cleaning procedure. When the first portion of toluene has been sucked into the bulb or ring of the regulator, refill the reservoir with toluene, close the tap and place both corks in position. Hold the regulator in a horizontal position with the bulb or ring hanging downwards. Heat the bulb while in this position, then very quickly turn the regulator upright, remove the corks, open the tap and cool the bulb. Repeat this process of heating, cooling and adding more toluene until the regulator is completely filled, i.e. until toluene overflows from the capillary tube when cool. As the bulb fills with toluene so the regulator should be tilted more and more until during the last stages of filling, it is completely inverted. Great care must be taken during filling not to allow any water to enter with the toluene. This will cause a cloudiness in the toluene. If this should happen the regulator must be emptied, cleaned, dried and filled again.

(2) Displace a portion of the toluene by filling the reservoir with mercury and opening the tap. The mercury will fall down the vertical tube towards the bulb, while the toluene is displaced upwards through the capillary tube. Add more mercury until the vertical tube is completely filled and the excess partially fills the capillary tube and reservoir. Remove any free toluene floating on the surface of the mercury with a coiled spill of filter paper. Pour clean mercury into the trough, place the stopper carrying the two electrode needles in position and the thermoregulator is ready for use.

CLEANING OF GLASSWARE

It is often of vital importance to have glassware which is completely clean and grease free. This can be achieved by filling it with chromic acid cleaning solution. When freshly prepared, the acid need only be in contact with the glass for 15 minutes. When using old acid or when cleaning extremely greasy glassware, it should be left in contact with the glass for some hours. After the requisite time, the acid should be drained from the glassware which should then be rinsed 12 times with tap water and twice with distilled water. Clean glassware may be dried in an oven with the exception of accurately calibrated equipment. This should never be heated on any account. Before cleaning any apparatus in this way, it must be rinsed thoroughly to remove any trace of organic substance which will reduce the acid.

The following solution is suitable for cleaning grade B glass. For grade A glass, nitric acid should be used instead of sulphuric acid in the cleaning fluid as less heat is produced during the cleaning reaction.

Dissolve 30 g of sodium or potassium dichromate in 100 ml water.
Make up 1 litre with concentrated sulphuric acid, cooling the mixture while adding the acid (always add the acid to the water).

This cleaning mixture should be made up in a Pyrex vessel and stored in a stoppered glass bottle.

If, during the preparation or use of chromic, or indeed any acid, a spillage should occur, it should be neutralized immediately and then completely cleared away. For this purpose a jar of technical grade sodium carbonate should be kept near the washing up bench so that it can be used for neutralizing large spills. A 20 per cent solution is useful for small spills.

Similarly, should an accident occur when using caustic solutions, the spillage should be neutralized with a 20 per cent solution of acetic acid and then washed away with clean water.

If the skin is splashed by acid or caustic, the area should be washed well with plenty of water and then the neutralizer should be applied in a 2·0 per cent solution. A further rinsing with clean water should follow.

Acid cleaning can be dispensed with if a cleanser is used which is manufactured specifically for laboratory glassware. These cleansers are supplied in a concentrated form either as powder or liquid and they should be diluted and used in accordance with the instructions provided. Although the concentrates are fairly expensive, when diluted they compare favourably with the cost of the acid cleaning solutions. They will remove grease, inorganic matter and resins from smooth glass surfaces, but are not so useful for sintered glassware. Many are ideal for radioactive decontamination and most are also bactericidal. Normally there is no detrimental effect to the skin unless the hands are immersed in the cleaning solution for a long time.

A list of some of the products which are available is given below:—

Haemo-sol (powder)	RBS-25 (liquid)
Pyro-neg (powder)	Decon-75 (liquid)
Quadralene (powder)	(Decon-75 has superseded RBS-25)

Cheaper liquid detergents such as Teepol or Lissapol can be used for general cleaning of laboratory glassware, when absolute chemical cleanliness is not essential. Teepol in particular removes the natural oils of the skin, and so rubber gloves are advisable. Glassware cleaned with any of these detergents must be thoroughly rinsed, i.e. at least 8 times with tapwater and 3 times with distilled water.

GRADUATED GLASSWARE

In the botanical laboratory a range of graduated glassware is essential to prepare solutions for many operations from media-making to volumetric analysis. Descriptions of the apparatus normally required, in addition to beakers, test-tubes, etc., are given below.

BURETTES

Generally, burettes are made to contain volumes of 25, 50 and 100 ml. Semi-micro and micro burettes hold smaller volumes with a range between 1 ml and 10 ml. Both series of burettes are calibrated with graduations of 0·01 ml to 0·2 ml usually dependent upon the overall volume.

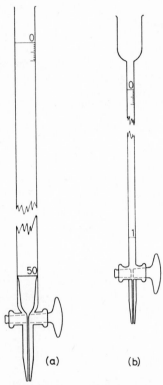

Figure 16. (a) *Standard burette;*
(b) *microburette*

The conventional burette tap (*Figure 16*) is made entirely of glass although a slightly more expensive one can be obtained which is made of the plastic Teflon. Another type of glass stopcock of the conventional pattern has the ground surfaces of the barrel and key impregnated with Teflon. A diaphragm type of Teflon stopcock (*Figure 17*) is also available. Burettes with plastic or plastic impregnated taps are suitable for use with caustic solutions or indeed with any solution which may cause the ground surfaces of untreated glass stopcocks to stick. An additional advantage with the conventional plastic, plastic impregnated glass, and diaphragm types is that no lubricant is needed. On the other hand the barrel and key of the untreated glass stopcock must be carefully and thoroughly lubricated before and after use (p. 60).

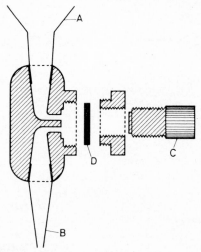

Figure 17. An exploded diagram of a diaphragm stopcock
(a) *body of burette;* (b) *jet;* (c) *adjusting screw;* (d) *rubber diaphragm.*

The diaphragm type must be assembled very carefully to ensure leakage-proof joints but once this has been done it provides a very delicate control over the volume and rate of flow of the liquid which is being dispensed during a titration.

After rinsing with a few ml of the required solution, the burette is filled from the top with the aid of a small funnel. The solution is then run out until all the air bubbles have been forced out of the jet. More solution is added if the level of the meniscus has fallen below the zero mark. Should any difficulty be experienced when filling semi-micro and micro burettes, a simple mouthpiece can be attached to the neck of the burette so that the solution can be drawn up to the zero mark.

All burettes should be filled and used in a vertical position. When using any graduated glassware, the level of the meniscus should always be read at eye level to avoid error due to parallax. If a piece of cardboard which has the lower half blackened is held behind the burette with the dividing line of the cardboard 1 or 2 mm below the level of the meniscus, then the bottom of the meniscus will appear as a dark line and the position can be recorded accurately.

As previously mentioned, untreated glass stopcocks must be lubricated. A small amount of white vaseline should be applied to the dry key which is then placed in the barrel and rotated. When the entire barrel is coated with vaseline it will appear transparent. If an excess of lubricant is applied the bore of the tap may become blocked. If this happens during titration, it can be unblocked in the following manner.

Record the level of the meniscus on the graduated scale and then place a small beaker below the jet. Insert a piece of fine fuse wire into the jet Withdraw it quickly, opening the tap simultaneously. This should be repeated until the solution flows freely. The meniscus level should be recorded again before resuming titration. To free a persistent blockage, the burette is taken from its holder, after recording the meniscus level and with the tap open, the jet is held under hot running water until the solution runs freely. The jet is cooled and rinsed with distilled water. The outside of the burette is wiped with a clean cloth or paper tissue and replaced in the holder. The meniscus level is recorded and the titration resumed.

When solutions are being dispensed from a burette, the left hand should be placed round the stopcock so that the tap is operated with the thumb and first two fingers. In this way there is no tendency for the key to be pulled from the barrel as might happen if the right hand were used. The right hand is then free to manipulate the receiving flask. If the key is fitted with a retaining clip, or if a Mohr burette or one fitted with a diaphragm stopcock is used the right hand may be used to control the flow of solution if the operator so prefers.

PIPETTES

The pippetes used for volumetric work fall into two groups: (a) bulb pipettes and (b) cylindrical pipettes (*Figure 18*).

The bulb pipette is designed to deliver accurately one specific volume whereas the cylindrical pipette can deliver any volume over the range for which it is calibrated. The former is the more accurate of the two and should be used whenever possible.

Both types of pipette are filled in the same manner. A quantity of the solution to be measured is poured into a beaker and the tip of the pipette placed under the surface of the liquid. The solution is sucked up into the pipette to a point beyond the graduation mark on the bulb pipette or the top of the graduated scale on the cylindrical type. The solution is held in the pipette by placing the index finger firmly

over the mouthpiece. The pressure of the finger is released slightly
and the solution allowed to run out until the meniscus has fallen to
either the graduation or the zero mark. The pipette is now ready for

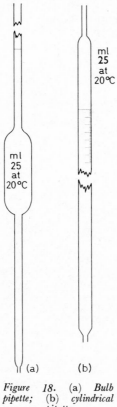

Figure 18. (a) *Bulb
pipette;* (b) *cylindrical
pipette*

delivery. The bulb pipette should be run out completely and allowed
to drain before touching the tip of the pipette against the side of the
receiving vessel. On no account should it be blown out. Unless a
blow-out pipette is used the cylindrical pipette should be allowed to
deliver the required amount, taking care to allow the solution to
drain down the walls of the pipette. This is to ensure that the correct
volume is delivered.

When pipetting concentrated acids, alkalis, and poisons *an external
means of suction must be used.* Various types of rubber bulbs are marketed
for this purpose, e.g., ' Pumpett '.

Cylindrical pipettes are normally graduated in two ways, (a) for delivery from a top zero mark down to the required graduation, and (b) for delivery from a top zero mark down to the tip of the jet. A third type of graduation having the zero mark on the stem just above the jet can be obtained from some manufacturers.

Cylindrical pipettes are normally made in capacities of 1, 2, 5, 10 and 25 ml. Bulb pipettes can be obtained in various capacities from 1 to 100 ml.

Most manufacturers are colour coding both bulb and cylindrical pipettes. This coding is carried out either by fusing a band of colour into the glass, or by etching a patch of colour on the suction tube section of the pipette. Provided that they are not from different manufacturers this colour coding is useful when selecting certain required capacities from assorted pipettes. As yet there is no standard colour code.

As it is possible to obtain these pipettes in several grades with respect to the accuracy of calibration, it is advisable to study the manufacturers' catalogues before deciding upon a particular grade. Apart from bulb and cylindrical pipettes there are numerous pipettes designed for specific purposes. Most of them are of the cylindrical type but with smaller capacities than the general purpose pipettes, and for this reason they are usually made of tubing with a capillary bore. Although primarily intended for clinical use, e.g. blood pipettes, etc., they are invaluable in the botanical laboratory for such things as 'spotting' chromatograms, plating out cell suspensions, enzyme assays and plating radio-active solutions prior to counting.

In addition there are micro-pipettes with automatic zeroing devices, which have been calibrated to a very great degree of accuracy and to within a given tolerance stated on the packaging of each individual pipette. They can be obtained in capacities ranging from 0·005 ml to 0·25 ml.

SEMI-AUTOMATIC AND AUTOMATIC DISPENSERS

Burettes with semi-automatic filling devices can be obtained from several manufacturers. In each case the burette is connected to a reservoir of the required solution and is refilled by means of a small finger pump.

Semi-automatic pipettes (*Figure 19*) can be obtained which are connected to an external reservoir in a similar fashion to the automatic burette, and these are used for repetitive work.

The most recent innovation in the semi-automatic and automatic dispenser field is that of the syringe pattern. Syringes have been used for many years for clinical work, e.g. hypodermic syringes, and therefore need to be accurately calibrated. They can be used in the botanical laboratory complete with hypodermic needle for introducing solutions into the side arm bulb of Warburg flasks during an experiment, or into a flask, containing a specific atmosphere, which is sealed with a vaccine stopper, i.e. the needle will pierce the rubber stopper, and the resultant tiny hole will reseal itself when the needle is withdrawn.

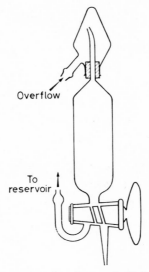

Figure 19. A semi-automatic pipette

If the needle is removed from the syringe and a duo-valve assembly attached, the syringe can be used to dispense in rapid repetition. The duo-valve is connected by polythene or rubber tubing to a reservoir of the liquid being dispensed. The solution is drawn from the reservoir by means of the non-return mechanism of the duo-valve and ejected through the nozzle of the syringe into the receiver.

One fully automatic dispenser which also has a non-return valve is the 'Zippette' (*Figure 20*) made by Jencons of Hemel Hempstead, Herts. The amount of liquid dispensed can be adjusted over a given range. Three models are available, one dispensing up to 4 ml, one up to 10 ml and the last up to 30 ml.

The same firm market the 'Repette', a device of the hypodermic syringe pattern but with modifications which allow for multiple deliveries from one filling of the syringe. Each aliquot is delivered with a high degree of accuracy. This syringe is in fact capable of doing all that the 'Zippette' will do but with greater accuracy and has the advantage of being capable of dispensing far smaller volumes of liquid. It is necessarily more expensive.

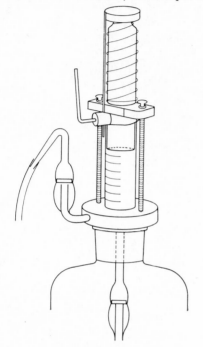

Figure 20. A Jencon's 'Zippette'

Automatic dispensers are available from a number of manufacturers apart from those described above and some have the added advantage of dispensing media aseptically if required.

When using syringes, care must be taken to expel any air-bubbles before collecting the aliquot.

When using all syringe type dispensers extreme caution must be taken to clean the barrel and plunger thoroughly; applying silicone liquid to avoid sticking between the two ground surfaces. If cleaning is impracticable immediately after use, a thorough rinsing with water is essential.

MEASURING CYLINDERS

Volumes of any solutions can be dispensed with a lesser degree of accuracy by using a measuring cylinder. These cylinders are available in a large range of capacities from 5 ml to 2 litres. The cylinder which is used should be as close in capacity to the volume required to be measured as possible. In the past the spouts and bases were prone to chipping, but the introduction of plastic bases and sponge rubber sleeves have helped to eliminate this problem.

Apart from the usual spouted type, stoppered measuring cylinders are available with either interchangeable ground glass or plastic stoppers.

VOLUMETRIC FLASKS

The volumetric flask is graduated to contain one specific volume of solution at one specific temperature, usually 15° or 20°C. The flask has a pear-shaped bulb, a long narrow neck upon which is the graduation mark and a stopper (*Figure 21*). They are obtainable in capacities of 5 ml up to 2 litres. Some manufacturers supply one

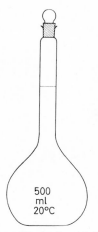

500
ml
20°C

Figure 21. A volumetric flask

further capacity of 5 litres. Recently a volumetric flask of 1 ml capacity has been brought on to the market which has a wide neck. This modification simplifies the introduction of the chemical into the flask and also facilitates cleaning. Plastic stoppers and screw caps can be obtained instead of a ground glass stopper.

It is in the volumetric flask that the accurate solutions used in volumetric analysis are prepared. The substance to be diluted can either be placed directly in the flask and water added, or it can be initially diluted in a small beaker and washed into the flask. This is facilitated by using a small funnel placed in the neck of the flask, the diluted substance being poured down a glass rod through the funnel into the flask. The beaker should be rinsed out several times. The

c*   65

former method is useful when preparing dilute solutions from concentrated ones but it is not advised when using solid materials. In this case the latter method is the better of the two.

Graduated test-tubes can be used for preparing small quantities of standard solutions, i.e. 1–10 ml.

Comparatively rough measurements of volume can be made in graduated beakers. Solutions of approximate strength can be prepared, *in situ*, using these beakers which are obtainable in glass or plastic.

It is not advisable to use concentrated acids in the cheaper, disposable plastic beakers. Many solvents attack the plastic type on *long standing*. Any residual solvent should be rinsed from the beaker immediately after use if thorough cleaning is not convenient at that time.

CALIBRATION AND CLEANING OF GRADUATED GLASSWARE

Although the glassware previously described can be obtained very accurately calibrated, it may be necessary for some reason to re-calibrate a piece of apparatus. In this case the glassware should be filled with water to the graduation mark. This water should then be transferred to a tared beaker, weighed and the temperature recorded. The exact volume of the pipette or burette can be calculated if a textbook of physical constants is used to obtain the specific gravity of the water at different temperatures.

Flasks may be calibrated in a similar way by weighing the flask empty and then filling with water to the graduation mark.

All glassware used for volumetric work should be kept clean and grease free, using either chromic acid cleaning solution or one of the proprietary brands of cleanser (p. 56, 57). Glass burette taps should be greased after each cleaning.

VOLUMETRIC ANALYSIS

STANDARD SOLUTIONS

A standard solution contains a known amount of substance, which has been accurately checked against a primary standard. The concentrations of these solutions are usually expressed in 'normalities'. A 'normal' solution contains 1 gram-equivalent weight of a substance per litre of solution. The gram-equivalent weight of an element or a compound is the number of grams of the substance which will combine with, or take the place of, 1 g of hydrogen, 8 g of oxygen or 1 gram-equivalent of any other substance. For example, hydrochloric acid contains 1 atom of hydrogen replaceable by 1 atom of a metal per molecule of the acid.

$$2HCl + Zn = ZnCl_2 + H_2$$

It may be noticed that two molecules of hydrochloric acid are required to balance the equation but, in fact, only one atom of hydrogen is required to be replaced by the atom of metal. One molecule of hydrochloric acid is therefore equivalent to 1 atom of hydrogen and hence the gram-equivalent weight is equal to the molecular weight, in this case 36·5.

On the other hand, if sulphuric acid is used in place of hydrochloric acid, then the equation would be

$$H_2SO_4 + Zn = ZnSO_4 + H_2$$

In this case one molecule of sulphuric acid supplied two atoms of hydrogen which are replaced by the metal. Therefore one molecule of sulphuric acid is equal to two atoms of hydrogen and the gram-equivalent weight is equal to half the molecular weight, i.e. $^{98}/_2 = 49$.

When the equivalent weight of a substance has been determined, the required solutions may be prepared, for example normal 1·0N, 0·5N, 0·1N, 0·01N or 2N, 3N, etc. Care should be taken not to confuse normal (N) solutions with molar (M) solutions. A molar solution contains the molecular weight of the substance in 1 l. of distilled water. Therefore a 0·1M solution would contain $^1/_{10}$th the molecular weight in 1 l.

Care must be taken when preparing dilute standard solutions of concentrated acids or other compounds to consider the specific gravity of the substance to be diluted. A textbook of constants (see bibliography) will provide tables of normalities with corresponding specific gravities for various acids.

Solutions should be prepared in accurately calibrated glassware. High grade stoppered measuring cylinders can be used, but it is preferable to use volumetric flasks (p. 65). After standardization, the solution should be transferred to clean *dry* containers for storage.

TITRATION

When a series of solutions have been made and standardized, it is reasonable to suppose that, if a known volume and concentration of a sample to be analysed is mixed with a volume of a standard solution, giving an equal concentration of reacting substances in solution, then the percentage of the reacting substance in the sample may be calculated. This is the process known as titration. One solution is placed in a burette, or a microburette, which is held vertically on a clamp stand. The other solution is pipetted into the reaction vessel and a drop of the appropriate indicator solution is added if required. The reaction vessel should be placed beneath the tip of the burette on a white tile which provides a suitable background for observing any colour change. The solution in the burette should be run into the reaction vessel, which should be swirled with the right hand to mix the contents thoroughly, until a permanent colour change has taken place. This colour change is called the 'end-point'. In this instance this is the point at which the reacting substances are present in equal concentrations. To determine this point accurately, a series of three titrations should be made. The first will serve as a rough estimation of the amount of standard solution required. The last two should be accurate. The solution should be added quickly to within 1 ml of the estimated end-point, which should then be approached slowly drop by drop until the colour change takes place. The average of the two volumes of solution used in these two titrations should be taken. From the result of the titration the amount of the reacting substance in the sample and therefore the normality of the solution can be calculated, using the equation

$$V_A \times N_A = V_B \times N_B$$

where V_A is the volume (in ml) of a solution of known normality N_A required to complete the reaction with volume V_B, of a solution of an unknown normality N_B.

The most widely used titrations in a botanical laboratory are:

1. Acid–base titrations
2. Precipitation titrations
3. Oxidation and reduction titrations

Details are given below for the preparation of some standard solutions required in each section. Analytical grade chemicals should be used whenever possible.

(1) *Acid–Base Titrations*

Decinormal (0·1N) sodium carbonate (primary standard):—Since a normal (1·0N) solution of sodium carbonate contains one gram-equivalent weight (53 g Na_2CO_3) per litre, a decinormal (0·1N) solution contains 53/10 or 5·300 g/litre. Pure dry anhydrous sodium carbonate must be used for this solution, which is a primary standard. Analytical grade sodium carbonate can be used after heating to a constant weight at 260°C ($\frac{1}{2}$ hour) and cooling in a desiccator. Alternatively, analytical grade sodium bicarbonate can be converted to anhydrous carbonate by heating to constant weight at 260°C ($1\frac{1}{2}$ hours) and cooling in a desiccator

$$2NaHCO_3 = Na_2CO_3 + CO_2 \uparrow + H_2O \uparrow$$

Since pure anhydrous sodium carbonate is very hygroscopic it is necessary to weigh the requisite amount quickly. For this reason it is better to take quickly an approximate weight in a closed bottle and weigh it accurately than to adjust the amount to exactly 5·300 g.

The accurately weighed sodium carbonate should be washed out of the weighing bottle into a beaker and completely dissolved in a small amount of distilled water (50 ml). This solution should be transferred to a 1 litre volumetric flask and diluted with distilled water to within a few ml of the graduation mark on the neck of the flask. The final adjustment should be made drop-wise with a pipette.

An example of the calculation of the normality is as follows:

Weight of weighing bottle $+ Na_2CO_3 = 12·358$ g
Weight of weighing bottle empty $= 7·013$ g
Weight of Na_2CO_3 $= 5·345$ g

Approximate strength when made up to 1 litre $= 0·1N$ but an exact $0·1N$ solution would contain

$$5·300 \text{ g } Na_2CO_3/\text{litre}$$

the prepared solution will be slightly more concentrated than $0·1N$ or

$$\frac{5·345}{5·300} \times 0·1N$$
$$= 0·1009N$$

The solution should be labelled '$0·1009N$ sodium carbonate'. This means that 1 ml of this solution would require 1·009 ml of $0·1N$ acid to neutralize it.

Standard Acid Solutions

Hydrochloric acid is most frequently employed for volumetric analysis. Sulphuric acid is used occasionally and nitric acid very rarely. The preparation and standardization of a normal (1·0N) hydrochloric acid is given in detail below together with the initial preparation of normal (1·0N) sulphuric acid.

Normal (1·0N) hydrochloric acid—The concentrated acid available commercially is between 10 and 12N. Since the specific gravity is about 1·18, approximately 90 ml of the concentrated acid are required for 1 litre of a normal (1·0N) solution. Place 500 ml of distilled water in a 1 litre volumetric flask and using a small funnel and glass rod, add 90 ml acid from a measuring cylinder. Make up to the 1 litre mark with distilled water and mix thoroughly. The acid can be standardized against 0·1N sodium carbonate but when titrating two solutions one against the other it is wise to use solutions of approximately the same normality. Therefore the prepared 1·0N hydrochloric acid solution must be diluted before standardization can proceed.

Take a 100 ml volumetric flask containing approximately 50 ml distilled water add 10 ml of the prepared 1·0N solution, measured with a bulb pipette. Make up to the graduation mark with distilled water and mix thoroughly. Rinse and fill a 50 ml burette with this solution. Pipette 25 ml of standard sodium carbonate solution into a 100 ml Erlenmeyer (conical) flask, together with one or two drops of an appropriate indicator, e.g. screened methyl orange. The carbonate is then titrated with the acid in the manner described previously (p. 67, 68) until the end-point is reached, i.e. when the colour of the solution in the flask *just* changes from green to grey.

The indicator selected for this titration, screened methyl orange, changes colour at pH 3·46 (see p. 43). At this pH the carbonic acid liberated by the addition of acid to sodium carbonate does not effect the indicator. If, however, an indicator with a higher change point is used, e.g. methyl red with a change point of pH 5·0, the flask containing the carbonate should be heated near the end-point to drive off carbon dioxide and the titration finished with the solution still hot.

Example calculation:

25 ml of 0·1009N sodium carbonate required:

Titration	1	2	3
	25·2	24·5	25·0 ml of acid

or 24·75 ml of acid (being the average of titrations 2 and 3)

Normality of the acid solution

$$= \frac{25 \cdot 00}{24 \cdot 75} \times 0 \cdot 1009N \text{ (normality of the carbonate solution)}$$

$$= 0 \cdot 1019N$$

This solution was prepared by diluting the approximately normal solution by exactly tenfold. Consequently the normality of the originally prepared 1·0N hydrochloric acid solution

$$= 1 \cdot 019N$$

∴. 1 ml of this solution has the neutralizing power of 1·019 ml of an exactly 1·0N solution.

To prepare an exactly 1·0N solution the following dilutions should be made:

1 ml should be diluted to 1·019 ml
1,000 ml should be diluted to 1,019 ml
980·37 ml should be diluted to 1,000 ml

The solution prepared initially should always be slightly *more* concentrated than the exact strength required; it can then be diluted as necessary.

Normal (1·0N) sulphuric acid—An approximate dilution is made by placing 500 ml distilled water in a volumetric flask and adding 30 ml of concentrated sulphuric acid very slowly. The flask should be cooled under cold running water during the addition. Make up to 1 litre mark. Mix thoroughly and standardize as described above for hydrochloric acid.

An appreciable amount of heat is generated during the dilution of many substances including some acids. Since volumetric flasks are calibrated to hold the required volume at one specific temperature, usually 20°C, it is essential to cool the contents of the flask continuously under cold running water throughout the dilution. The last addition of water, bringing the meniscus up to the graduation mark, should be carried out at 20°C.

Standard Alkali (Basic) Solutions

Sodium hydroxide is the most commonly used alkali for standard solutions. It may be obtained in either pellet or stick form, with a purity of approximately 98 per cent; a small percentage of carbonate is always present. It is also extremely hygroscopic. For elementary work, the carbonate present may be disregarded, but some titrations require a carbonate free solution. Therefore the preparation of both the carbonate adulterated solution (a) and the carbonate-free solution (b) will be given.

Normal (1·0N) sodium hydroxide solution

(a) Weigh 42–43 g of solid sodium hydroxide. Do this quickly and approximately to reduce deliquescence using a weighing bottle or small beaker. Wash the sodium hydroxide into a larger beaker and immediately add 100 ml distilled water. Stir with a glass rod and when no more solid appears to be dissolving transfer the solution to a 1 litre volumetric flask. Add more water to the remaining solid in the beaker and continue until all the sodium hydroxide has dissolved. Wash out the beaker and add the washings to the solution in the 1 litre flask. The solution, which will be hot, should be allowed to cool before making up to volume.

(b) Sodium carbonate is insoluble in saturated sodium hydroxide solution and a virtually carbonate-free solution can be prepared by diluting saturated sodium hydroxide solution, which is about 16N, with carbon dioxide free water.

Place about 350 g sodium hydroxide in a 1 litre beaker and add 500 ml water. Allow to stand, stirring occasionally until the solution is cool and no more sodium hydroxide dissolves. Transfer the rather viscous liquid to a polythene bottle containing about 50 sodium hydroxide pellets. On standing, the carbonate present will settle to the bottom of the bottle. A carbonate-free sodium hydroxide solution, approximately 1·0N can be made by diluting 60 ml of the clear liquid to 1 litre with freshly boiled and cooled distilled water.

The solutions prepared in (a) and (b) are approximately 1·0N and must be standardized against 1·0N hydrochloric acid. The standardized solution (a) should be stored in a polythene bottle or plastic stoppered Pyrex glass bottle and labelled appropriately. The carbonate free solution should be stored in a polythene aspirator, the neck of which should be closed with a bung fitted with a soda lime tube.

TABLE 4

Type of titration	Indicator to be used
Strong acid—strong base	Bromo-thymol-blue
Strong acid—weak base	Screened methyl orange or methyl red
Weak acid—strong base	Phenolphthalein
Weak acid—weak base	No suitable indicator

These are simple indicators for acid-base titrations. Other indicators required for more complicated titrimetric methods may be found in a textbook on volumetric analysis.

(2) *Precipitation Titrations*

The two solutions most likely to be required are decinormal (0·1N) silver nitrate and decinormal (0·1N) sodium chloride. The theory governing precipitation titrations or indeed any of the titrations mentioned will not be discussed here but it can be found in a comprehensive textbook on volumetric analysis (see bibliography).

Decinormal (0·1N) sodium chloride—Weigh accurately 5·846 g of sodium chloride. Dissolve in a little distilled water, transfer to a 1 litre volumetric flask and make up to volume. Mix and transfer to a labelled Pyrex glass bottle.

Decinormal (0·1N) silver nitrate—Heat a quantity of silver nitrate to 120°C for 2 hours. After cooling it in a desiccator, weigh accurately 16·989 g, dissolve and make up to 1 litre in a volumetric flask with distilled water. Standardize as follows using dichlorofluorescein as an adsorption indicator. Pipette 25 ml of 0·1N sodium chloride into a 100 ml Erlenmeyer flask. Add 0·5 ml of the adsorption indicator dichlorofluorescein. Titrate with 0·1N silver nitrate (in diffuse light) as rapidly as possible. As the pink colouration following the addition of silver nitrate becomes more persistent, continue the titration more slowly until the end-point is reached. At this point the whole of the precipitated silver salt will turn deep pink. The normality of the silver nitrate solution may be calculated using the equation given previously (p. 68). Standard solutions of silver nitrate should be stored in amber glass bottles.

Indicators used for precipitation titrations—Adsorption indicators have superseded all other indicators and so will be the only ones mentioned here. Those most commonly used are:

Indicator	Preparation	End point colour
Fluorescein	0·2 g in 100 ml 70 per cent alcohol	deep pink
Dichlorofluorescein	0·1 g in 2 ml 0·1N NaOH→100 ml 70 per cent alcohol	deep pink
Eosin	0·5 g in 100 ml 70 per cent alcohol	deep pink
Di-iodomethyl-fluorescein	1 g in 100 ml water	blue–red

(3) Oxidation and Reduction

The most frequently used oxidation–reduction titration in a botanical laboratory is the titration of iodine with sodium thiosulphate, using starch as an indicator. In using this method, a solution of oxidant is allowed to react quantitatively with potassium iodide in an acid solution and the liberated iodine is titrated.

Another useful oxidation–reduction titration is that of using a potassium permanganate solution which can be standardized against 0·1N ferrous ammonium sulphate.

The preparation of the standard solutions required for the above titrations are given below.

Decinormal (0·1N) sodium thiosulphate—Weigh out 25 g sodium thiosulphate, dissolve and make up to 1 litre in a volumetric flask, with distilled water. Standardize against potassium iodate as follows.

Prepare an accurate 0·1N solution of potassium iodate by dissolving 3·567 g of the solid per litre of solution. Pipette 25 ml of this solution into a 250 ml Erlenmeyer flask, add about 1 g of potassium iodide and 3 ml of 2N sulphuric acid. Titrate the liberated iodine with the prepared thiosulphate solution until pale straw in colour, add a few drops of 1 per cent starch solution and continue titration until the colour changes from blue to colourless. Calculate the normality of the thiosulphate from the results obtained.

Sodium thiosulphate solutions are not stable and should be prepared and standardized as required. They are best kept in darkness.

Decinormal (0·1N) iodine solution—Weigh 20 g of potassium iodide, dissolve in 30–40 ml of distilled water and transfer to a 1 litre volumetric flask. Introduce into this flask approximately 12·7 g iodine. Stopper the flask and shake until all the iodine has dissolved. Make up to the graduation mark with distilled water. Store in an amber bottle. Standardize this iodine solution against freshly standardized 0·1N sodium thiosulphate using starch as indicator.

1 per cent starch solution—Take 1 g of soluble starch, make into a thin paste with a little water and pour into 100 ml of boiling distilled water. Cool and add 2 g of potassium iodide. Keep in a stoppered bottle with 1 or 2 drops of chloroform to preserve the solution. Use 2 or 3 drops per titration.

Decinormal (0·1N) ferrous ammonium sulphate—Weigh accurately 39·213 g of ferrous ammonium sulphate. Transfer to a 600 ml beaker, add 400 ml of distilled water and 20 ml of concentrated sulphuric acid. Stir carefully with a glass rod until dissolved. Transfer to a 1 litre volumetric flask, cool under running cold water and make up to the graduation mark. Bottle and label.

Decinormal (0·1N) potassium permanganate—Weigh approximately 3·2 g potassium permanganate crystals. Transfer to a 1½ or 2 litre Pyrex glass beaker and add 1 litre of distilled water. Place a large clock glass over the beaker and bring the solution to boiling point slowly. Boil gently for 15 min, then allow to cool to room temperature. Filter through a pad of glass wool held in a filter funnel and store in an amber glass bottle. Standardize as follows.

Place 25 ml of 0·1N ferrous ammonium sulphate solution in a 250 ml conical flask and titrate with the prepared permanganate solution until the first *permanent* pink colour appears.

Calculate the normality of the potassium permanganate solution from the equation given previously (p. 68).

MICRO DIFFUSION APPARATUS

Apart from the estimation of total nitrogen by the Kjeldahl method, a volumetric method of measuring liberated ammonia has been evolved by Conway (1942) [3]. This method works in conjunction with the Kjeldahl digestion of the sample which is being analysed. The nitrogen is liberated as ammonia and this is absorbed by boric acid and titrated directly with standard acid.

Apparatus Used for Diffusion and Absorption (Conway Unit)

A small circular dish divided into two compartments is used (*Figure 22a*). The diameter to the outer edge should be approximately 67 mm and the depth of the outer compartment 10 mm. The diameter of the inner compartment should be approximately 40 mm and its depth 5 mm. Each unit is fitted with a glass lid which is ground on one side.

Solutions Used with the Conway Unit

Boric acid—10 g of boric acid (A.R.), dissolved in a little water is transferred to a litre volumetric flask. To this is added 200 ml absolute alcohol and 700 ml glass distilled water.

Mixed indicator—0·033 g bromo-cresol green and 0·066 g methyl red are mixed and made up to 100 ml with absolute alcohol in a volumetric flask.

Boric acid solution plus indicator—A 1 per cent solution plus 0·00033 per cent bromo-cresol green and 0·00066 per cent methyl red. To 1 l. of 1 per cent boric acid, 10 ml of mixed indicator is added and made up to 1 l. with water.

Standard hydrochloric or sulphuric acid—N/100 (1 ml N/100 acid = 0·14 mg ammonia).

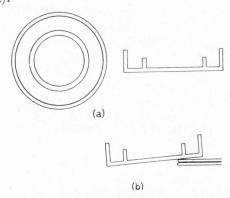

(a)

(b)

Figure 22. A Conway unit: (a) plan and side view of the unit; (b) the unit tilted on two pennies

Saturated potassium carbonate—110 g of hydrated potassium carbonate or 87 g of anhydrous potassium carbonate are dissolved in 100 ml water. The saturated solution is decanted into a large conical flask, some glass beads added to stop bumping, and boiled for 10 min, first vigorously and then gently. If a glass funnel is inserted in the neck of the flask, this will act as a crude reflux condenser. After boiling, the neck of the flask is closed with a rubber bung. The solution is cooled before using.

White Vaseline—This is also needed.

Method of Use

The boric acid (1 ml) should be pipetted into the central chamber. The unit is tilted slightly, supported by two pennies (*see Figure 22b*). The sample is pipetted into the outer compartment. Vaseline is smeared on the ground side of the lid which is placed on the unit so as to leave a small gap. Approximately 1 ml of saturated potassium carbonate is added, from a rough pipette with a rapid delivery, to the opposite side of the outer compartment to which the sample was

75

added. The unit should be closed immediately, sliding the lid lightly in position. The pennies are removed and the dish swirled carefully to avoid mixing inner and outer contents. A blank should be set up, leaving out the sample. The units are allowed to stand until the liberated ammonia has been completely absorbed. The solution is titrated with N/100 acid until the end point is reached (a colour change of the indicator from green to pink). The volume of acid used is noted and the percentage of ammonia present calculated.

Conway units may be used for several estimations where liberation, diffusion and absorption are effected, e.g. estimation of alcohol concentration.

Cleaning of Units

Excess grease should be removed with cotton wool, after which the dishes may be scrubbed carefully with warm water and detergent, rinsed thoroughly, placed in a beaker or shallow dish and covered with chromic acid cleaning fluid. They are left for 24 h. After this time they are removed from the acid, rinsed 20 times individually with tap water, then twice with distilled water. They are then placed upside down in a drying oven taking care not to touch the inside of the dish at any time after removing it from the acid. The slightest amount of grease deposited on the glass by the fingers, will necessitate further cleaning. Alternatively, a laboratory cleanser (p. 57) can be used.

The lids should be cleaned with cotton wool soaked in ether.

When not in use it is advisable to wrap the dishes and lids in clean paper, or at least stack the dishes upside down.

PRECAUTIONS IN THE LABORATORY

Poisons, in general, should not be kept in a small laboratory, but rather in a central store attached to a group of laboratories. If this procedure is not practicable, then any poisonous substance should be stored away from other chemicals in a locked drawer or cupboard. A strict check should be kept on any substance issued, using a card index system or record book. The record should include, the name of the substance, the amount issued, the date and the name of the person to whom it was issued. One responsible person should be in charge of the poison stock, and care should be taken not to allow the key to be used by anyone other than the person in charge of a practical class.

Flammable and toxic liquids should also be stored well away from other substances. Here again, ideally, bulk supplies of solvents should be stored in a central store. This store should be substantially built and away from inhabited buildings. If solvents must be kept in an actual laboratory, the volumes should be kept down to the minimum requirements and they should be stored in a cool place. When dispensing toxic liquids, a fume cupboard should be used. When using flammable liquids great care should be taken to remove all naked flames. Do not assume that because a bunsen is 20 ft away, although on the same bench, it is safe to use a flammable liquid. This is not the case as heavy vapour from a bottle of volatile liquid will drop down the side of the container and roll along a bench top until it reaches the end where it will fall to the floor. If however it reaches a naked flame on the way a serious accident will result as the vapour ignites and flashes back to the source.

SODIUM AND PHOSPHORUS

Small quantities of sodium and phosphorus may be kept in a laboratory, although, as with the previously discussed chemicals, it is safer to keep both these metals away from the general store. Neither chemical may be handled with the fingers, forceps should be used instead.

Sodium
Sodium may be purchased in either pellet or stick form. It should be stored in a wide necked jar under liquid paraffin (light grade).

Phosphorus
Both the red and yellow forms can be purchased. The latter should be stored under water in a wide necked jar and must be inspected regularly to ensure that it is still completely immersed. This is particularly important as yellow phosphorus will ignite spontaneously if allowed to come into contact with the air.

ACCIDENTS

Accidents in the laboratory range from superficial cuts to falls, poisoning and burns, all of which may be accompanied by shock. No accident, however small, should pass untreated. Even the smallest cuts must be disinfected and dressed (this is particularly important in a bacteriological laboratory). More serious accidents should be dealt with in the appropriate way and when first aid has been correctly administered the accident should be reported to the proper authorities. All establishments, whether equipped with laboratories or not, are required by law to carry an accident book in which all accidents apart from extremely trivial ones, must be reported. If, because of the seriousness of the accident, the casualty is unable to see to the essential formality themselves, a responsible witness or medical officer should see that it is completed for them.

Every laboratory should be equipped with a first aid cabinet, placed in an accessible place. It is a good plan to place a book about first aid in or on top of the cabinet, along with the telephone number of the staff medical officer or nearest doctor.

RADIOISOTOPES

USES AND HAZARDS

Radioisotopes may be used extensively in the field of botany to trace metabolic pathways both in micro organisms and higher plant life. Some isotopes are more dangerous biologically than others. Many used for botanical research are not on the whole of the most dangerous. In fact, when proper precautions are taken during their use, they are often less hazardous than some dangerous chemicals. Various excellent handbooks are available, giving precise instructions for the design and use of laboratories, for various types of radioactive work. A list of such books is given at the end of this section. Provided that the concentrated radioisotopes are shielded with the correct barrier for the ionizing radiation they are then emitting, the chief hazard is one of contamination during the use of the diluted substance. A list of precautions are given below, which if strictly observed will reduce the fear of contamination.

Precautions
1. The use of all isotopes other than those of very low toxicity, for example ^{14}C should be confined to a special 'hot' laboratory.
2. Radioisotopes of low toxicity and small quantities, for example, not greater than the maximum permissible body burden, may be used in the general laboratory. In this case a corner of the laboratory should be set aside for this purpose. Bench space should be covered with disposable, bitumen-lined paper and the sink should be supplied with hot water.
3. All hot laboratories or hot sections of general laboratories should be provided with several large notices to show the presence of radioactive chemicals and contaminated surfaces, to unsuspecting personnel.
4. Soiled waste should be placed in a foot-operated pedal bin. Liquid of high activity should not be flushed down the drain, but collected in a glass carboy. Both the pedal bin and the carboy should be clearly labelled to indicate their contents. Radioactive waste should be disposed of by an authorized person.
5. No mouth operations should be allowed in the vicinity of radioisotopes, i.e. no mouth pipetting, glass blowing, smoking, drinking or eating. No mouth operated wash bottles should be used and there should be no licking of labels.

6. If a gas or vapour is evolved during a reaction it should be carried out in a fume cupboard, fitted with an efficient extractor fan which will get vapour away from surrounding buildings.

7. Regular blood counts should be arranged and film badges should be worn to measure exposure to any but soft radiation.

8. Forceps or tongs should always be used to increase the distance between the person and the radioisotope, and so to guard against radiation. Surgical rubber gloves may be used if there is a danger of the skin becoming contaminated. When using rubber gloves a paper tissue should be interposed between the glove and such things as taps, etc., to reduce the risk of spreading contamination.

9. A small portable monitor should be kept in any laboratory having radioisotopes.

10. The bench top and the hands should be cleaned scrupulously when work is concluded and always monitored after cleaning.

11. All containers should be held in trays during use to contain spills.

12. Spills should be attended to immediately and then monitored.

13. Every piece of apparatus used in an operation should be labelled with specially designed self-adhesive radioisotope tape. All glass apparatus should be cleaned in hot water and then in chromic acid cleaning solution. After cleaning, the glassware should be monitored and, if free from radiation, the adhesive labels removed.

14. Paper tissues and towelling should be used to wipe pipette tips or mop up spills.

15. Laboratory coats must be worn by all operators. All protective clothing must be cleaned thoroughly and regularly.

16. In all establishments where radioisotopes are in use, there should be a person in authority to whom the operators may take such queries as may arise during their work.

17. Counting apparatus should be segregated from the areas of preparative work. No radioactive substances should be allowed near such apparatus except prepared samples for counting and standard sources. Rubber gloves should be removed before entering counting rooms.

18. It must be realized that, with proper precautions, work with radioisotopes is relatively safe although work of this type can, because of ignorance, cause a great deal of nervous stress. A nervous or an ignorant operator is a potential danger not only to him or herself but to other operators in the vicinity.

It is therefore essential for all operators to understand fully the physical properties and hazards of the radioisotopes he or she is using and to attend all lectures or meetings which might be provided by the establishment for the purpose of educating research workers, technicians and students.

REFERENCES

[1]Weston, W. H. (1942). 'A Petri Dish Holder for Mechanical Stages.' *Science* **95**, 415

[2]Cole, S. W. (1942). *Practical Physiological Chemistry*, 9th ed. Cambridge; Heffer

[3]Conway, E. J. (1947). *Micro Diffusion Analysis and Volumetric Error*, 2nd ed. London; Crosby Lockwood

BIBLIOGRAPHY

Balances
Macnevin, W. M. (1957). *The Analytical Balance—Its Care and Use.* Ohio; Pub. Inc. Saudusky
Microscopes
Barer, R. (1956). *Lecture Notes on the Use of the Microscope*, 2nd ed. Oxford; Blackwell
Cosslett, V. E. (1951). *Practical Electron Microscopy*, 1st ed. London; Butterworths
Duddington, C. L. (1960). *Practical Microscopy*, 1st ed. London; Pitman
Frey-Wyssling, A. (1959). *Die Pflanzliche Zellwand*, 1st ed. Berlin; Springer-Verlag
Hallimond, A. F. (1956). *Manual of the Polarising Microscope*, 2nd ed. York; Cooke, Troughton & Simms
Martin, L. C., and Johnson, B. K. (1958). *Practical Microscopy*, 3rd ed. London; Blackie
McLung, C. E. (1961). *McLung's Handbook of Microscopical Technique*, 3rd ed. New York; Hoeber
Preston, R. D. (1952). *The Molecular Architecture of Plant Cell Walls*, 1st ed. London; Chapman and Hall
Taylor, E. W. (1949). 'Phase Contrast Microscope.' *J.R. micr. Soc.* **69**, 49
Wischnitzer, S. (1962). *Introduction to Electron Microscopy*, 1st ed. Oxford; Pergamon
Colorimetry
Findlay, A. (1955). *Practical Physical Chemistry*, 8th ed. London; Longmans Green
Squirrel, D. C. M. (1964). *Automatic Methods in Volumetric Analysis*, 1st ed. London; Hilger and Watts
Walsh, J. W. T. (1953). *Photometry*, 2nd ed. London; Constable
Wright, W. D. (1958). *The Measurement of Colour*, 2nd ed. London; Hilger and Watts
Volumetric Analysis
Belcher, R., and Nutten, A. J. (1960). *Quantitative Inorganic Analysis*, 2nd ed. London; Butterworths
Garside, J. F., and Claret, P. A. (1955). *Experimental Chemistry* (Part I) 1st ed. London; Pitman
Hodgman, C. D., Weast, R. C. and Selby, S. M. eds. (1959). *Handbook of Chemistry and Physics*, 41st ed. Ohio; Chemieal Rubbcr Pub. Co.
Sutton, F. (1955). *A Systematic Handbook of Volumetric Analysis*, 13th ed. London; Butterworths
Vogel, A. I. (1961). *A Textbook of Quantitative Inorganic Analysis Including Elementary Instrumental Analysis*, 3rd ed. London; Longmans Green

BIBLIOGRAPHY

Radioisotopes

Bacq, Z. M., and Alexander, P. (1955). *Fundamentals of Radiobiology*, 1st ed. London; Butterworths

British Safety Council (1961). *Safety Spotlight—Isotopes*, London; British Safety Council

Broda, E. (1960). *Radioactive Isotopes in Biochemistry*, 1st ed. Amsterdam; Elsevier

Comar, C. L. (1955). *Isotopes in Biology and Agriculture*, 1st ed. New York; McGraw-Hill

Faires, R. A., and Parks, B. H. (1960). *Radio-isotope Laboratory Techniques*, 2nd ed. London; Newnes

H.M. Stationery Office (1957). *Code of Practice for the Protection of Persons Exposed to Ionising Radiations*. London; H.M. Stationery Office

Jefferson, S. (1960). *Radio-isotopes—A New Tool for Industry*, 2nd ed. London; Newnes

Ministry of Labour (1964). *Code of Practice for the Protection of Persons Exposed to Ionising Radiations in Research and Teaching*

Precautions

Gaston, P. J. (1964). *The Care, Handling and Disposal of Dangerous Chemicals*, I.S.T. Publication. Aberdeen; Northern Publishers

Guy, K. (1965). *Laboratory First Aid*, 1st ed. London; Macmillan

General

Edwards, J. A. (1960). *Laboratory Management and Techniques*, 1st ed. London; Butterworths

Guy, K. (1962). *Laboratory Organization and Administration*, 1st ed. London; Macmillan

CHAPTER 2

PRESERVING, FIXING AND EMBEDDING

COLLECTION OF MATERIAL

If it is possible to have access to open spaces or to be within easy reach of a country district, the collection of common specimens is a simple matter. Interesting or excess fresh material should be preserved and, in this way, a good stock of specimens can be built up to provide material which is difficult to obtain or that is wanted out of season. There are also several Botanical Supply Units which do their best to procure any required material.

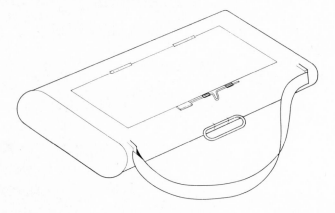

Figure 23. A vasculum

When collections are made, it is most important to ensure that the material does not dry out or deteriorate before it can be preserved. A vasculum (*Figure 23*) is useful for the collection of small plants and so are various sizes of polythene bags.

Where it is necessary to preserve small pieces of material in the field, specimen tubes containing the required fixative should be carried.

A pair of secateurs is needed for cutting woody material, a sharp knife for softer material, an old scalpel for prising specimens from bark, etc., and a small fork for digging up rootstocks. Waterproof receptacles are necessary for algae and aquatic plants. It is also useful to have a drag and line. A special plankton net is essential for collecting phytoplankton[1].

Large fleshy fungi can be wrapped in newspaper and carried in a basket or box, while smaller specimens can be put in polythene bags or envelopes. Pteridophytes are usually found growing in damp places and should preferably be fertile when collected.

Lichens are found growing on various media such as rocks, bark, soil or leaves and should be collected with samples of these materials. A geological hammer and chisel are necessary for collecting lichens growing on rocks.

Pine needles should be collected about July when they are mature but soft. They should not be collected in late autumn or winter when they are brittle and have large amounts of resinous matter in the cells.

PREPARATION OF MATERIAL

The preparation of material falls into two groups:

1. Material which is to form a collection of preserved specimens for general anatomical study and which will be used without embedding.
2. Material which has to be embedded because it is fragile or because a number of sections, usually serial sections, are required.

Obviously smaller pieces of material must be prepared when they are to be infiltrated with an embedding medium.

Group 1

Woody twigs can be cut into pieces about $1\frac{1}{2}$ in. in length with secateurs but softer stems and roots are better cut with a sharp knife. The cut should be made straight across the material so that the minimum of trimming is required before sectioning.

Small leaves can be preserved entire but it is necessary to cut larger leaves so that the fixative can penetrate quickly. These must not be chopped indiscriminately, however.

Mosses and liverworts should have any soil or debris carefully washed away if they are to be preserved in liquids. Mosses are better stored dry and when needed they can be soaked in water.

All material can be stored in wide-mouthed glass jars with ground glass lids. Any general fixative such as formalin alcohol or formalin-aceto-alcohol can be used, as the material can remain in these liquids indefinitely.

Where it is possible it is preferable to cut sections without embedding the tissue because of the time factor and the possibility of artefacts (see Chapter 3, hand sectioning and sledge microtome).

LABELLING AND INDEXING

Jars containing preserved material are labelled with the full name of the specimen, date, place of collection and the reference letter and number of the collection.

Key index cards are drawn up, choosing letters of the alphabet to cover a particular section. This is a flexible system and can be adapted to the size and requirements of the collection.

For example, A–D stems, E–F roots, G–I leaves, J–K inflorescences, etc. Dicotyledons may be distinguished from monocotyledons as required. Other letters can denote divisions of the plant kingdom M–N bryophytes, O–P pteridophytes and so on.

One key index card is chosen to cover one sub-section and, as each new specimen is added to the collection, its number is added to the key card. There are several methods of numbering but a useful one is to keep a different series of numbers for each key card. For example, the card having the letters A–D uses numbers beginning with 1 (*Figure 24*). The next key card having the letters E–F would be characterized by using all numbers beginning with 2 and so on.

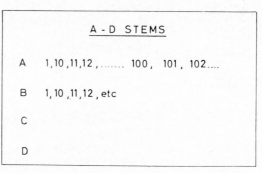

Figure 24. A key card with all the numbers beginning with 1

Ordinary index cards (*Figure 25*) are written for each specimen in the collection and filed alphabetically.

The jars containing the specimens are stored according to the letter on the label, thus dividing the collection into sections; the first section containing stems, the next roots and so on. To find a particular specimen the name is looked up in the alphabetical index of cards. The letter and number on the card, record where it is to be found in the collection.

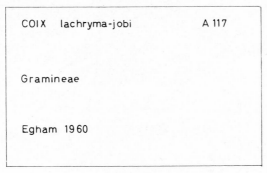

COIX   lachryma-jobi   A 117

Gramineae

Egham 1960

Figure 25. An ordinary index card

Hand Samples of Timber

Samples usually measure $2^1/2 \times 5 \times ^1/2$ in. and each one is labelled with its name and country of origin. If a large collection is being made there should be some system of filing, each sample having a collection number.

PREPARATION OF TIMBER SAMPLES FOR SECTIONING

First of all small cubes about $^1/2$ in. square, preferably having true tangential and radial faces (*Figure 26*), are cut from the block of wood. When the transverse surface of the specimen is viewed through a hand lens, the rays can be seen running across the block. The side which is cut parallel to the direction of the rays is the radial face and the side cut at right angles to it is the tangential face.

A chisel is used to trim the radial and tangential faces of the cubes.

The air must be expelled from the cubes by boiling them in a beaker of water until they become waterlogged and sink. This process can be hastened by removing the cubes from boiling water, plunging into cold water for a few minutes and then replacing them in the boiling water.

Most cubes have to be softened before they can be sectioned by hand or by a sledge microtome. Softening can be carried out by Franklin's method[2], using equal parts by volume of glacial acetic acid and hydrogen peroxide (20 vol.).

The cubes are placed in a flask containing this solution and boiled gently under a Liebig condenser (*Figure 27*). This is an excellent method and very successful for all types of wood.

The times of softening vary with different woods and even different specimens of the same wood, but directly the cube begins to have a whitish appearance it must be removed and washed thoroughly in running water for 12–24 h. This whitish wood is trimmed off the cube, which is then ready for sectioning provided it has true transverse, radial and tangential surfaces.

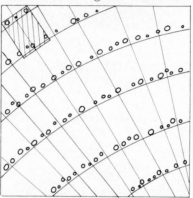

Figure 26. The shaded portion of the block marks the position of a cube which would have true tangential and radial faces

The softened cubes can be stored in wide-mouthed jars or specimen tubes containing a mixture of glycerine and alcohol (30 per cent glycerine and 70 per cent alcohol). Very soft woods like balsa wood are an exception and only need placing in 70 per cent alcohol without any previous softening process.

When indexing timber collections, the samples should be divided into two groups, hardwoods and softwoods. These are misleading terms and bear no relation to the wood being hard or soft. The softwoods are conifers and the hardwoods are dicotyledons. These two groups should be indexed alphabetically.

Group 2. Preparation Prior to Fixing and Embedding

Material which is to be fixed must be cut very carefully so that the tissues are not crushed. A razor blade is very useful for this purpose. Root apices should be cut 4–5 mm long and stem tips should have the older leaves removed to expose the apex. Leaves which are to be embedded should be cut along a vein (see *Figure 28*).

FIXING

The aim of fixation is to kill and preserve plant cells and their contents so that they are not distorted in any way.

In practice this aim is not completely attainable because one part of the cell is not fixed as well as another part. It is therefore important to know, before killing and fixing, for what purpose the cell is to be examined in order that the right fixative can be chosen. These fall roughly into two main groups:

(1) Those that fix cells in relation to each other and can be used for material that is to be studied anatomically.
(2) Those that fix the cell contents for cytological study.

This latter group falls into two types: (*a*) those that give an acid fixation image and (*b*) those that give a basic fixation image.

Fixatives giving an acid fixation preserve the chromatin, nucleoli and spindle fibres[3] but not the cytoplasm and cytoplasmic inclusions such as mitochondria.

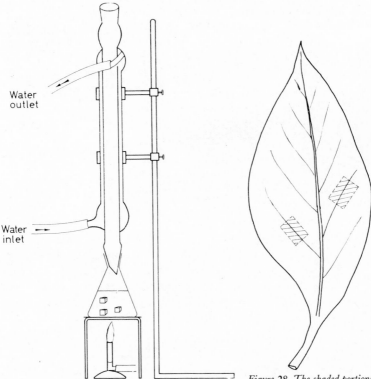

Water outlet

Water inlet

Figure 27. Cubes being softened by boiling in a mixture of hydrogen peroxide and glacial acetic acid under a Liebig condenser

Figure 28. The shaded portions mark the positions of the pieces of leaf wanted for sectioning in relation to the whole structure

Fixatives giving a basic fixation image preserve the mitochondria but not the resting chromatin and spindle fibres.

The pH of the fixative is important. It is possible to raise the pH of a fixative with an acid fixation image by the addition of an alkali and so preserve both chromatin and mitochondria[4].

It is very important that the fixative should penetrate the plant cells quickly, as the sooner the cells are killed and fixed the more natural their appearance. To this end, the air contained within the cells must be expelled, allowing penetration of the fixative. To hasten this process the following method is used.

Two jars are needed, one to hold the material and the fixative, the other to act as a trap between the first jar and the vacuum pump. This trap prevents any water being sucked back into the fixative (*Figure 29*).

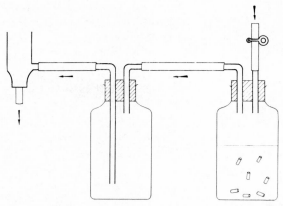

Figure 29. Expelling air from the specimens

The apparatus is connected to a water vacuum pump which is turned on full. The pinch clip on the jar holding the material is released at intervals, as the change in pressure facilitates the sinking procedure which usually shows that all air is expelled from the specimens.

It is quite obvious that for fixing difficult material, special fixatives are necessary and it is impossible to include all of them but a selection has been made to cover most general needs.

Formalin Alcohol

	parts by volume
Ethyl alcohol	15
Distilled water	10
Commercial formalin	1

This is a general fixative and preserving fluid which is adequate for most anatomical material, especially woody twigs. The material can be left in this mixture indefinitely.

Formalin-aceto-alcohol F.A.A.

50 or 70 per cent ethyl alcohol	90 ml
Glacial acetic acid	5 ml
Commercial formalin	5 ml

This is a general fixative for stems, roots and leaves, etc. Material can be left in this mixture indefinitely.

Formalin-propionic-alcohol F.P.A.

Propionic acid can be used instead of glacial acetic acid as in the preceding formula. This mixture is sometimes preferred to the formalin-aceto-alcohol for fixing bryophytes and pteridophytes.

Weak Chrom-acetic[3]

10 per cent aqueous chromic anhydride	2·5 ml
10 per cent aqueous acetic acid	5 ml
Distilled water to	100 ml

This can be used for filamentous algae and fungi and also for bryophytes.

Medium Chrom-acetic

10 per cent aqueous chromic anhydride	7 ml
10 per cent aqueous acetic acid	10 ml
Distilled water to	100 ml

The addition of 0·5 per cent saponin helps the penetration power of the fixative. This mixture is very useful for root tips and stem apices. The material should be fixed for at least 24 h and washed in running water for about the same length of time.

Dioxan Fixative[5]

Dioxan	50 ml
Commercial formalin	6 ml
Glacial acetic acid	5 ml
Distilled water	50 ml

This is a good fixative for unicellular and filamentous algae and fungi.

Dioxan fumes are harmful and care should be exercised when this liquid is being used.

Chamberlain's Chrom-osmo-acetic

Chromic anhydride	1 g
Glacial acetic acid	3 ml
1 per cent aqueous osmic acid	1 ml
Distilled water	100 ml

A good fixative for freshwater algae and filamentous fungi.

Sass' Modified Bouin's Fluid

1 per cent aqueous chromic acid	50 ml
Saturated aqueous picric acid	35 ml
Commercial formalin	10 ml
Glacial acetic acid	5 ml

This fixative is useful for buds and anthers of Liliaceae.

Farmer's Fluid

	parts by volume
95 per cent ethyl alcohol (or absolute)	3
Glacial acetic acid	1

Carnoy's Fluid

	parts by volume
95 per cent ethyl alcohol (or absolute)	6
Chloroform	3
Glacial acetic acid	1

These two fixatives are useful for rapid smear preparations (see Chapter 4).

Randolph's Modified Navashin's Fluid (CRAF)

Solution A	Chromic acid	1 g
	Glacial acetic acid	7 ml
	Distilled water	92 ml
Solution B	Neutral formalin	30 ml
	Distilled water	70 ml

Equal quantities of solutions A and B should be mixed just before using and the material fixed for 12–24 h. The material can be washed afterwards in 70 per cent alcohol.

Flemming-type Medium Chrom-osmo-acetic Mixture

1 per cent chromic acid	50 ml
10 per cent acetic acid	10 ml
2 per cent osmic acid	10 ml
Distilled water	30 ml

There are numerous variations of Flemming-type fixatives and they are very useful for cytological studies.

Osmic acid preserves chromosome structures very well but it blackens tissues and it is often necessary to bleach the fixed material before staining.

Taylor's Chrom-osmo-acetic for Smears

10 per cent aqueous chromic acid	0·20 ml
10 per cent aqueous acetic acid	2·00 ml
2 per cent osmic acid in 2 per cent chromic acid	1·50 ml
Distilled water	8·30 ml
Maltose (approximately)	0·15 ml

Osmic Acid Fumes

The fumes of osmic acid kill as efficiently as the solution. Spores, zygospores and small unicellular algae, etc., may be fixed by using osmic acid fumes. These fumes are extremely irritating and care should be taken when using osmic acid. Solutions of osmic acid are very quickly oxidized by the presence of the least trace of organic matter such as dirt or dust. Therefore it is important that containers and utensils are thoroughly clean when preparing the solution, which is made up just prior to use.

Zirkle-Erliki Fluid (Basic fixation image)

Potassium dichromate	1·25 g
Ammonium dichromate	1·25 g
Cupric sulphate	1·00 g
Distilled water	200·0 ml

The material should be fixed for 48 h and then washed thoroughly in water. This fixative is useful for preserving mitochondria but chromatin is dissolved[6].

Fixative for Plant Cytoplasm[7]

10 per cent commercial formalin	100 ml
Normal sodium hydroxide	1 ml
Pyrogallol	7 g

The material should be fixed for 12–24 h and rinsed with running water before starting to dehydrate.

The effects of this fixative produce very little plasmolysis and no vacuolar precipitates.

Fixative for both Nuclei and Mitochondria[4]

Copper dichromate	5 g
Cupric oxide	1 g
10 per cent aqueous solution of acetic acid	1 ml
Distilled water	200 ml

This fixative must be made up at least 24 h before use. It should be shaken frequently and the excess copper oxide allowed to settle. If used too soon, the fixation image will be that of chromic acid. The material should be fixed for 36–48 h and then the fixative should be washed out with 70 per cent alcohol. The dehydration time should be kept to a minimum, otherwise the mitochondria will be dissolved out of the peripheral cells.

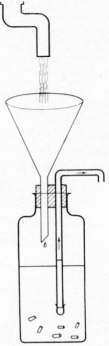

*Figure 30. Washing specimens
after fixing*

Artifacts—These can be caused by distortion of the constituents of
the cells or by the deposition of extraneous objects within them[8].
The former are more common and can be produced by the fixative
or by subsequent treatment.

Common artifacts are coagulation of protoplasm and the thickening of nuclear and cell membranes. The standard of fixation can only
be judged by comparing the fixed material with living cells.

Difficulties arise in electron microscopy for, at higher magnification levels, more artifacts may become apparent. After fixation the
fixing fluid must be washed out of the material to prevent precipitation of extraneous matter.

Washing—It is necessary after a number of fixatives, especially
chromic acid mixtures, to wash the plant material in water. Alcoholic
fixatives are washed out with alcohol or an alcohol-water mixture.
A simple way of washing small pieces of material is to set up the

following apparatus. Two holes are drilled in the cork of a wash bottle. Through one hole is passed a funnel and through the other hole a bent piece of glass tubing to serve as an outlet for excess water. A piece of gauze is tied on the end of the tubing inside the bottle, to prevent the material from being washed away.

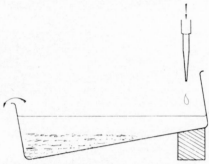

Figure 31. Washing a large quantity of filamentous algae

The funnel is placed under a tap and water is allowed to run slowly through the apparatus (see *Figure 30*).

An alternative method is to use a specimen tube or jar covered with muslin which is held in position by a rubber band. One end of a piece of glass tubing is drawn out to a fine nozzle which is inserted through the muslin, the other end is attached to the water supply by a piece of rubber tubing.

Washing in running water should be continued for several hours. Large quantities of filamentous algae and fungi can be washed by placing them in a trough inclined at a slight angle and allowing water to run slowly into the trough (*Figure 31*).

Unicellular algae and fungi can be washed by centrifuging (see Chapter 4).

After washing is completed, dehydration is necessary as water is not miscible with paraffin wax solvents.

DEHYDRATION AND INFILTRATION

Dehydration and Infiltration with Paraffin Wax

Dehydration must be gradual to prevent distortion of the cells and their contents, so the specimens are taken through a graded series of alcohols.

Stock solutions of 5, 10, 15, 20, 30, 50, 70, 85 and 95 per cent alcohol by volume are made up, diluting with distilled water. Commercial alcohol can be assumed to be 100 per cent for this purpose as a graded series is being used.

The material is allowed to remain in each percentage for a minimum time of 30 min. Sometimes 1–2 h are necessary depending on the size and nature of the specimens. From the 95 per cent alcohol they are passed to commercial alcohol and then into absolute alcohol. A second change of absolute alcohol is necessary in which the specimens should be allowed to remain overnight.

No material should be allowed to remain too long in any of the alcohol solutions weaker than 50 per cent.

Material which is needed for anatomical study can be taken up through a wider spaced series of alcohols, 15, 35, 70 and 95 per cent with 2 h immersion in each solution. The finer details of the cell contents will be destroyed but this does not matter if the relationship of cell structure is to be studied.

From absolute alcohol it is necessary to transfer the specimens to a paraffin wax solvent such as chloroform and this is also done in gradual stages by immersion in the following solutions:

(1) 1 part chloroform: 2 parts absolute alcohol.
(2) 1 part chloroform: 1 part absolute alcohol.
(3) 2 parts chloroform: 1 part absolute alcohol.
(4) Pure chloroform.

Two hours are usually necessary for each change although sometimes 1 h is sufficient. For difficult material the changes can be made in 25 per cent stages. Chloroform is to be preferred to xylene which renders the tissues brittle.

Before infiltrating with wax there should be a change of the pure chloroform. The specimen tube or container holding the material can then be put in a warm place (the top of an embedding oven is useful) and shavings of wax can be added gradually. This infiltration can take from 24 h to several days and as long as the temperature does not exceed 35°C, the tissues are not damaged. When the wax begins to solidify around the sides of the tube, it is time to continue the infiltration by placing the material in pure molten wax inside the embedding oven on the top shelf. There should be several changes of pure wax until there is no trace left of the chloroform. Small delicate material should not be allowed to remain in the oven for more than 2 h. After the final change of pure wax, the container is placed on the lower shelf of the oven and the material is ready for embedding.

A method, quoted by Johansen[3], in which tertiary butyl alcohol is used instead of chloroform, is excellent, as tertiary butyl alcohol is also a solvent of paraffin wax. Dehydration proceeds as usual to the 50 per cent alcohol stage and then the specimens are passed through the following series of tertiary butyl alcohol (Table 5).

TABLE 5

Series No.	Commercial alcohol	Absolute alcohol	Tertiary butyl alcohol	Distilled water
1	40 ml	—	10 ml	50 ml
2	50 ml	—	20 ml	30 ml
3	50 ml	—	35 ml	15 ml
4	50 ml	—	50 ml	—
5	—	25 ml	75 ml	—

From 50 per cent alcohol the material is transferred to the first grade of the series of tertiary butyl alcohol solutions and then on through this series. After the fifth solution, the material is passed to pure tertiary butyl alcohol. There should be at least two changes of this solvent, in one of which the material should be left overnight. The material is then transferred to a mixture of equal parts of liquid paraffin and tertiary butyl alcohol for 1 h.

A specimen tube can then be filled two-thirds full of melted wax and allowed to solidify but not completely harden. The material is placed on top of the solidified wax and just covered with the mixture of liquid paraffin and tertiary butyl alcohol. The tube is then placed on the upper shelf in the embedding oven and the material is left to infiltrate slowly as it sinks down into the wax. It should be allowed to remain in the oven for 1 h after it has sunk to the bottom of the tube. There should be two changes of pure wax before embedding.

When a large number of specimens, for example root tips, have to be dehydrated a useful method is to set up the following apparatus[9]. A Buchner funnel, covered by a half a Petri dish, is held in a clamp. A length of tubing controlled by a screw clip is connected to the end of the funnel and leads to a waste bottle (*Figure 32*).

Finely perforated cylindrical baskets can be made to contain the specimens. These are placed inside the Buchner funnel and the screw clip is tightened. The funnel is filled with fluid, which is allowed to remain for the required length of time, when the screw clip is released and the procedure is repeated with the next solvent.

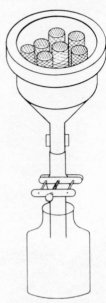

Figure 32. Apparatus for dehydrating a number of specimens. The funnel is held in position by a clamp

Dehydration and Infiltration with Ester Wax

Dehydration through a series of alcohols can be carried out as for paraffin wax, but the procedure can be cut by adding chips of ester wax when the material is in equal quantities of absolute alcohol and chloroform. It is not necessary to go into pure chloroform, as ester wax tolerates a percentage of alcohol.

Another method is to use 2-ethoxy-ethanol (ethylene glycol monoethyl ether) for dehydration[10]. The tissues are taken through the alcohols into 70 per cent alcohol and then through the following mixtures of 2-ethoxy-ethanol and 70 per cent alcohol.

    (1) 1 part 2-ethoxy-ethanol: 2 parts 70 per cent alcohol.
    (2) 1 part 2-ethoxy-ethanol: 1 part 70 per cent alcohol.
    (3) 2 parts 2-ethoxy-ethanol: 1 part 70 per cent alcohol.

Finally the material is brought into pure 2-ethoxy-ethanol and shavings of ester wax can be added in the same way as for paraffin wax. The material is transferred to pure ester wax of which there should be at least two changes.

Dehydration and Infiltration with Polyester Wax

Dehydration through a series of alcohols is carried out until 96 per cent alcohol is reached. Polyester wax is then added gradually. Two changes of pure polyester wax are needed before embedding. If kept in a molten state this wax tends to become softer so only a sufficient quantity for the job in hand should be melted.

Dehydration and Infiltration of Water Soluble Wax

Aquax (as supplied by G. T. Gurr) is a mixture of polyethylene glycols of varying molecular weights. The specimens are placed in a series of solutions of Aquax and distilled water at room temperature. It can be used in stages of 25 per cent but, with more delicate material, a closer series is necessary. A method for using polyethylene glycols has been described[11], using wax of a low molecular weight to dehydrate and then infiltrating in a mixture of two harder waxes each having a high molecular weight. After fixation the material is washed in running water for several hours before transferring to a 25 per cent aqueous solution of polyethylene glycol 400 in a wide-mouthed stoppered jar. It is then taken through a series of polyethylene glycols 50, 80, 95 per cent and finally into pure polyethylene glycol.

The time for this dehydration is usually 15 min–2 h depending on the material.

It is then infiltrated with mixtures of polyethylene glycols 1500 and 4000. These are prepared by melting them together and filtering in an oven at a temperature between 59° and 61°C. To this mixture add 1 per cent Tween 20 to accelerate penetration.

A little of the embedding mixture is placed in a container and allowed to congeal but not harden. The dehydrated tissue is then placed on the top of the wax and the container placed in the oven until the material has sunk. This process is repeated until the material is completely infiltrated.

EMBEDDING
EMBEDDING MEDIA

Paraffin Waxes

These can be obtained with various melting points which normally range from 45° to 60°C. The most useful one for general purposes is 52°C but mixtures of the different waxes sometimes produce better results when cutting ribbons. Generally speaking, the thinner the sections required, the harder the wax used.

Fibrowax

This is an embedding medium consisting of paraffin wax with the addition of plastic polymers. It has a melting point of 57°–58°. Difficult materials are easier to section in Fibrowax than in paraffin wax and the compression in the sections is reduced to a minimum.

The usual solvents are used and it is heated in the same way as paraffin wax.

Paraplast

Paraplast is a similar embedding medium to Fibrowax and it has a melting point of 56°–57°C.

Ester Wax

Ester wax 1960 is an improvement on the ester wax introduced by Steedman in 1947. It is a very useful wax as it has a low melting point (47°–48°C) but is harder than paraffin wax. The compression of the wax when cutting sections is considerably less than with paraffin wax and there is no trouble with static electricity. Also sections below 5 μ are cut with ease.

Ester wax must not be kept in a molten state longer than overnight as the condition of the wax is impaired.

Polyester Wax

Polyester wax[12] has a very low melting point of 38°C. It is useful for embedding very delicate material and has the advantage of being soluble in ethyl alcohol. It will tolerate 5–10 per cent water in this solvent.

Water Soluble Waxes

These waxes can be used with advantage where dehydrating reagents will damage tissues or cell contents. They are usually polyethylene glycols or their esters. Because of the hygroscopic nature of the waxes with low molecular weights, difficulties arise in mounting the sections. Serial sections are not easily obtained, although application of a 25 per cent solution of beeswax in chloroform, brushed on to the upper and lower surfaces of the block, is sometimes successful[13].

These water soluble waxes are useful for embedding and supporting fresh plant material to be cut on a freezing microtome either with or without the use of carbon dioxide[14].

Celloidin

The lengthy infiltration techniques, using celloidin for embedding hard and difficult materials, can now be replaced almost entirely by the use of ester wax or by cutting the material direct in a sledge microtome.

EMBEDDING BATHS AND OVENS

There are various types of embedding baths and ovens on the market which can be heated by gas or electricity.

Baths

The top of an embedding bath is fitted with pots and tubes for holding molten wax in which specimens can be infiltrated.

Separate thermostatically controlled pots for containing wax are sold, usually for use when embedding with an automatic processor. Only electrically heated baths are thermostatically controlled.

Ovens

Both gas and electrically heated ovens can be thermostatically controlled when the temperature reaches a set level. This should be a few degrees above the melting point of the wax used. Care must be taken to top up the water in the jacket of gas ovens occasionally and no gas appliance must be placed in a position where a sudden draught could blow out the flame. Molten paraffin wax can be stored inside the oven in beakers or in a separate unit in the top, as illustrated in *Figure 33*.

Metal beakers should certainly be used for storing wax in gas heated ovens, as there is serious risk of a fire if a glass beaker breaks and molten wax drips on to the flame.

Vacuum ovens—These are built to be connected to a vacuum pump which expels the air from the inside of the oven and also the material. They are not usually used for botanical material unless large quantities of material are being handled, but a vacuum procedure does quicken the infiltration process and is often used in conjunction with freeze drying.

An exhausting head, which is connected to a vacuum pump to expel the air from the specimen, can easily be made to fit any thermostatically controlled paraffin pot[15]. This head consists of a vacuum gauge, and two gas stopcocks, one for the connection to the vacuum pump, and the other used as an air valve. At the base of the head, a large rubber bung fits through an opening in a metal plate, and a gasket seals the apparatus to the embedding pot. When embedding is complete under vacuum, the pump valve is closed and the air valve opened.

Casting Blocks with Paraffin Wax

It is an advantage to use wax that has been kept in a molten state for a week or longer as more even textured blocks result.

Paper trays or L-pieces can be used for block making. Paper trays can be made by folding pieces of paper to the required size.

Figure 33. An embedding oven
(By courtesy of A. Gallenkamp and Co. Ltd.)

L-pieces are L-shaped pieces of metal, usually brass, which can be placed together on a suitable base to form a box. They are used in pairs and are adjusted so that a block of the required size is obtained (*Figure 34*).

The inside and base of the L-pieces are smeared with glycerol and placed on a piece of brass or glass also smeared to prevent the wax sticking.

The molten wax is poured carefully into the paper tray or L-pieces; then the specimens are removed from their container of molten wax with warmed forceps, placed into the block and orientated with warmed mounted needles. This should be carried out as quickly as possible to prevent the formation of air bubbles within the block. If the material is delicate, then a spatula must be used instead of forceps for transferring from the molten wax to the block. Specimens may be embedded singly, or a number in one block, for example root tips. The tips should all face the same way along one side of the block, preferably outwards. Enough space should be left between the specimens to enable each one to be cut out in a separate block when required (*Figure 35*).

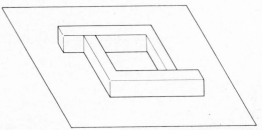

Figure 34. L-pieces set up on a sheet of metal or glass ready for embedding

A skin should be allowed to form on the surface of the wax block and then it should be carefully immersed in cold water to harden. When this is complete the L-pieces can be detached from the block.

Vital information can be scratched on the blocks, which are wrapped in paper and stored in small cardboard boxes. Any further details can be recorded on the paper in which the blocks are wrapped.

Several methods have been described for casting blocks in multiple moulds. Silicone rubber moulds[16] have the advantage of being flexible for the removal of the blocks.

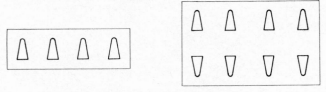

Figure 35. Root tips orientated in wax blocks

Casting Blocks with Ester Wax

When using ester wax, the L-pieces can be smeared with glycerol or Mayer's albumen[10].

A sufficient quantity of wax for the block making is heated to about 10°C above its melting point and poured into the L-pieces.

101

The wax is left for a few moments until a thin layer solidifies at the sides of the block. The surface of the block is melted with a warm spatula, and the specimen is put into the block and orientated. The L-pieces are then surrounded with cold water but the block is not immersed. The surface of the block should be kept liquid while the rest of the wax is solidifying, otherwise air bubbles appear. This is done by touching the surface of the block with a heated spatula and filling in with molten wax if required.

Casting Blocks with Polyester Wax

The wax is cast in L-pieces as previously described but it is not cooled with water. It is left to harden overnight on the bench at room temperature. Very thin sections of the embedded material are best cut several days after making the block. Polyester blocks should be handled with forceps because of the low melting point of the wax.

Casting Blocks with Water Soluble Waxes

The L-pieces are smeared with Mayer's albumen and filled with molten wax. When a skin forms on the surface it is melted with a heated spatula. The specimens should be orientated along the sides of the block, because when polyethylene glycols solidify, they often show signs of cracking in the middle of the block. The surface of the block is kept liquid while the rest of the wax is solidifying. Then it is left to cool and harden at room temperature or in a refrigerator. The blocks should be wrapped in metal foil for storage purposes.

Double Embedding

This is not usually necessary for plant material but it can be of use with difficult material. Where it is necessary to infiltrate with Aquax and to obtain serial sections, the material can be passed from Aquax through chloroform and into paraffin wax. This means that the outside of the block is paraffin wax and serial sections can be obtained quite successfully.

Automatic Processing

Several firms manufacture automatic tissue processors, one of which, the Elliott model, is illustrated in *Figure 36*.

Automatic dehydration, embedding, and staining can be carried out by these instruments. The material is placed in one of the perforated containers which can have either fine or coarse perforations and which can be subdivided to hold different specimens. These containers fit into a carrier which is attached to a transfer arm and will be moved automatically, according to the timing control, through the whole series of dehydration fluids and embedding media. Discs can be prepared by cutting notches in them at intervals according to the time needed in each solvent. For dehydration, a 24 h disc is used but, for most staining schedules, a 1 h disc is prepared. There is also a delayed starting switch to facilitate processing over the weekend.

Figure 36. Shandon–Elliott Automatic tissue processor
(By courtesy of Shandon Scientific Company Ltd.)

For staining, special racks to hold the slides can be attached to the transfer arm and automatic staining procedures carried out. (See also the automatic slide stainer, p. 147). Although some of the first models on the market were mainly for medical laboratories obviously dealing with larger specimens, there are now models with various modifications which can be very useful in botanical work.

PREPARATION AND EMBEDDING FOR THE ELECTRON MICROSCOPE

This work is becoming increasingly important and a summary has been made of some of the methods with a reference list for further reading.

FIXATION

Fixation can be carried out using buffered osmium tetroxide[17,18] or potassium permanganate solutions[19, 20, 21].

In the search for fixatives which will preserve cell structure so that it is not distorted or degraded, the use of dialdehydes[22] has been suggested to provide enhanced fixation. This suggestion has been borne out by practical results[23] and improved preservation of proteinaceous components has been demonstrated by using glutaraldehyde as a fixative.

Glutaraldehyde fixation has also revealed cytoplasmic structures which have not hitherto been demonstrated by other methods of fixation[24].

Caulfield's Buffered Osmium Tetroxide

2 per cent osmium tetroxide	4 ml
Veronal-acetate buffer	1 ml
Distilled water	2 ml
0·1N HCl	1 ml

Adjust the pH to 7·4 with HCl and then add 0·015 g of sucrose per ml of fixative.

Veronal-acetate Buffer for Caulfield's Fixative

Sodium veronal (barbitone sodium)	2·94	g
Sodium acetate	1·94	g
Distilled water to	100	ml

Luft's Buffered Permanganate

1·2 per cent aqueous potassium permanganate	12·5 ml
Veronal-acetate buffer	5·0 ml
Distilled water	2·5 ml
0·1N HCl	5·0 ml

The pH should be adjusted to 7·5 with HCl.

Veronal-acetate Buffer for Luft's Fixative

Sodium veronal	2·89	g
Sodium acetate (anhydrous)	1·15	g
Distilled water to	100	ml

This buffer is stable for a few months at 4°C.

Fixation with Luft's buffered permanganate must be carried out at 4°C if the specimens are to be embedded in methacrylate. It is usually better to embed in an epoxy or polyester resin when employing a permanganate fixative.

Unlike osmium tetroxide, potassium permanganate is insoluble in oils and fats.

Glutaraldehyde Fixative

A 6 per cent solution of glutaraldehyde buffered to a pH 7·0 in phosphate is frequently used. The material is fixed for about two hours followed by washing in buffer solution and further fixation in osmium tetroxide as described above. These processes can be carried out at 4°C.

Small amounts of sucrose can be added to either the glutaraldehyde or the washing buffer to enhance osmotic buffering.

Kellenberger's Standard Fixative[25]

This has been found to give good fixation of bacteria and other micro-organisms. The solutions required are as follows:

1. *Veronal-acetate buffer (Michaelis)*
Sodium veronal	2·94 g
Sodium acetate (hydrated)	1·94 g
Sodium chloride	3·40 g
Distilled water to	100 ml

2. *Kellenberger buffer*
Veronal-acetate buffer	5·0 ml
Distilled water	13·0 ml
0·1N HCl	7·0 ml
M-CaCl$_2$	0·25 ml

The pH is adjusted to 6·0 with HCl.
This buffer must be made up just before it is required.

3. *Kellenberger fixative*
Osmium tetroxide	0·1 g
Kellenberger buffer	10 ml

4. *Washing fluid*
Uranyl acetate	0·5 g
Kellenberger buffer	100 ml

5. *Tryptone medium*
Bacto-Tryptone (Difco)	1·0 g
Sodium chloride	0·5 g
Distilled water	100 ml

About 30 ml of culture is centrifuged; the pellet is suspended in 1 ml of Kellenberger fixative and 1 ml of tryptone medium and left overnight at room temperature. It is then re-centrifuged after adding 8 ml of Kellenberger buffer. The pellet is re-suspended in a small quantity of warm agar and a drop placed on a glass slide. This is allowed to set and is then cut into small cubes which are placed in the washing fluid for 2 h at room temperature.

EMBEDDING MEDIA[26]

Methacrylates

These have been in use as embedding media for some years but, although embedding times are short for animal tissues, plant material requires considerably longer. The polymerization process is uneven, resulting in considerable shrinkage and distortion in the blocks. Modifications to reduce polymerization damage have been described (a) by the addition of a small quantity of uranyl nitrate[27], and (b) by removing oxygen from the embedding media[28.]

Sections from methacrylate blocks are unstable under the electron beam[29] because of volatilization of the resin. Although easy to cut, methacrylate has been largely replaced by other embedding media.

Epoxy Resins

Mixtures containing Araldite[30] are used to produce blocks which harden uniformly and with much less shrinkage than with methacrylates. Infiltration, however, is more difficult and usually takes longer. Modifications have been made to ensure complete penetration and to hasten the infiltration process[20].

Work on the Epon epoxy resins has produced mixtures based on Epon 812[31, 32] which penetrates the specimens more readily than Araldite mixtures.

Embedding techniques using Epon 812 have been devised successfully[33].

In Great Britain a similar resin is sold under the trade name of 'Epikote' 812.

Polyester Resins

These also harden uniformly with little shrinkage. Blocks made from Vestopal W[34] are free from polymerization damage and are stable under the electron beam.

Various embedding materials have been tried and their uses and draw-backs have been summarized[35].

Water Soluble Embedding Media

These water soluble embedding media are becoming increasingly important. Aquon[36] is extracted from Epon 812 and, although the procedure is lengthy, it is an advantage to avoid dehydration in alcohol or acetone.

Water soluble methacrylates are also becoming important[37] and it has been found that the formation of artifacts is reduced[38].

A number of other water soluble media are on trial and successful results are being obtained.

Gelatin Capsules

Empty capsules can be obtained from Parke Davis Ltd., Hounslow, Middlesex, England. Number 1 capsules are widely used and are convenient for embedding specimens of a millimetre or two in length. Number 2 capsules are smaller and need less trimming for minute objects. It is important to use the correct size capsule if there is only one fixed chuck on the microtome.

Specimen grids 3 mm in diameter fit snugly into Number 4 capsules for storage or transport purposes if a grid box is not available.

When they are filled with the embedding mixture, the capsules can be supported in wire baskets (made by wrapping copper wire round a pencil) or in holes punched out of thin card which is bent over to make a stand (see *Figure 37*).

BEEM capsules are available which are moulded to reduce the amount of trimming.

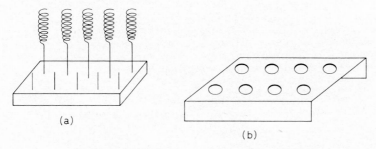

Figure 37. (a) wire holders; (b) paper holder for capsules

DEHYDRATION

Washing is not usually necessary after fixing and the specimens can be dehydrated through a graded series of alcohol and water if they are to be embedded in methacrylate or epoxy resins.

Polyester resins are insoluble in alcohol and specimens should be dehydrated through a graded series of acetone and water.

The easiest way to dehydrate the specimens is to keep them in a small specimen tube; the solvents can be removed and added with a fine pipette.

Embedding with Methacrylates

Methacrylate vapour is harmful and all operations should be carried out in a fume cupboard.

To prevent polymerization occurring, an inhibitor is supplied with the methacrylate and this must be removed before embedding. A measured volume of methacrylate with half the volume of 5 per cent sodium hydroxide is shaken in a separating funnel. The mixture will separate out and the bottom layer containing the hydroquinone (inhibitor) is drained away. The procedure is repeated until the bottom layer is colourless, showing that all the hydroquinone has been removed. The sodium hydroxide is removed by adding distilled water, shaking and draining the bottom layer. This is repeated several times. The methacrylate is filtered and stored overnight in a corked flask containing a little solid sodium sulphate (anhydrous). It is finally stored in a glass-stoppered bottle containing a drying agent at 4°C.

Methacrylate Mixture for Embedding

The *n*-butyl methacrylate is mixed with 10–20 per cent methyl methacrylate. Benzoyl peroxide is used as the catalyst and 0·5–2·0 g is added to the mixture of methacrylates. The procedure is as follows:

(1) Remove the absolute alcohol from the tube containing the specimens and replace it by a mixture of equal parts absolute alcohol and methacrylates (without the catalyst).
(2) Replace by methacrylate without catalyst.
(3) Replace by methacrylate plus catalyst.

The specimens must be left in these mixtures for at least 45 min, probably much longer, according to the material being handled.

(4) Remove the specimens carefully with a fine pipette and place each one into a dry gelatine capsule of a convenient size.
(5) Fill the capsule with a fresh mixture of methacrylate plus catalyst and press the cap down. Label the capsule with ink.
(6) Place the capsules in a tray filled with methacrylate and harden overnight in an incubator at 60°C.

Embedding with Araldite

The embedding mixture is made up as follows:

Araldite M (Ciba resin CY 212)	10·0 ml
Hardener 964B (Ciba HY 964)	10·0 ml
Dibutyl phthalate	1·0 ml
Accelerator 964C (Ciba DY 064)	0·5 ml

The Araldite and the hardener are warmed before mixing.

The absolute alcohol (or acetone if prefered) is removed from the tube containing the specimens which are then passed through the following series of Araldite and alcohol mixtures at 48°C:

(1) 20 per cent Araldite in absolute alcohol for 1 h
(2) 50 per cent Araldite in absolute alcohol for 1 h

(3) 70 per cent Araldite in absolute alcohol for 1 h
(4) Araldite mixture without accelerator for 24 h
(5) Another change of this mixture for 24 h
(6) Araldite mixture plus accelerator for 24 h at room temperature.

The specimens are placed in dry gelatine capsules which are filled with the Araldite mixture plus the accelerator.

The capsules are left for 24 h at room temperature, then placed in an incubator at 48°C for 24 h and finally the temperature is increased to 60°C for a further 24 h.

Embedding with Epikote (Epon)

A convenient method of embedding with Epikote is to prepare two mixtures A and B using different hardeners in each. The final embedding medium is a mixture of A and B plus an accelerator[32]. This final mixture will only keep for a short period before hardening but separately the A and B mixtures will keep for several months and are preferably stored in sealed polythene containers in a refrigerator.

The two hardeners, dodecenyl succinic anhydride DDSA and methyl nadic anhydride MNA, can be obtained from Ciba (A.R.L.) Limited, Duxford, Cambridge. The Epikote resin and the accelerator, benzyl dimethylamine BDMA, can be obtained from Shell Chemical Company Limited, 15–17 Great Marlborough Street, London, W.1.

Mixture A (soft)	Epikote 812	62 ml
	DDSA	100 ml
Mixture B (hard)	Epikote 812	100 ml
	MNA	89 ml

The following table gives a series of mixtures of various hardnesses.

MIXTURE A	MIXTURE B	BDMA	
10 ml	0 ml	0·15 ml	soft
7 ml	3 ml	0·15 ml	
5 ml	5 ml	0·15 ml	medium
3 ml	7 ml	0·15 ml	
0 ml	10 ml	0·15 ml	hard

After absolute alcohol in the final stage of dehydration, the specimens may be placed in propylene oxide for 1–2 hours to aid the penetration of the embedding mixture. Each specimen is allowed to settle in the end of a pipette before being transferred to the capsule so that a minimum of propylene oxide is introduced. It is recommended that the specimen is changed through the final resin more than once. The capsules can be filled with the embedding mixture prior to the introduction of the specimen if this will sink to the bottom of the capsule. It is sometimes an advantage to drill a small hole in the end of a hardened capsule and then to introduce the specimen plus resin into the hole. This method often facilitates correct orientation of specimens (see *Figure 38*).

The capsules are placed in an incubator at 35°C for 12 hours when the temperature is increased to 45°C for a further 12 hours and finally increased to 60°C for 12 hours. Alternatively, the capsules can be hardened at 60°C overnight. In either case they are best left for a day or two after hardening before sectioning.

Embedding with Epikote (Epon)–Araldite mixture

A method has recently been described[39] which uses a mixture of Epikote 812 and Araldite M (CY 212).

A convenient mixture has been found to be:

Epikote	25 ml
D.D.S.A.	55 ml
Araldite M (CY 212)	15 ml
Dibutyl phthalate	2 ml

The mixture can be hardened by the addition of 3 per cent BDMA. The embedding procedure is essentially the same as that used for Epikote alone.

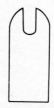

Figure 38. A drilled capsule

This mixture has been found in some cases[39] to have advantages over Epikote or Araldite used alone. It is easy to cut and gives good tissue preservation.

Durcupan ACM is supplied by Fluka, A. G., Buchs, S. G., Switzerland, and is equivalent to Araldite M (Ciba product CY 212).

It should be noted that the accelerator benzyl dimethylamine (BDMA) must be handled with care as it may cause severe dermatitis.

Embedding with Vestopal

The embedding mixture is made up by adding 1 per cent initiator (benzoyl peroxide) and 0·5 per cent activator (cobalt napthenate) to Vestopal W.

The initiator and the activator should not be mixed together as they may explode. All the ingredients should be stored separately in the dark at 4°C.

After dehydration, drops of Vestopal can be added to the container at 15 min intervals for several hours. The top is left off the container overnight to allow the rest of the acetone to evaporate. The following morning, the Vestopal mixture is added and the specimens are left to infiltrate for 6–8 h.

A drop of Vestopal is added to the gelatine capsule before transferring the specimen. The capsules are filled with fresh Vestopal mixture and placed in an incubator at 60°C for 24 h with the tops off.

Embedding in Water Soluble Media

Mixtures of ordinary bacteriological gelatine have been used and specimens passed through three 10 per cent mixtures of gelatine. The immersion should be 30 min to 1 h in each stage. The final solution is poured into a Petri dish and allowed to solidify. Small cubes are cut from this and placed in a vacuum desiccator under reduced pressure for 6 h to harden.

Aquon procedures[36] are lengthy, but worthwhile results have been obtained where it is necessary to avoid dehydration in alcohol or acetone.

Freeze Drying for electron microscopy

This is becoming increasingly important in techniques connected with the electron microscope although there are difficulties in adapting techniques so that they are suitable for all material.

This method has the great advantage of cutting out dehydration.

FREEZE DRYING AND FREEZE SUBSTITUTION

Both freeze drying and freeze substitution rely on the same primary process of rapidly freezing the tissue to approximately $-170°C$. This operation is commonly effected by plunging the material into a 'quenching' fluid which is immersed in liquid nitrogen. This part of the procedure is critical as it is essential that the ice crystals formed are submicroscopical. This is only brought about by very rapid cooling. Pieces of tissue (which have been cut as small as possible) are immersed in an 8 to 10 per cent solution of methylcyclohexane in isopentane which is being cooled in liquid nitrogen. This obtains a freezing temperature of approximately $-175°C$.

Following the freezing procedure, the ice crystals must be removed with as little disturbance to the cell structure as possible; either by dissolving the ice in alcohol (freeze substitution) or by evaporating the frozen water under vacuum (freeze drying). In the former case alcohol-soluble substances will be removed from the material whilst in the latter process they remain. However, freeze substitution gives better tissue preservation than conventional chemical fixation and being less complex than freeze drying is therefore more commonly used.

The frozen material which is to be freeze substituted is immersed in alcohol (absolute ethyl or methyl) at below –30°C. For this purpose a dry ice–acetone mixture has been found satisfactory and gives a temperature of about − 60°C. The material should be in sealed tubes and left totally immersed in the cold bath for 24 hours, the dry ice being replaced as necessary. One or more changes of alcohol are made for subsequent periods of 24 hours. The alcohol is replaced by toluene and during further changes of toluene is slowly brought to room temperature and embedded in the normal manner. None of the solutions used in the freeze substitution procedure are adequate fixatives and hence the first solution having fixing properties into which the tissue is placed following embedding becomes the effective fixative.

It is customary to make provision for fixation prior to embedding because this may be done by placing the material in 70 per cent ethanol at about 60°C for an hour, or by using acidified 95 per cent ethanol (containing approximately 0·3 per cent acetic acid) for half an hour. As an alternative to these methods it is possible to fix the tissue whilst the substitution process is taking place. A 1 per cent solution of osmium tetroxide in acetone at − 60°C has been found useful for such fixation and is used instead of the alcohol in the normal substitution process. The fixation dehydration is allowed to take place for up to a week, after which the material is washed in two or three changes of acetone at the same low temperature, brought to room temperature and embedded.

In freeze drying, the tissue must again be maintained at below − 30°C during the course of the removal of the water. The crystals of frozen water may be removed either under high vacuum, or in a stream of moving gas at a lower vacuum. Following the drying process, which may take place for a number of days, the material is embedded in wax (or resin) whilst maintaining the vacuum.

Moving gas freeze drying apparatus has been described by Jensen which involves sucking dry carbon dioxide gas or nitrogen over the frozen material, and through a desiccant to remove water vapour. The vessel containing the specimen is immersed in some type of cold bath (such as the acetone–dry ice bath mentioned above) thus maintaining the low temperature.

The alternative to this type of apparatus is the high vacuum tissue drier such as the Speedivac Pearse tissue drier, where a thermoelectric element maintains the low temperature whilst the tissue is dried. Then the current may be reversed thus warming the specimen as it is embedded in wax or resin, the whole process being carried out without release of vacuum.

REFERENCES

[1] British Museum (Natural History) (1957). *Instructions for Collectors, No. 10,* 6th ed. London; British Museum

[2] Franklin, G. L. (1946). 'A Rapid Method of Softening Wood for Microtome Sectioning.' *Trop. Woods* **88**, 35

[3] Johansen, D. E. (1940). *Plant Microtechnique,* 1st ed., New York; McGraw-Hill

[4] Zirkle, C. (1927). 'Some Fixatives for Both Nuclei and Mitochondria.' *Science* **66**, 400

[5] McWhorter, F. P. and Weier, E. (1936). 'Possible Uses of Dioxan in Botanical Microtechnique.' *Stain Tech.* **11**, 107

[6] Zirkle, C. (1934). 'Amines in Cytological Fixing Fluids.' *Protoplasma* **20**, 473

[7] Marengo, N. P. (1952). 'Formalin Pyrogallol as a Fixative for Plant Cytoplasm.' *Stain Tech.* **27**, 209

[8] Baker, J. R. (1958). *Principles of Biological Microtechnique,* 1st ed. London; Methuen

[9] Duffield, J. W. (1940). 'Time Savers for Fixing and Dehydration.' *Stain Tech.* **15**, 57

[10] Steedman, H. F. (1960). *Section Cutting in Microscopy,* 1st ed. Oxford; Blackwell

[11] Fell, K. R. and Rowson, J. M. (1955). 'Water Soluble Embedding Media and Permanent Mountants for Use in Histological Work with Botanical Materials.' *J.R. micr. Soc.,* Series III **75**, 111

[12] Steedman, H. F. (1957). 'Polyester Wax. A New Ribboning Embedding Medium for Histology.' *Nature, Lond.* **179**, 1345

[13] Wade, H. W. (1952). 'Notes on the Carbowax Method of Making Tissue Sections.' *Stain Tech.* **27**, 71

[14] McLane, S. R. Jr. (1951). 'Higher Polyethylene Glycols as a Water Soluble Matrix for Sectioning Fresh or Fixed Plant Tissues.' *Stain. Tech.* **26**, 63

[15] Weiner, S. (1957). 'A Simplified Vacuum Embedder.' *Stain Tech.* **32**, 195

[16] Cunningham, R. H. and Wighton, D. C. (1962). 'Silicone Rubber Multiple Molds for Paraffin Embedding.' *Stain Tech.* **37**, 54

[17] Palade, G. E. (1952). 'A Study of Fixation for Electron Microscopy.' *J. exp. Med.* **95**, 285

[18] Caulfield, J. B. (1957). 'Effects of Varying the Vehicle for OsO_4 in Tissue Fixation.' *J. biophys. biochem. Cytol.* **3**, 827

[19] Luft, J. H. (1956). 'Permanganate—A New Fixative for Electron Microscopy.' *J. biophys. biochem. Cytol.* **2**, 799

[20] Mollenhauer, H. H. (1959). 'Permanganate Fixation of Plant Cells.' *J. biophys. biochem. Cytol.* **6**, 431

[21] Bradbury, S. and Meek, G. A. (1960). 'A Study of Potassium Permanganate Fixation for Electron Microscopy.' *Quart. J. micr. Sci.* **101**, 241

[22]Sabatini, D. D., Bensch, K. and Barrnett, R. J. (1963). 'The Preservation of Cellular Ultrastructure and Enzymatic Activity by Aldehyde Fixation.' *J. Cell. Biol.* **17**, 19–58

[23]Ledbetter, M. C. and Porter, K. R. (1963). 'A Microtubule in Plant Cell Fine Structure.' *J. Cell. Biol.* **19**, 239–250

[24]Ledbetter, M. C. and Gunning, B. E. S. (1964). 'Glutaraldehyde-osmic Fixation of Plant Cells.' *Symp. on Botanical Applications of Electron Microscopy. J. R. micr. Soc.* **83**, 331

[25]Kellenberger, E., Ryter, A. and Sechaud, J. (1958). 'Electron Microscope. Study of DNA—Containing Plasmas. II. Negative and Mature Phage DNA as compared with Normal Bacterial Nucleoids in Different Physiological States.' *J. biophys. biochem. Cytol.* **4**, 671

[26]Glauert, A. M. (1962). 'A Survey of Embedding Media for Electron Microscopy.' *J. R. micr. Soc.* **80**, 269–277

[27]Ward, R. T. (1958). 'Prevention of Polymerization Damage in Methacrylate Embedding Medium.' *J. Histochem. Cytochem.* **6**, 398

[8]Moore, D. H. and Grimley, P. M. (1957). 'Problems in Methacrylate Embedding for Electron Microscopy.' *J. biophys. biochem. Cytol.* **3**, 255

[29]Cosslett, A. (1960). 'The Effect of the Electron Beam on Thin Sections.' *European Regional Conference on Electron Microscopy.* Delft. p.678

[30]Glauert, A. M. and Glauert, R. H. (1958). 'Araldite as an Embedding Medium for Electron Microscopy.' *J. biophys. biochem. Cytol.* **4**, 191

[31]Finck, H. (1960). 'Epoxy Resins in Electron Microscopy.' *J. biophys. biochem. Cytol.* **7**, 27

[32]Luft, J. H. (1961). 'Improvement in Epoxy Resins in Embedding Methods.' *J. biophys. biochem. Cytol.* **9**, 409

[33]Craig, E. L., Frajola, W. J. and Greider, M. H. (1962). 'An Embedding Technique for Electron Microscope Using Epon 812.' *J. Cell Biol.* **12**, 190

[34]Ryter, A. and Kellenberger, E. (1958). 'L'inclusion au Polyester pour l'ultramicrotomie.' *J. Ultrastructure Res.* **2**, 200

[35]Low, F. N. and Clevenger, M. R. (1962). 'Polyester Methacrylate Embedments for Electron Microscopy.' *J. Cell Biol.* **12**, 615

[36]Gibbons, I. R. (1959). 'An Embedding Resin Miscible with Water for Electron Microscopy.' *Nature, Lond.* **184**, 373

[37]Wichterle, O., Bartl, P. and Rosenberg, M. (1960). 'Water Soluble Methacrylates as Embedding Media for Preparation of Ultra Thin Sections.' *Nature, Lond.* **186**, 494

[38]Rosenberg, M., Bartl, P. and Lesko, J. (1960). 'Water Soluble Methacrylate as an Embedding Medium for the Preparation of Ultra Thin Sections.' *J. Ultrastructure Res.* **4**, 298

[39]Mollenhauer, H. H. (1964). 'Plastic Embedding Mixtures for use in Electron Microscopy.' *Stain Tech.* **39**, 111–114

BIBLIOGRAPHY

Feder, N. and Sidman, R. L. (1958). 'Methods and Principles of Fixation by Freeze Substitution.' *J. biophys. biochem. Cytol.* **4**, 593–602

Jensen, W. A. (1962). *Botanical Histochemistry*, 1st ed. San Francisco; Freeman

Kay, D. (1961). *Techniques for Electron Microscopy*, 1st ed. Oxford; Blackwell

Mercer, E. H. and Birbeck, M. S. C. (1961) *Electron Microscopy. A Handbook for Biologists.* 1st ed. Oxford; Blackwell

CHAPTER 3

SECTION CUTTING AND MOUNTING

RAZORS AND MICROTOME KNIVES

There are three main types of razors and microtome knives; wedge shaped, plano-concave and hollow ground. All three types of razors are useful for hand sectioning but the wedge shaped microtome knife is the most useful for general purposes when sectioning mechanically.

Good sections can be obtained with safety razor blades but a properly sharpened razor produces the best results. It cannot be over emphasized that the razor must be sharp and this means constant honing and stropping. A new razor has not necessarily an edge sharp enough to produce successful sections.

Knives must never be laid on the bench when not in use but should be replaced in their boxes.

Stones and Strops

If the knives and razors are kept in good condition a coarse stone is not required. A Belgian yellow stone, on which oil is used as a lubricant, and a slate stone, on which a soap solution is used, are two useful fine stones. These stones must be cleaned after use by washing off the soap solution with water and removing the oil with xylene. Occasionally the water stone may be cleaned with a little xylene.

The stones must not be too narrow and, for sharpening microtome knives, should be at least 3 in. wide and 12 in. long.

The leather strop should be mounted on a block of wood. A flexible strop should not be used unless stretched very tightly, because if it bends while the knife is being moved up and down, it removes the edge obtained by sharpening. A small amount of jeweller's rouge or stropping paste should be rubbed into the leather of the strop occasionally.

All stones and strops should be covered when not in use to prevent any dust settling on them.

Sharpening on a Stone

Plano-concave and wedge shaped microtome knives must always have a back fitted to give the correct angle for sharpening. These backs are supplied by the makers and either screw or slip on to the back of the knife and must always be fitted in the same way. If there is no mark on the back, a scratch with a file will show which end fits nearest to the handle of the knife. The slip-on backs are the easiest to use.

The knife is always sharpened with the edge of the blade facing the direction of movement and should be moved diagonally from one end of the stone to the other (*Figure 39*).

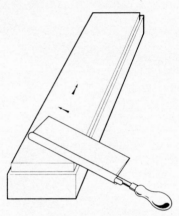

Figure 39. Honing a microtome knife

At the end of each stroke it is turned over on its back without being lifted from the stone. Pressure should not be exerted on the blade as the knife overlaps the edge of the stone.

Razors are sharpened in the same manner and are easier to handle as the whole of the blade is supported at the same time, provided a wide stone is used. Plano-concave razors are only honed on the one side, any slight burr of the edge being removed with one or two strokes on the flat side. Razors and knives should not be left until they are blunt before being re-sharpened, as some considerable time can be spent producing a suitable 'edge'. After sharpening they should be wiped dry and replaced in their boxes.

Sharpening on Plate Glass

Microtome knives can be sharpened very successfully on a piece of plate glass using a silver polish, e.g. Silvo as a lubricant.

This method of sharpening should only be used if the knife is new, as a knife which has been sharpened on a stone will be slightly bowed and therefore not suitable because only part of the blade will make contact with the glass. A back must be fitted to the knife before sharpening in the same manner as for sharpening on a stone.

The Shandon Scientific Company market a knife sharpening machine which makes use of a rotating plate glass table on which the knife is sharpened using Silvo or Three-in-One oil. This machine can be set to sharpen one or both sides of the knife and has a damping system to prevent the edge being damaged when the knife is turned over from one side to the other. It also has a mechanism for reproducing the correct bevel angle.

The knives should have two holes drilled in the back so that they can be fitted to the arm of the machine.

Stropping

This should be done sparingly, usually only five or six strokes. Stropping does not sharpen the knife but produces a finer edge. Naturally when stropping, the back of the knife precedes the edge, otherwise the leather would be cut.

HAND SECTIONING

All types of material can be sectioned by hand with the use of the correct razor. Hand sectioning is a quick method of obtaining a few sections or for identification of specimens when embedding or microtoming are not necessary.

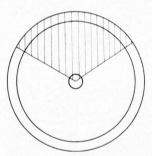

Figure 40. The shaded portion of the diagram marks the area of an adequate transverse section of a stem

Figure 41. One method of supporting a piece of woody stem for sectioning

A wedge shaped or plano-concave razor is required to cut hand sections of timber and these sections must consist only of a very small portion of the surface. The cubes can be softened in the same way as for microtoming. Usually twigs can be cut without this treatment but, when cutting a transverse section, only a portion of the surface area is cut. This is quite adequate, provided that the section shows all the tissues from the bark to the pith (*Figure 40*).

Much thinner sections can be obtained in this way than by attempting to cut a 'whole' section.

Not everyone finds it comfortable to cut in the same way but the following is one example of how to take a transverse section.

The material should be held firmly between the fingers and thumb of one hand, with the end of the material supported by the fourth finger (*Figure 41*).

The stem of the razor should be held between the thumb and the first two fingers, with the handle at right angles to the blade, gripped between the second and third fingers (*Figure 42*). In this way both the material and the razor are held firmly.

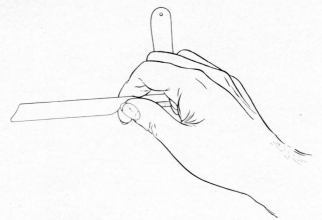

Figure 42. Method of holding a razor for hand sectioning

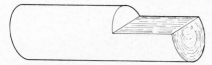

*Figure 43. A portion cut away from a twig
ready for longitudinal sectioning*

To cut longitudinal sections from twigs, a portion of the stem is cut away as shown in *Figure 43*. The material is held between the thumb and first finger, supported underneath by the other fingers (*Figure 43*).

The method of cutting transverse sections of soft stems is the same as for woody material. There is an alternative method for cutting longitudinally, provided that the material is not tough. With a razor blade two cuts are made two-thirds of the way through the material

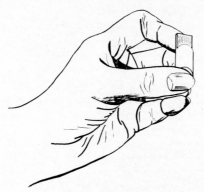

Figure 44. Material held in a position for sectioning longitudinally. Care must be taken that the first finger is below the cut portion of the twig

Figure 45. Position of cuts in a soft piece of stem prior to sectioning

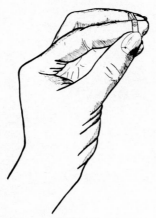

Figure 46. Position of soft stem for longitudinal sectioning

as shown in *Figure 45* and the two end-pieces bent downwards at right angles.

The material is then laid over the first finger and held by the thumb and second finger (*Figure 46*).

For cutting very soft, small, or thin specimens, pith or carrot can be used as support and a hollow ground razor is useful.

When hand sections of leaves are required, a vertical cut can be made across a piece of elder pith and the portion of leaf material inserted. A section of the pith and the leaf is then cut.

For small pieces of roots and stems, a hole can be made in the pith and the material inserted. Part of the supporting pith can be trimmed away so that there is less surface area to be cut. The trimming of any material should be done with a razor blade or with part of the razor that is not used for sectioning.

When cutting sections of any type of material, both the specimen and the razor must be kept wet. If cutting preserved material, the razor must be kept flooded with 70 per cent alcohol but if cutting fresh material water is substituted. On no account should the specimen be allowed to dry out.

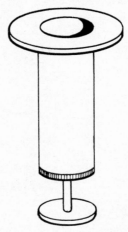

Figure 47. A hand microtome

The sections can be removed from the razor with a finger or a soft brush and placed in either 70 per cent alcohol or water. Pin dishes and specimen tubes containing 70 per cent alcohol are useful for holding and storing sections. Soft haired brushes, sizes 3 and 5, or section lifters are useful to transfer sections from one liquid to another.

A hand microtome may be used to support material for sectioning. It consists of a metal tube with a platform top and a screw for adjusting the thickness of the sections (*Figure 47*). The material should be supported by two pieces of cork just below the level of the platform or by filling the cavity around the material with molten wax which is allowed to solidify.

Woody materials are difficult to cut in a hand microtome because they can rarely be clamped firmly enough. A plano-concave razor should be used with a hand microtome. A big disadvantage with a hand microtome is that the razor is blunted by continual movement across the platform.

Bench Microtome

This is similar to the hand microtome but it is clamped to the bench instead of being held in the hand.

MECHANICAL SECTIONING

SLEDGE MICROTOME

The sledge microtome (*Figure 48*) is used to obtain sections of timber, and any other material which is firm enough to be held in the object clamp, either by itself or supported between pieces of cork. Sections of leaves, stems and roots can be obtained very successfully by this method.

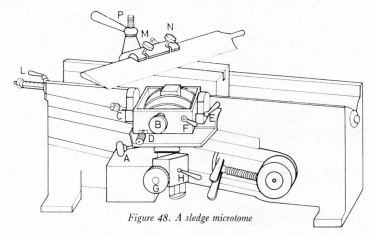

Figure 48. A sledge microtome

The object clamp is made fast by screw A and the material held fast in the clamp by screw B. To orientate the material C and D can be used, and E and F to clamp them in position.

E   121

By turning G the whole object clamp is raised and can be locked in position by H. The thickness of the sections is set by L. The knife is held in position by the two screws M and N, and P controls the direction of the knife to the block. By P, at the side of the knife holder, is an adjustment for the angle of cutting. This angle should be 10 degrees when cutting most timbers and the knife should be at a fairly oblique angle to the material. Knives 8–10 in. long are used for this work and are gradually adjusted so that each part of the blade is used in turn.

Trimming Cubes of Wood

The cubes should be trimmed so that they have true transverse, radial and tangential faces.

Orientation of Cubes

When transverse sections are needed, the cube is orientated in the clamp so that the rays run parallel to the length of the microtome but occasionally, with difficult material, it can be an advantage to orientate the block with the rays running at right angles to the length of the microtome. Also with difficult material the cut should be made very obliquely across the cube.

Cutting

To cut a section, the knife, which is supported on a block running between two grooves, is pushed right back against L. This movement raises the knife so that the correct thickness of section is cut. The knife is then brought forwards smoothly over the cube and the section is slid on to the knife with a soft brush.

Figure 49. Diagram of the transverse surface of a block of Douglas Fir showing the dark bands of late wood

It is important that both the knife and the specimen are kept flooded with 70 per cent alcohol. To prevent serious rolling of the sections, they should be allowed to remain on the knife for a short time before transferring to a dish of 70 per cent alcohol. Timber sections are usually cut at 18–20 μ, although thicker ones are some-times necessary. When a number of sections are being cut, it is advisable to examine them under the microscope from time to time, to make sure that the tissues are not torn.

Additional Softening Process

In some woods, such as the Douglas Fir, there are hard bands of late wood which can be seen running across the transverse surface of the cube inter-spaced with softer bands of early wood (*Figure 49*).

The late wood bands show up clearly, as they are darker in colour than the bands of early wood.

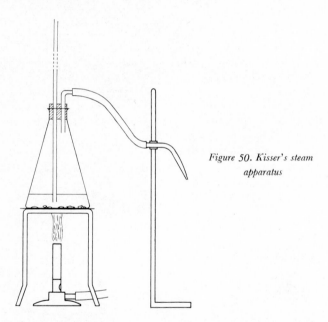

Figure 50. Kisser's steam apparatus

When cubes like these are subjected to the softening process, described on p. 85, the bands of late wood cannot be softened sufficiently without disintegration of the early wood. This process, therefore, can be carried out only to the stage when the early wood has been rendered soft enough to section easily. Kisser's steam method can then be employed to soften the late wood while the sections are being cut.

The apparatus is set up as shown in *Figure 50*.

A conical flask is fitted with a long length of glass tubing to act as a safety valve, while another is bent and drawn out to a fine nozzle at one end so that steam can be directed on to the cube of wood held in the object clamp of the microtome. Porous chips or pieces of flower pot are placed in the bottom of the flask to prevent bumping and the flask should not be more than a third full of water. A jet of steam can be produced by boiling the water in the flask and this jet is directed on to the surface of the cube while the sections are being cut. Steam which is supplied by tap is extremely useful.

Care should be taken after using steam to see that the knife and all parts of the microtome are thoroughly wiped dry. The microtome is dismantled and all parts are coated with a thin lubricating oil such as Three-in-One. The parts are then re-assembled and the microtome is covered with an oily rag and enclosed by a dust cover.

Cutting Wax Blocks

Blocks of ester wax can also be clamped in a sledge microtome and cut. The knife should move straight towards the operator over the block and a dry brush held in one hand steadies the section against the knife. As the next section is cut, the first section is freed from the knife and can be lifted off and placed on a slide or in a dish of xylene to dissolve the wax. This method of cutting is useful when sections of 30 μ or more are needed, as these thick sections cannot be cut on a rotary microtome.

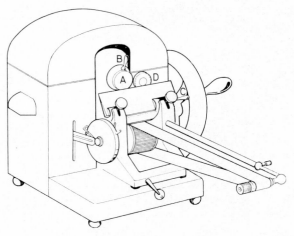

Figure 51. A rotary microtome

MECHANICAL SECTIONING

ROTARY MICROTOME

A rotary microtome (*Figure 51*) is used to obtain serial sections of embedded material.

The block holder A is orientated and clamped into position by lever B. The angle of the knife is set by adjusting C, and a good cutting angle is 5 degrees.

The thickness of the sections is controlled by D. A ribbon conveyor belt is not altogether necessary but is useful to support very thin sections. Knives which are 5–6 in. long are used in a rotary microtome.

CAMBRIDGE ROCKER MICROTOME

This is also used to obtain serial sections of embedded material (*Figure 52*).

Two screws A and B hold the knife in a fixed position and the object holder C is secured by D. The string E is adjusted so that the material is cut when the handle F is moved along the graduated scale G. This is set for the thickness of the sections, each division usually equalling 2 μ. The knurled screw H is turned anti-clockwise to reset the machine when M has risen to the top of H.

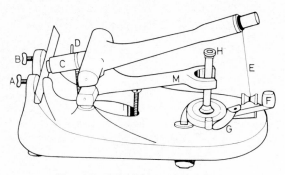

Figure 52. A Cambridge rocker microtome

TRIMMING BLOCKS AND CUTTING SECTIONS FOR ROTARY AND CAMBRIDGE ROCKER MICROTOMES

Paraffin Wax Blocks

The blocks, each one usually containing one specimen, are trimmed with a scalpel so that the embedded material is visible.

The surface of the object holder is covered with molten wax which is allowed to set. The wax block is attached to the object holder by melting the under surface of the block with a heated spatula, at the same time pressing it down on to the holder. The spatula can be heated again and a little more wax added to anchor the base of the block. This can be cooled by placing it under a cold tap for a few seconds.

Metal object holders are supplied with microtomes but wooden holders[1] may be made so that a number of wax blocks can be mounted separately at the same time. The blocks can be stored on these holders until needed.

When the block is mounted on the holder it should be finally trimmed so that the specimen is centrally placed (*Figure 53 a and b*).

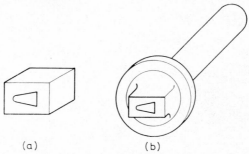

(a)   (b)

Figure 53. (a) Trimmed wax block; (b) block mounted on the specimen holder

The sides of the block, which are in a horizontal position in relation to the knife, should be parallel to one another, otherwise a curved ribbon will result (*Figure 54b*).

One or both sides of the block, which are in a vertical position in relation to the knife, can be cut at a slight angle. This enables the operator to see the length of each individual section in the ribbon and is useful when the embedded material cannot be seen easily when cut (*see Figure 54a*).

Each length of wax ribbon should be detached from the knife and supported over two mounted needles. The ribbons are laid in rows on a sheet of plain paper, with the first cut ribbons placed nearest the operator and the serial sections running from left to right.

At room temperature, paraffin sections can be cut at thicknesses from 5–12 μ. If sections of 3–5 μ are required, the use of a cold room is almost essential as, at this thickness, the wax will fail to ribbon properly at room temperature.

Paraffin wax sections should be cut at a speed of 80–100 sections/min.

If there is undue compression of the sections owing to the room temperature being too high, the use of a cold room for cutting is valuable because it is not always possible to embed in a wax with a higher melting point. If a cold room is not available the wax block and knife can be cooled by ice, cold water or a thermoelectric power pack (see p. 131). A simple device to contain ice cubes can be made and attached to the knife holder, with a drainage tube to carry the water away from the microtome[2].

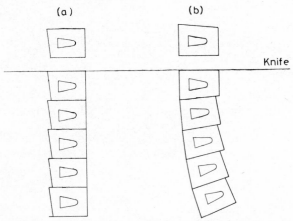

Figure 54. (a) *Wax block trimmed so that a straight ribbon is obtained;* (b) *sides of the block which are horizontal to the knife edge are not parallel so a curved ribbon is produced*

Another method is to have a water jacket which can be filled with cold or warm water to adjust the temperature of the knife[3] but this is inclined to be messy. The best method of cooling is by the use of a thermoelectric power pack although the use of CO_2 gas[4] is a cheaper proposition. Static electricity can be troublesome when handling paraffin wax ribbons; the ribbons are attracted to parts of the microtome and knife so they are often broken in the attempts to remove them. When the specimens are embedded in ester wax, however, this difficulty does not arise.

If difficulty is experienced in obtaining a complete ribbon, moistening the back edge of the knife with a finger will often help.

Ester Wax Blocks

Blocks of ester wax may be warmed slightly in an oven to facilitate trimming but they must not be left in too long as this impairs the properties of the wax. The blocks are trimmed and mounted on the object holder, in the same manner as paraffin blocks, but they should be allowed to set at room temperature for a few minutes and not placed under running water.

The speed at which ester wax blocks are cut[5] is about 30–50 sections/min which is slower than for paraffin wax. There is not nearly so much compression of the sections and it is usually easier to work with ester wax than with paraffin wax.

Polyester Wax Blocks

Blocks of polyester wax should not be handled on account of the low melting point of the wax. They should be moved with forceps and trimmed with a safety razor blade. Mounting on the object holder is the same as for ester wax.

Sections are cut at the same speed as for paraffin wax, i.e. 80–100 sections/min.

Water Soluble Waxes

Ribbons are difficult to obtain from these blocks which are best used where single sections are required. When serial sections are necessary, however, some ribbons can be obtained by painting a 25 per cent solution of beeswax in chloroform on to the upper and lower surfaces of the block[6].

Mounting Paraffin Wax Ribbons

Clean slides are smeared with a little adhesive, usually Mayer's albumen (see p. 136) or Haupt's adhesive (see p. 136). To avoid confusion in the order of the serial sections, the slides should be labelled before mounting the ribbons. This is done by scratching the slides with a diamond pencil.

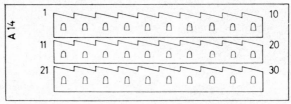

Figure 55. Wax ribbons mounted on a microscope slide

The wax ribbons are then cut into lengths which will fit conveniently under a 2 in. cover glass, allowing for the slight stretching which takes place when the wax is warmed.

According to the width of the ribbon, two or three rows can be arranged on the slide (*Figure 55*) using mounted needles or a small fine haired brush. If Mayer's albumen is used, the ribbons are floated on a little distilled water and the slides placed on a slide drier or similar source of heat to correct any compression of the wax. When the ribbons are completely stretched, the water is drained off and the slides are left to dry in a convenient place. They must be protected from dust.

When Haupt's adhesive is used, the ribbons are floated on 3 per cent formalin.

A thermostatically heated water bath can be used to stretch the ribbons and they are then mounted on the slides and left to dry.

Mounting Ester Wax Ribbons

Clean slides are smeared with Mayer's albumen in the same manner as for paraffin ribbons. The slides are flooded with distilled water and after the expansion of the sections this is drained off. The slides are then placed in a drying oven at 40–45°C.

Mounting Polyester Wax Ribbons

Mayers albumen is not a satisfactory adhesive for polyester ribbons and a carbohydrate adhesive appears to be the best.

A solution of amylopectin is excellent[5] (see p. 137). A few drops should be smeared on a clean slide and dried overnight before using.

Mounting Soluble Wax Ribbons

It has been found that either a rubber cement or a gelatine adhesive (p. 137) is successful in holding the water-soluble ribbons on the slide.

The gelatine adhesive is smeared thinly on the slides and the carbowax sections mounted. The slides are placed in a warm place for about 15 min and then in a drying oven.

The rubber cement is smeared quickly on the slide in a thick layer[7]. The ribbons are placed on this and the slide flooded with lighter fuel. The slides are placed on a slide drier and more lighter fuel added to keep the ribbons afloat as they are flattened. The slides are then dried as the lighter fuel evaporates.

FREEZING MICROTOME

The freezing microtome (*Figure 56*) should be firmly clamped to the bench and a piece of cardboard or thin wood inserted between the clamp and the bench to preserve the surface.

A secures the freezing stage and B raises or lowers the whole stage. C and D control the angle of the knife to the block. At the far end of runner E is a scale which is set for the thickness of the sections. On a Reichert model it is marked from 1–6 and each division equals 5 μ.

F is opened and closed to let the CO_2 through the freezing stage in short bursts, as this freezes the material quickly. It is important that the CO_2 is liquid when it reaches the stage of the microtome, otherwise it will not freeze the material sufficiently.

G controls the CO_2 for cooling the knife so that it is approximately the same temperature as the section being cut.

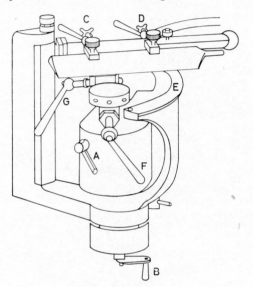

Figure 56. A freezing microtome

The degree of freezing is important. If insufficiently frozen the section will just disintegrate on the knife edge, and if frozen too hard it will chip.

When cutting, the top of the frozen material should be slightly thawed by resting a finger on it for a moment or moistening it with a brush dipped in 70 per cent alcohol.

The freezing microtome is particularly useful for cutting fresh material but fixed material can also be sectioned. Tissues that have been immersed in fixatives containing alcohol, should be washed under running water for at least 12 hours, as alcohol inhibits freezing.

It is possible to cut sections of fresh material by flooding the object stage with water, freezing it, attaching a small piece of material and freezing again. Distortion of the material takes place and a medium is necessary to support it while sections are being cut.

A solution of 5 per cent agar[8] made up in distilled water may be used, but a solution of gum arabic, as described by Sass, is often found to be superior.

A syrupy aqueous solution of gum arabic is made with the addition of a few crystals of carbolic acid[9]. The object stage should be spread with gum and then frozen. The specimen should be dipped in the gum, placed on the stage and frozen. More gum can be added until the specimen is well supported, each addition being frozen.

Polyethylene glycols are also useful as a water soluble matrix for sectioning fresh or fixed plant tissues[10]. The stage of the freezing microtome is coated with the water soluble wax, the material arranged in it and hardened. More wax is added and also hardened. The material is not frozen and only enough CO_2 is let through to set the wax quickly.

An aqueous syrupy solution of polyvinyl alcohol can also be used as a matrix.

Freezing adaptations can be obtained from the makers of both the Sledge and Cambridge rocker microtomes and a device for the adaptation of a Rotary microtome has been described[11].

Thermoelectric Freezing

Thermoelectric freezing is fast and capable of close temperature control. Attachments from the power pack can be connected to the stage and the knife of microtome. Normally this type of apparatus is used in conjunction with a sledge or freezing microtome but it can be used with certain rotary machines provided that wedge-shaped knives are used which are 40 mm or more in width.

An anti-roll plate (manufactured by De La Rue Frigistor Ltd., Langley, Bucks., England) can be fitted on the knife to prevent the sections from curling.

Although it is expensive, thermo-electric freezing is extremely valuable for cutting sections of fresh botanical materials and it can also be used to cool paraffin blocks, thus eliminating the need for a cryostat.

ULTRA-THIN SECTIONING

ULTRA MICROTOMES

These microtomes are designed to produce sections for examining under the electron microscope. The sections need to be very thin indeed and their thickness is measured in ångström units (Å), 1 Å being equivalent to $^1/_{10,000}$ μ. Sections can be cut automatically or by a manual feed.

The LKB ultrotome III (*Figure 57*) provides an excellent instrument for cutting ultra-thin sections. The specimen holder can be orientated in any plane and the block can be cut transversely or longitudinally. It has added advantages that capsules can be trimmed accurately in the chuck of the machine and that the edge of the glass knife can be determined by focusing the microscope and reading the angle from the scale on the side arm.

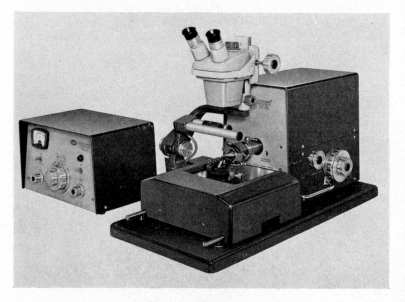

Figure 57. LKB ultrotome III
(By courtesy of LKB Instruments Ltd.)

Knives

Glass or diamond knives[12] can be used. The method of making glass knives was first described in 1950[13] and the basic principles have not changed, although modifications have been devised[14]. Strips 1 in. wide are cut from a sheet of plate glass or optical glass and each strip is cut into shorter pieces, each one having a cutting angle of about 45 degrees. Plate glass is easier to break but the edge of the knife is soon blunted. Optical glass is much harder to break but each knife has a longer life. The edge and cutting angle of the knife are very important. The edge of the knife should be examined under the microscope to make sure that it is up to standard. The exact cutting angle can be measured by placing the knife carefully on a piece of marked graph paper and moving the knife until the tip is parallel to one of the marked lines.

If it is possible, the glass knives should be made just before they are to be used so that the edge is not damaged by dust particles. Several knives can be conveniently placed in a Petri dish in readiness for a period of cutting.

Diamond knives are very expensive and, ideally, a set of knives with different cutting angles is necessary to cover all requirements. A diamond knife holder has been described[15] which is easily interchangeable with glass knives.

Strips of glass for hand breaking or for the Knife Maker can be obtained from LKB Instruments Ltd. (London address: 137 Anerley Road, S.E.20).

Special glass pliers[16] which can be adjusted and set to the thickness of the glass are available from Sommers & Maca Glass Machinery Co., 5501 W. Ogden Avenue, Chicago, Illinois, U.S.A.

LKB Knife Maker

Although this instrument is expensive it is an extremely valuable piece of equipment for an institution where a great deal of work is done in the electron microscope field. It produces glass knives with a highly reproducible edge angle and the scoring angle can be set from 40° to 55°. It is simple to operate and saves a considerable amount of time.

Trimming Blocks

The specimen blocks are trimmed to the shape of a pyramid with the top cut flat, which enables a very small area of the block to be cut. Simple devices for accurate trimming have been described[17,18,19]. If longitudinal sections of the material are needed, the block is sawn longitudinally by rubbing it against a blade set at the required height. A special specimen holder is used to take the block.

Cutting Sections

Metal troughs can be used but these are difficult to keep clean and it is often better to use waterproof adhesive tape. This must be attached to the knife, taking care that the ends of the tape do not foul the edge. The sides of the trough or the tape are sealed to the knife by using a high melting point wax.

Sections from methacrylate blocks can be cut on to 70 per cent alcohol in water. Vestopal blocks are usually cut on to 10 per cent acetone in water. Araldite and Epon blocks can be cut on to distilled water but the surface tension of the water presents some difficulties. Araldite is better cut on 20 per cent acetone. A modification is suggested to obtain flat sections by using a drop of water on a bakelite block, which is glued to the knife[20]. This has been improved by using a wedge made of brass, easily clamped to the diamond knife holder[15] and by using a hydraulic device for the withdrawal of the water from under the ribbon[21].

Whatever liquid is chosen, it must be absolutely clean and free from all dust particles. A hypodermic syringe is useful for filling the trough and adjusting the level of the liquid.

Single sections should be cut by the manual control and examined under the microscope. The thickness can be assessed by the colour. Serial sections can be cut by setting the automatic control but a check must be made to ensure that a section is cut each time the arm is lowered, otherwise a ribbon of uniform thickness will not be obtained.

Preparation of Specimen Grids

The sections are collected on grids which are usually coated with Formvar and then with carbon (Formvar is the trade name of a grade of polyvinyl formal).

Formvar films can be cast on glass[22] either by smearing a drop of 0·5–1 per cent Formvar in chloroform or ether on to a glass slide, or by dipping a chemically clean slide into a small container of the Formvar solution. The slide is held vertically in the solution until any bubbles of air rise to the surface. It is then carefully withdrawn and the end touched with a piece of filter paper to remove any excess Formvar. When the Formvar is dry, the edges of the slide are scraped with a razor blade to free the film. This is floated off by inserting the slide carefully at an angle into a dish of Pyrex distilled water. Breathing on the film prior to immersion in the water often facilitates this procedure. A number of grids can be arranged close together on the floating film with the shiny sides of the grids in contact with the Formvar. A clean slide is placed over the grids and film, which are pressed down at an angle into the water and which are removed as the slide is turned over and withdrawn. Now on the glass slide are the specimen grids covered by the Formvar film.

The carbon film is cast over the Formvar film by the evaporation of carbon[23, 24]. The grids can be removed from the slide and examined under a phase contrast microscope to make sure that the carbon film has not shattered.

Thinner films can often be obtained by employing a 'dip grid' method instead of casting on glass. Each grid is dipped into a solution of 1 per cent Formvar in chloroform or ether and allowed to dry in the air[25] before coating with carbon. A quick method of washing single grids is by using a burette filled with a solution of 50 per cent ether and 50 per cent acetone[26].

Mounting

Sections from methacrylate and Araldite blocks can be flattened by chloroform vapour[27] if necessary but care must be taken that the sections do not explode.

To remove the sections from the trough, a coated grid is held by a pair of watchmaker's forceps and placed either over the ribbon, coated side downwards, or brought up underneath the ribbon which is detached from the knife. A ring made of thin wire can also be used to lift out the sections which are supported on a water film held by the wire. The sections can be lowered on to a specimen grid under a binocular microscope.

AN ULTRA FREEZING MICROTOME[28]

This combines the ultra-microtome with freeze-drying and shadow casting installation in the same vacuum container.

Staining

Staining of ultra thin sections is carried out so that they are easily visible under the electron microscope. This is often necessary with sections from Araldite blocks. Usually, heavy metals such as uranium or lead[29,30,31] are employed but potassium permanganate[32] and other substances are equally valuable.

REPLICA TECHNIQUES FOR ELECTRON MICROSCOPY

For the study of the surface topography of specimens which are opaque to electrons, the preparation of replicas has proved most useful. Many techniques for the preparations of replicas have been described[33,34], and these are to a large extent determined by the nature of the material being examined.

Replicas are usually produced by a single or by a two stage technique. In the single stage technique, the surface of the specimen is coated with the material which will form the actual replica to be viewed in the microscope. In the two stage technique however, the first replica has a second layer of another material deposited upon it, the initial replica being removed.

The initial replica is commonly of plastic which can be deposited from solution in a volatile liquid, polymerized *in situ* or made by warming a thermoplastic and pressing it against the specimen. In the former case, a solution of Formvar in chloroform has commonly been used, although the resolution is not great and it may be difficult to strip from the surface of the specimen. By careful control of the concentration of the Formvar solution the replica may be made thin enough to be used as the final replica for a single stage technique.

In the case of polymerizing material *in situ* (such as methacrylate monomer) or using thermoplastics (such as polystyrene) the primary replica may only be used as the initial stage in a two stage technique.

Vacuum deposited carbon can also be used in a single stage technique. This involves careful backing and stripping of the carbon film from the specimen, followed by dissolving away the backing film leaving the carbon film to be viewed.

Two stage replica techniques involve the formation of a primary replica in much the same way as described above with the addition of a deposit of carbon, silicon monoxide or silica upon this. The primary replica is dissolved away and the vacuum deposited film is examined in the electron microscope.

If the replica, whether single or double stage, is viewed directly, it will be found to have very little inherent contrast. For this reason the specimen, the intermediate replica or the final replica can be "shadowed" with a heavy metal (such as gold palladium) which is evaporated under high vacuum from a source which is so positioned that the metal will impinge upon the surface of the specimen (or replica) at an angle. The result of this is that, according to the surface sculpturing of the shadowed film, there will be local accumulations of the metal thus producing electron opaque areas in the replica which increase the overall contrast obtained.

MOUNTING OF SECTIONS

ADHESIVES

Mayer's Albumen

Fresh white of egg	50 ml
Glycerol	50 ml
Thymol	A few crystals

The mixture should be well shaken and filtered through several thicknesses of cheese cloth.

Haupt's Adhesive

Pure gelatine	1 g
Distilled water	100 ml
Phenol crystals	2 g
Glycerol	15 ml

First the gelatine is dissolved in the water at a temperature of about 30°C. Then the phenol crystals and glycerol are added. The solution is stirred and filtered.

Amylopectin Adhesive[5]

(1) Boil 1 l. of water and while boiling, add 1·5 g Nipa ester No. 82121.

(2) Cool 200 ml of the solution to room temperature and add 2 g amylopectin. Stir until the powder forms a suspension (it will not dissolve), and then pour it slowly into the 800 ml of water which should still be boiling.

(3) Cool but do not filter. Shake before using.

Baker's Albumen[35]

0·9 per cent aqueous sodium chloride	100	ml
Sodium p-hydroxybenzoate	0·2 g	
Dissolve and add fresh white of egg	100	ml

The solution is well stirred and centrifuged until the supernatant fluid is quite clear. It is decanted and used as Mayer's albumen.

Giovacchini's Modification of Gelatine Adhesive[36]

Gelatine	15	g
Distilled water	55	ml
Glycerol	50	ml
Phenol	0·5 g	

The gelatine is dissolved in the water by heating, then the glycerol and phenol are added.

MOUNTANTS

Weak Glycerin

Glycerol	30 ml
Distilled water	70 ml

Add 2 or 3 crystals of thymol.

Lactophenol

This consists of equal quantities of phenol crystals, lactic acid, glycerol and distilled water. It can be purchased already prepared.

Glycerin Jelly

This can be made up but is better purchased as neutral glycerin jelly. Dye can be added to make this a useful mountant but it must be melted before use.

Gurr's Water Mountant

This is a valuable mountant which can also be coloured with dye. There is less trouble with air bubbles when using this mountant than there is with glycerin jelly.

Gelvatol

Gelvatol is the trade name for a series of polyvinyl alcohol resins. Polyvinyl alcohol has been used by various people for mounting specimens, but not all grades are suitable for this purpose. Gelvatol has replaced the Solvar[37] which was successful as a mountant.

Stock Solution

Gelvatol 20–30	20 g
Distilled water	100 ml

This is allowed to soak and dissolve overnight and is then filtered through glass wool. To prepare for use:

Stock solution	50 parts
Lactic acid	25 parts
60 per cent aqueous phenol	25 parts

Material may be preserved, cleared and permanently mounted in this solution.

Canada Balsam

Enough neutral resin is added to xylene to make a liquid of syrupy consistency. This can be made thicker, if required, by the addition of more resin, or thinner with the addition of xylene.

Canada balsam can be purchased in solution, which has the advantage of not drying up when left for any length of time but, when used as a mountant, it also takes a proportionally longer time to dry.

Euparal

This is purchased in solution and can be diluted with Euparal essence. It does not dry as quickly as Canada balsam.

MOUNTING PROCEDURE

Microscope slides should be of good quality glass, the ground edges having a whitish colour rather than a greenish-blue colour. The most useful size is 3 in. × 1 in. and about 1 mm thick.

Cover glasses are available in a range of grades and sizes. Useful sizes for sections of plant material are $3/4$ in. and $7/8$ in. square.

For mounting three sections of timber $7/8$ in. × $1^1/2$ in. cover glasses are used, for serial sections $7/8$ in. × 2 in. cover glasses are used, as described on p. 128. Grade 2 cover glasses can be used for low power work and some preparations for class work. Grade 1 should be used for more precise work and Grade 0 for oil immersion work.

Round cover glasses must be used for preparations which require ringing, otherwise square ones are cheaper.

Ringing

This is a process to seal the cover glasses of temporary mounts, thus rendering the preparations more permanent. The operation is carried out on a turntable (*Figure 58*) and the edge of the cover glass is sealed. Either Glyceel or gold-size can be used for this work. The slide is clipped on to the turntable which is marked out with rings. These enable the cover glass to be orientated. A small amount of medium is applied to the edge of the cover glass with the tip of a fine brush and the turntable rotated while the brush is held still.

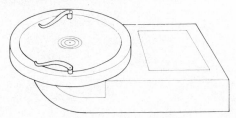

Figure 58. A ringing table

Temporary Mounts

Fresh sections, and sections that are not needed for prolonged study, can be mounted in a drop of water. As this dries out quite quickly, however, weak glycerin is widely used as a temporary mountant.

Glycerin jelly preparations are semi-permanent and can be made more permanent by ringing the slides.

Permanent Mounts

Euparal and Canada balsam are widely used for mounting ordinary material where special refractive indices are not required.

Experience will soon show the quantity of mountant to use, but a rough guide is given here. The thickness of the specimen is important, as bulky material obviously requires more mountant than very thin flat material.

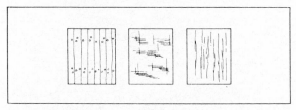

Figure 59. Arrangement of timber sections on a slide; from left to right transverse section, radial longitudinal section, tangential longitudinal section

One small drop is usually enough when using $^3/_4$ in. square cover glasses, and one large drop for $^7/_8$ in. square cover glasses. When long cover glasses are used, a smear of mountant should be placed along the length of the cover glass as well as two or three drops on the material on the slide.

Timber sections are usually arranged on a slide from left to right, transverse section (T.S.), radial longitudinal section (R.L.S.) tangential longitudinal section (T.L.S.) (*Figure 59*).

One end of the cover glass is lowered on to the slide and supported by a finger, while the other end is gently lowered by a mounted needle. This operation must be carried out carefully to avoid trapping air bubbles under the cover glass. The slides can be dried on a slide drier for two or three days.

Inexpensive slide driers can be made by utilizing half-sized biscuit tins. A hole is cut in one side, so that a lamp holder can be fitted, and a series of ventilation holes are punched round the other sides. A 40W bulb is placed inside and the lid fitted back into position (*Figure 60*).

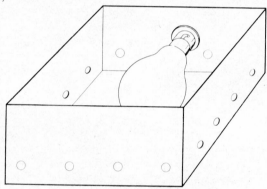

Figure 60. A slide drier

Small pieces of lead can be used to weight down large cover glasses in order to procure perfectly flat preparations.

When the slides are completely dry, any excess balsam can be removed from the edges of the cover glass with a razor blade, then the remainder wiped off with a cloth soaked in xylene. The preparations are then labelled permanently.

STORAGE OF SLIDES

For a small number of slides, slotted wooden boxes can be obtained but these are only suitable for permanent mounts. If the slides need to be stored in a flat position, cardboard folders each holding 6–12 slides are available. These folders are contained in special boxes.

For sets of slides, large cardboard folders are useful. Each folder is partitioned and holds 20 slides (*Figure 61*).

The name is written on the end of the folder and a number of folders can be stacked on top of one another.

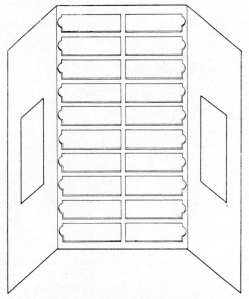

Figure 61. A cardboard slide holder

For a large collection of slides, filing cabinets are available which can be built up in units as the collection expands. Each section consists of a number of drawers on runners. There are drawers to take 3 in. × 1 in. slides in an upright position. The slides can be packed together or separated by using a spiral spring. There are also units where temporary mounts can be stored singly in a horizontal position. These units are very useful, as lantern slides and wax blocks can also be stored in the same cabinet.

Other small metal units are available for storing slides in an upright position. Metal holders, each containing four slides, are stacked in a box-like container.

REFERENCES

[1]Chute, H. L., Fulleron, R. L. and O'Meara, D. C. (1958). 'Tissue Blocks on Wood Holders.' *Stain Tech.* **33**, 245

[2]Cooper, K. W. (1937). 'Cooling Device for the Microtome.' *Stain Tech.* **12**, 25

[3]Duffield, J. W. (1941). 'Temperature Control for Microtome Knives.' *Stain Tech.* **16**, 123

[4]Schechtman, A. M. (1941). 'A Convenient Cooling Method in Paraffin Sectioning.' *Stain Tech.* **16**, 85

[5]Steedman, H. F. (1960). *Section Cutting in Microscopy*, 1st ed. Oxford; Blackwell

[6]Wade, H. W. (1952). 'Notes on the Carbowax Method of Making Tissue Sections.' *Stain Tech.* **27**, 71

[7]Yos, D. A. (1961). 'The Mounting of Carbowax Sections with Lighter Fluid and Rubber Cement.' *Stain Tech.* **36**, 163

[8]Evenden, W. and Schuster, C. E. (1938). 'The Use of Agar as a Matrix for Sectioning Plant Material with the Freezing Microtome.' *Stain Tech.* **13**, 145

[9]Sass, J. E. (1958). *Botanical Microtechnique*, 3rd ed. Des Moines; Iowa State Press

[10]McLane, S. R. Jr. (1951). 'Higher Polyethylene Glycols as a Water Soluble Matrix for Sectioning Fresh or Fixed Plant Tissues.' *Stain Tech.* **26**, 63

[11]Strike, T. A. (1962). 'A Device for Adapting the Rotary Microtome to Frozen Sectioning.' *Stain Tech.* **37**, 188

[12]Fernàndez-Moran, H. (1953). 'A Diamond Knife for Ultra-thin Sectioning.' *Exp. Cell Res.* **5**, 255

[13]Latta, H. and Hartmann, J. F. (1950). 'Use of a Glass Edge in Thin Sectioning for the Electron Microscope.' *Proc. Soc. exp. Biol., N.Y.* **74**, 436

[14]Cameron, D. A. (1956). 'A Note on Breaking Glass Knives.' *J. biophys. biochem. Cytol.* **2**, 57

[15]Crandall, F. B. (1961). 'An Improved Diamond Knife Holder for Ultramicrotomy.' *Stain Tech.* **36**, 34

[16]Siakotos, A. N. and Maiolatesi, E. (1964). 'Glass-breaking Pliers for Ultramicrotomy.' *Stain Tech.* **39**, 171–172

[17]Boyde, A. (1960). 'Device for the Trimming of Blocks for Ultra-microtomy.' *J. Ultrastructure Res.* **3**, 398

[18]Danon, D. (1961). 'An Instrument to Trim Plastic Specimen Blocks for Electron Microscopy prior to Sectioning.' *J. biophys. biochem. Cytol.* **9**, 726

[19]Isaac, P. K. (1964). 'Mechanical Trimming of Embedded Blocks for Ultra Microtomy.' *Stain Tech.* **39**, 225–227

[20]Westfall, J. A. (1961). 'Obtaining Flat Serial Sections for Electron Microscopy.' *Stain Tech.* **36**, 36

[21]— and Healy, D. L. (1962). 'A Water Control Device for Mounting Serial Ultra Thin Sections.' *Stain. Tech.* **37**, 118

[22]Drummond, D. G. (1950). 'The Practice of Electron Microscopy.' *J.R. micr. Soc. Series III*, **70**, 1

[23]Bradley, D. E. (1954). 'Evaporated Carbon Film for Use in Electron Microscopy.' *Brit. J. appl. Phys.* **5**, 65

BIBLIOGRAPHY

[24]Barton, A. A. (1960). 'Carbon Coated Grids for Electron Microscopy.' *Stain Tech.* **35**, 287

[25]Bradley, D. E. (1953). 'A New Method of Making Electron Microscope Specimen Support Films.' *Nature, Lond.* **171**, 1076

[26]— (1954). 'A High Resolution Evaporated Carbon Replica Technique for the Electron Microscope.' *J. Inst. Met.* **83**, 35

[27]Birbeck, M. S. C. and Mercer, E. H. (1958). 'Applications of an Epoxide Embedding Medium to Electron Microscopy.' *J.R. micr. Soc. Series III*, **76**, 159

[28]Moor, H., Möhlethaler, K., Waldner, H. and Frey-Wyssling, A. (1961). 'A New Freezing Ultramicrotome.' *J. biophys. biochem. Cytol.* **10**, 1

[29]Watson, M. L. (1958). 'Staining of Tissue Sections for Electron Microscopy with Heavy Metals.' *J. biophys. biochem. Cytol.* **4**, 475

[30]Parsons, D. F. and Darden, E. B. (1960). 'A Technique for the Simultaneous Dirt Free Lead Staining of Several Electron Microscope Grids of Thin Sections.' *J. biophys. biochem. Cytol.* **8**, 834

[31]Normann, T. C. (1964). 'Staining Thin Sections with Lead Hydroxide without Contamination by Precipitated Lead Carbonate.' *Stain Tech.* **39**, 50–52

[32]Lawn, A. M. (1960). 'The Use of Potassium Permanganate as an Electron-dense Stain for Sections of Tissue Embedded in Epoxy Resin.' *J. biophys. biochem. Cytol.* **7**, 197

[33]Kay, D. (1961). *Techniques for Electron Microscopy*, 1st ed. Oxford; Blackwell

[34]Côté, W. A. Jr., Koran, Z. and Day, A. C. (1964). 'Replica Techniques for Electron Microscopy of Wood and Paper.' *Tappi* **47**, 477–484

[35]Baker, J. R. and Jordan, B. M. (1953). 'Miscellaneous Contributions to Microtechnique.' *Quart. J. micr. Sci.* **94**, 237

[36]Giovacchini, R. P. (1958). 'Affixing Carbowax Sections to Slides for Routine Staining.' *Stain Tech.* **33**, 247

[37]Metcalf, C. R. and Richardson, F. R. (1949). 'The Use of Polyvinyl Alcohol and Related Compounds as Mounting Media for Microscope Slides.' *Kew Bull.* **4**, 569

BIBLIOGRAPHY

Pease, D. C. (1964). *Histological Techniques for Electron Microscopy*, 2nd ed. London; Academic Press

CHAPTER 4

STAINS AND STAINING TECHNIQUES

INTRODUCTION

Certain parts of plant cells are acid in character and have an affinity for basic dyes. Chromatin within nuclei is acid in character and has a strong affinity for basic dyes. Cytoplasm has an affinity for acid dyes and is basic in character[1].

As with fixation, the pH plays a considerable part in staining procedures. The H-ion concentration at which any compound changes from an acid to a base in action is known as its isoelectric point. Therefore, a compound acts as a base or as an acid in any staining solution according to whether its isoelectric point is below or above the H-ion concentration of that solution; and cellular elements take a basic dye if the H-ion concentration of the staining solution is below its isoelectric point and an acid dye if above this[2].

Some compounds have an isoelectric range, rather than a point, as the change over is gradual[3].

The simple purpose of staining is to show up tissues more clearly and, for material which is to be viewed under a light microscope, various dyes are used.

Basic Stains

These consist of a coloured organic base usually combined with a colourless acetate, chloride or sulphate such as safranin, crystal violet, methylene blue, bismark brown, iodine green or haematoxylin.

Acid Stains

These consist of a metallic base, usually sodium or potassium, combined with an organic acid radical, such as light green, fast green, aniline blue or orange G.

Neutral Stains

These consist of mixtures of certain acid and basic dyes, for example neutral red.

Specific Stains

These only stain certain tissues. Some are highly selective, others only slightly so.

Staining processes may be either progressive or regressive.

Progressive Staining

The material is placed in dilute stain and gradually more stain is added until the desired intensity of colour is obtained.

This process can be watched under the microscope.

Regressive Staining

The material is placed in the staining solution, deliberately over-stained, and then differentiated. This is the more usual procedure.

Tissues can be stained *in toto*, as sections, or as smears.

Vital Staining

Certain non-toxic dyes can be introduced to the living plant in dilute concentrations.

Differentiation

Various reagents are used to differentiate the tissue and to remove the excess stain.

Acid alcohol is used after staining with safranin, clove oil after crystal violet and iron alum after Heidenhaim's haematoxylin.

Mordants

These are certain chemicals which help to condition the plant tissues so that they may be stained successfully. They may be used in three ways.

1. Before staining, for example iron alum as a mordant for Heidenheim's haematoxylin.
2. Combined with the staining solution, for example Delafield's or Harris's haematoxylin.
3. Following the stain, for example iodine or picric acid after staining with crystal or methyl violet.

BLEACHING

Sections from woody material containing gum or resin should be bleached before staining. A weak aqueous solution of sodium hypochlorite or domestic bleach is ideal.

Other sections may be discoloured but they should only be bleached if staining would be hindered by the darkened tissues. Hydrogen peroxide (20 vol.) can be diluted with water or 70 per cent alcohol to provide good bleaching solutions.

The blackening caused by osmic acid can be removed by immersing the sections in a solution of equal parts hydrogen peroxide (20 vol.) and water, or by chlorine water.

STAINING

This can be carried out on a slide, when only one or two sections are to be dealt with, or in watch glasses and specimen tubes for bulk staining.

When staining is carried out on a slide, the stains and reagents can be drained into a cloth held in one hand. Sometimes sections have a tendency to curl up and then they should have a cover glass placed over them. The reagents are applied on the slide at one edge of the cover slip and a piece of filter paper used to draw the liquid under the glass (*Figure 62*).

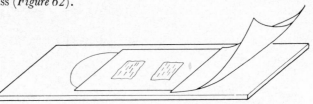

Figure 62. Irrigating sections on a slide

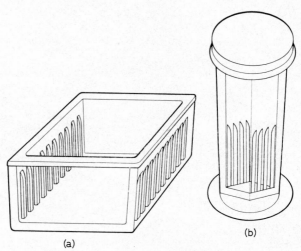

(a)   (b)

Figure 63. (a) A Stender dish; (b) A Coplin jar

Specimen tubes are useful for the bulk staining of timber sections and watch glasses for the bulk staining of sections of small stems, roots and leaves, etc. As a larger quantity of stain is used, it should not be thrown away but decanted into another bottle to be used again. This is an advantage with stains which mature with age.

When dealing with serial sections on slides, Stender dishes or Coplin jars are used (*Figure 63 a and b*).

Stender dishes are available in two sizes, each holding 20 slides at a time. Two slides are placed back to back and inserted in each division of the dish. The advantage of the larger dish is that it holds more liquid, although only the same number of slides, and is useful for reagents which remove excess stain.

Coplin jars hold 12 slides also placed back to back.

Automatic Staining

The Shandon–Elliott automatic stainer is a useful piece of apparatus which has two timing clocks covering one hour and half hour sequences respectively. Notches are cut in the timing discs in a similar manner to those of the automatic processor but the operation of this machine follows a different principle.

STAINING SCHEDULES

A counter stain is not needed for timber sections unless there is included phloem present.

To Stain Timber Sections (Method 1)
  (1) Place sections in 70 per cent alcohol.
  (2) Stain in safranin in 70 per cent alcohol for 15–30 min.
  (3) Wash sections in commercial alcohol.
  (4) Quickly pass through acid alcohol (2 drops HCl/100 ml commercial alcohol).
  (5) Wash in commercial alcohol.
  (6) Rinse in two changes of absolute alcohol allowing 2 min for each change.
  (7) Rinse in two changes of xylene allowing 2 min for each change.
  (8) Mount sections in Canada balsam.

This is a quick schedule and to obtain brilliant staining the acid alcohol should be made up of commercial alcohol and not 70 per cent alcohol.

To Stain Timber Sections (Method 2)
  (1) Place sections in the safranin stain and leave overnight.
  (2) Pass the sections through tap water to remove any deposits left by the stain.
  (3) Wash with 70 per cent alcohol.
  (4) Dehydrate with two changes of commercial alcohol.
  (5) Rinse in two changes of absolute alcohol.
  (6) Rinse in two changes of xylene allowing 2 min for each change.
  (7) Mount sections in Canada balsam.

Timber sections should not be passed through clove oil, as air bubbles become trapped in the rays.

147

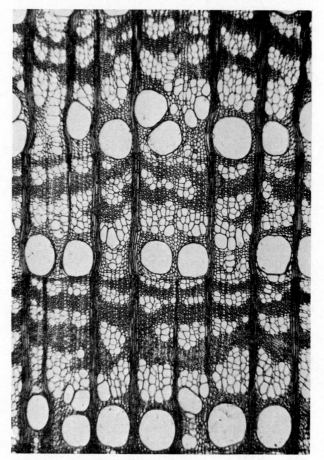

Figure 64. (a) *Transverse section of Ulmus glabra;*

Safranin and Light Green

This is used to double stain sections of stems, roots and leaves.

(1) Take sections from 70 per cent alcohol.
(2) Stain in safranin for 10–15 min. This time should be longer for sections of leaves.
(3) Wash in commercial alcohol until no more safranin is removed.
(4) Differentiate in acid alcohol.
(5) Wash once in commercial alcohol.
(6) Rinse in two changes of absolute alcohol; about 2 min for each change.

148

Figure 64. (b) Radial longitudinal section Ulmus glabra

(7) Counter stain with light green for 1–2 min.
(8) Clear in clove oil.
(9) Pass through two changes of xylene; about 2 min for each change.
(10) Mount in Canada balsam.

Using commercial alcohol to remove the excess safranin from the sections cuts down the staining time. If 70 per cent alcohol is used a much longer staining time is required.

As it is necessary that only the lignified cell walls should be stained by the safranin, the sections are de-stained in acid alcohol until this has been achieved.

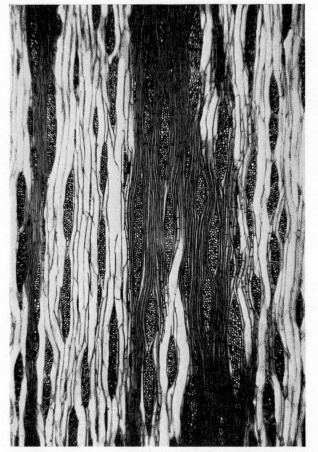

Figure 64. (c) Tangential longitudinal section Ulmus glabra

The amount of vascular tissue present in a section is quite a good guide to the length of time needed to stain in safranin. In a stem, as opposed to a leaf, there is usually more vascular tissue, so sections of most stems require less time staining in safranin than sections of leaves.

Safranin and Haematoxylin

    (1) Stain in safranin for 10–15 min.
    (2) Wash in commercial alcohol.
    (3) Differentiate in acid alcohol.

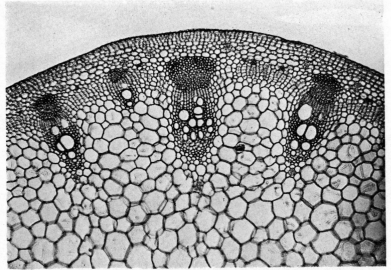

Figure 65. Transverse section of a portion of dahlia stem showing vascular bundles and the beginning of secondary thickening. This section was cut by hand and stained in safranin and light green

(4) Wash in commercial alcohol to remove all traces of acid.

(5) Stain in Delafield's or Harris' haematoxylin for 1–2 min.

(6) Pass through acidulated water to prevent the haematoxylin precipitating. Then wash thoroughly in tap water which should turn the haematoxylin blue. If this does not happen, add a trace of ammonia to the water.

(7) Wash in several changes of commercial alcohol.

(8) Dehydrate with two changes of absolute alcohol.

(9) Clear in clove oil.

(10) Rinse in two changes of xylene allowing 2 min for each change.

(11) Mount in Canada balsam.

If a milkiness is noticed when sections are transferred to xylene it usually means that dehydration is not complete. Either the sections were not left long enough in the absolute alcohol or the absolute alcohol had been standing for some time and had absorbed some water vapour. Occasionally it is caused through old xylene being used; often when it is used from a winchester that has been left standing with only a small quantity in the bottom of the bottle. Should this milkiness be noticed, the sections must be taken back immediately to absolute alcohol. If, when counter staining with light green, the cells take on a blackish appearance this also means that dehydration is not complete or that old reagents were used.

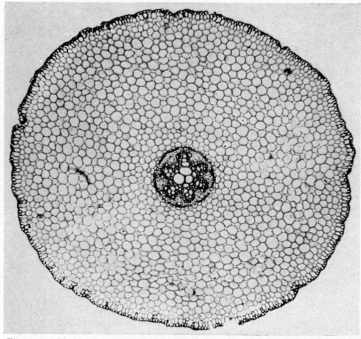

Figure 66. Transverse section of Ranunculus root showing the small stele and wide cortex. This section was cut by hand and stained in safranin and light green

Zimmerman's Stain

This is a quick stain for bulk material but differentiation is not always as clear as when two stains are used separately.

(1) Place sections in Zimmerman's stain for 10 min.
(2) Differentiate in absolute alcohol with 1 per cent acetic acid and 0·1 per cent iodine.
(3) Wash in two changes of absolute alcohol.
(4) Rinse in two changes of xylene.
(5) Mount in Canada balsam.

Lignified tissues are stained green.

Heidenheim's Haematoxylin and Orange G

This is a good stain combination for root tips and stem apices for anatomical study. Haematoxylin can be used alone for chromosome counts but crystal and methyl violet are usually better stains except for resting chromatin.

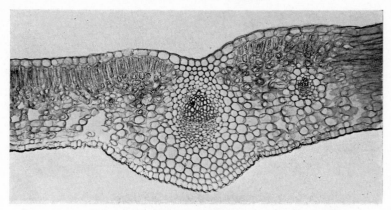

Figure 67. Transverse section of portion of Helleborus leaf showing the palisade tissue beneath the upper surface and the spongy mesophyll below. This section was cut by hand and stained in safranin and light green

When dealing with material which has been embedded, the wax must be removed before staining.

(1) Place the slides, with the ribbons attached, in xylene to remove wax.

(2) Place in a second change of xylene.

(3) Place in absolute alcohol for 5–10 min.

(4) Take down through a graded series of alcohols according to the material. If staining for anatomical study use 95, 70 and 35 per cent but if it is cytological material, the series of alcohols must be much closer together, e.g. 95, 85, 70, 50, 30, 20, 15, 10 and 5 per cent.

(5) Rinse in distilled water.

(6) Mordant in 4 per cent iron alum for 30 min–2 h but not longer. Only clear violet crystals of ferric ammonium sulphate should be used. Any yellowish crystals should be discarded.

(7) Rinse in distilled water.

(8) Stain in Heidenheim's haematoxylin for at least the same length of time as mordanting. Slides can be left in the stain for up to 24 h.

(9) 'Blue' in tap water.

(10) Rinse in distilled water.

(11) De-stain in 2 per cent iron alum, watching under a microscope. If de-staining a number of slides, they can be removed from the dish of iron alum to a dish of water after a minute or two and, if a cloudiness is noticed in the water, the process has been carried far enough.

(12) Wash under running water for 1–2 h.

(13) Dehydrate through graded series of alcohols.

(14) Rinse in two changes of absolute alcohol.

(15) Counter stain with orange G in clove oil for several minutes.

(16) De-stain with a mixture of equal parts of absolute alcohol, xylene and clove oil.

(17) Clear in two changes of xylene.

(18) Mount in balsam.

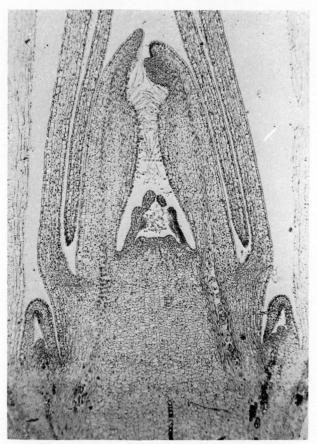

Figure 68. Median longitudinal section of sycamore apex in early stage of plastochron. A pair of leaf primordia has just formed so the apex is very flat. The section is stained in Heidenheim's haematoxylin and orange G

Crystal Violet-Iodine

(1) Place in a solution of 1 g iodine, 1 g potassium iodide in 100 ml distilled water for 15 min.
(2) Wash in distilled water.
(3) Stain in a 0·5–1 per cent aqueous solution of crystal violet for 1–2 h.
(4) Rinse in water.
(5) Place in iodine mixture for 15 min.
(6) Rinse in water.
(7) Place in 70 per cent alcohol containing a trace of picric acid.
(8) Finally dehydrate in 95 per cent and absolute alcohol.

Figure 69. Longitudinal section of Nardus root including part of the root cap region. Stained in Heidenheim's haematoxylin and orange G

(9) Rinse in two changes of xylene.
(10) Mount in balsam.

This is purely a cytological stain.

Johansen's Methyl Violet Method

(1) Take slides to water.
(2) Stain in 1 per cent aqueous solution of methyl violet 2B for 15 min.
(3) Place slides in water for up to 30 min.
(4) Differentiate each slide individually in 70 per cent and 95 per cent alcohol containing 0·5 per cent picric acid for about 10 sec.

155

(5) Immerse in 95 per cent alcohol containing a few drops of ammonia for about 15 sec.
(6) Rinse in two changes of absolute alcohol.
(7) If necessary, differentiate finally in clove oil for about 10 sec, but the slide must be checked under a microscope.
(8) Rinse in two changes of xylene. The second change should be left for about 2 h.

Stain for Fresh Plant Tissues

Thionine	1	g
Phenol	2·5	g
Water	100	ml

(1) Stain for 30 sec–2 min.
(2) Wash in water and mount in weak glycerin.

The lignified tissues are bright blue with other tissues purple to red.

This stain cannot be used for permanent preparations.

More usually temporary mounts of sections are stained in iodine or, if to show lignified tissue, in phloroglucinol and hydrochloric acid (see Chapter 6).

MAKING UP STAINS

Crystal Violet

A 1 per cent solution in distilled water can be made up but, as the violets wash out very quickly in the dehydrating alcohols, the stain should be mordanted.

A useful solution can be made up in clove oil.

Delafield's Haematoxylin

Solution A
Make up a saturated solution of ammonium alum.

Solution B
1 g haematoxylin dissolved in 6 ml absolute alcohol.

Add B to A drop by drop.

Expose to light and air for a week and then filter.

Add 25 ml glycerol and 25 ml methyl alcohol. Allow the solution to stand until the colour is sufficiently dark.

The solution should be filtered and kept in a tightly stoppered bottle for at least 2 months before using.

Fast Green FCF

Fast green FCF powder (0·5 per cent) is added to a mixture of equal parts methyl cellosolve, absolute alcohol and clove oil[4].

156

STAINING SCHEDULES

Gentian Violet

This is a mixture of violet coloured dyes. Crystal violet is better used as a substitute in any schedule quoting gentian violet.

Harris' Haematoxylin

Haematoxylin	5 g
Aluminium ammonium sulphate	3 g
50 per cent ethyl alcohol	1 l.

The haematoxylin and the alum are dissolved in the alcohol by heating. To this is added 6 g mercuric oxide (red powder) and the solution is boiled for 30 min. It is then filtered, cooled and 50 per cent alcohol is added to regain the original volume. A drop of HCl should be added to each 100 ml of solution.

Heidenheim's Haematoxylin

A 0·5 per cent solution in distilled water can be made up but a much more stable solution can be made up in methyl cellosolve.

Haematoxylin	0·5	g
10 per cent absolute alcohol	5	ml
Methyl cellosolve	100	ml
Distilled water	50	ml
Tap water	50	ml

If the red colour does not immediately appear a pinch of sodium bicarbonate should be added.

This solution is ready for use.

Iodine Green

1 per cent iodine green in 70 per cent alcohol.

Light Green S.F.

Light green	1 g
Clove oil	100 ml

This is heated in a water bath and filtered.

Loeffler's Methylene Blue

Methylene blue	0·5	g
1 per cent potassium hydroxide solution	1	ml
Commercial alcohol	30	ml
Distilled water	100	ml

The water is warmed to 50°C, the methylene blue stirred in and then the other ingredients added. The solution is then filtered.

Methyl Violet 2B

A 1 per cent aqueous solution is boiled, filtered and cooled.

157

Orange G

| Orange G | 1 g |
| Clove Oil | 100 ml |

Safranin O

| Safranin | 1 g |
| 70 per cent alcohol | 100 ml |

Zimmerman's Stain

| Iodine green 0·1 per cent aqueous solution | 9 parts |
| Acid fuchsin saturated aqueous solution | 1 part |

CYTOLOGICAL STAINING

Apart from temporary squashes, staining in cytology is a lengthy procedure.

Squashes or sections can be stained but squashes are usually made when it is possible.

In cytological staining it is necessary to concentrate on one part of the cell, as a single staining procedure does not show up all parts equally well.

Practically all root tips can be stained successfully by crystal or methyl violet, as these stains have a high affinity for dividing chromatin. They do not always stain resting chromatin, however, and for this stage iron haematoxylin should be used. Crystal and methyl violet are also used for the study of meiosis in anthers but they are not usually successful with the prophase stages. Iron haematoxylin is good for some buds and particularly for prophase stages.

The Feulgen reaction is very valuable and can always be used as a routine method.

MITOSIS AND MEIOSIS

Mitosis

Mitosis is the mechanism whereby the chromosomes duplicate and separate which means that the two daughter cells thus formed each have a similar set of chromosomes. For the convenience of description, mitosis can be divided into various phases.

Interphase—This is the 'resting' stage. In this stage the chromosomes are not visible in the nucleus which, under a light microscope, shows little definite structure except the nucleoli. The nucleus is enclosed in a nuclear membrane.

Prophase—The chromosomes become visible as thread-like structures. Each chromosome consisting of two chromatids which are often twisted round each other. At some point along the chromosome there is an undivided region called a centromere.

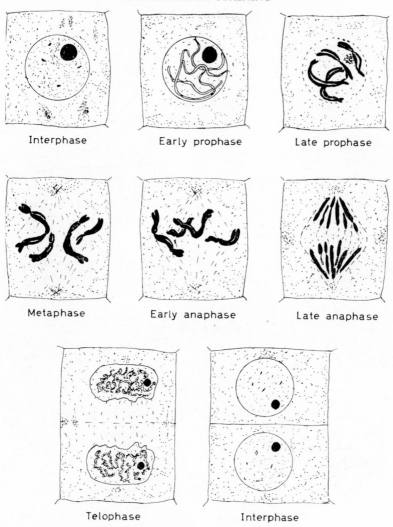

Figure 70. *Diagrammatic representation of mitosis in plants*

During the late prophase, the chromosomes shorten and thicken and the nuclear membrane disappears.

Metaphase—The chromosomes lie in the centre of the cell to form the metaphase plate. Each centromere is attached to the fibres of

159

the nuclear spindle. This phase is the best time for the examination of individual chromosomes.

The centromere of each chromosome divides and the two halves move apart drawing the chromatids towards the opposite poles of the cell.

Anaphase—This phase is reached when the chromatids begin to move towards the opposite poles of the cell.

Telophase—A nuclear membrane forms round each group of daughter chromosomes.

Meiosis

This generally takes place in reproductive cells. In the first meiotic division only one set of chromosomes passes into each daughter cell. The main difference between mitosis and meiosis lies in the fact that the homologous chromosomes pair and at this stage genetic crossing over occurs.

At the end of the first meiotic division each nucleus contains only half the number of chromosomes as the nucleus of a somatic cell.

The second division in meiosis is a mitotic division, involving the separation of the individual chromatids after the division of the centromeres.

SQUASH METHODS

Squashes are made for the investigation of cell contents and are invaluable for chromosome counts. Normal methods are limited to material in which the cells can easily be separated.

Apparatus

Chemically clean slides must be used. New slides and cover glasses are immersed in the chromic acid mixture (p. 56) used for cleaning glassware, for at least 24 h. They are then rinsed in running water and placed into 95 per cent alcohol until needed. Any slides that have previously had sections attached to them should not be used.

All slides should be marked with a diamond pencil to show on which side the squash is made.

A shallow square dish is necessary, preferably with a ridged bottom. Two pieces of thin glass rod cut to size can be substituted if a ridged dish is not available. The ends of the slides rest on the glass rod which prevents them touching the bottom of the dish.

A scalpel and mounted needles are also required.

Aceto-carmine Stain

A saturated solution of carmine in 45 per cent glacial acetic acid is made. This is boiled under a Leibig condenser for several hours, cooled and filtered.

A few drops of aqueous ferric acetate can be added to this solution to make iron-aceto-carmine which produces good results with some material. Care should be taken to use nickel, chromium plated or glass needles when dissecting material in iron-aceto-carmine, as the acetic acid acts on steel and an excess of iron may be precipitated. For the same reason it is better to use two slides, rather than a scalpel, to squash the material.

There are many variations in the techniques of making aceto-carmine squashes and several simple procedures are described here.

It is important to remember that there are definite daily cycles of division in some plants. Usually specimens fixed about midday are good for meiosis. Anthers are taken about a fortnight before they would normally shed any pollen. A test squash will soon show whether the desired stages are present. Tradescantia anthers can be used to demonstrate meiosis.

Seeds grown on blotting or filter paper provide root tips free from dirt and they should be cut as soon as they are visible. Cell division is very rapid. Broad bean and onion root tips are excellent for demonstrations. The metaphase can be arrested by pre-treating the ' root tips for 2 hours before fixation in 0·05 per cent colchicine.

For rapid preparations, the material can be fixed in Farmer's or Carnoy's fluid. Better fixation is often obtained in Navashin's fluid (CRAF) or any of the other cytological fixatives. Preparations can be made after a short immersion in the fixative but are better for a longer fixation time. Root tips seem to produce better preparations after fixing for 12–24 h.

Method 1—After fixing, the material is placed in a drop of aceto-carmine on a slide and squashed with a scalpel. If it does not squash readily, it can be teased out with mounted needles into longitudinal strips. Anthers can be cut in half and the pollen mother cells squeezed out by pressing from the uncut end with a curved mounted needle. The debris is removed from the slide and a cover glass applied.

The slide should be gently heated by passing it over the flame of a spirit lamp. The preparation must not boil.

For root tips more pressure is necessary to separate the cells. The slide is placed on a sheet of filter paper, covered with a second sheet and pressure applied. Care must be taken not to break the cover glass or to move it sideways along the slide. The cover glass can be sealed to prevent the preparation drying out while it is being studied.

Permanent preparations can be obtained by placing the slide face downwards in a shallow ridged dish, already described, containing Carnoy's fluid. When the cover glass falls off, the slide can be placed in a dish of 95 per cent alcohol to dehydrate the squashed material. Care must be taken not to touch the squashed material when the excess alcohol is wiped off the slide. A drop of Euparal is added, and a cover glass applied.

Good temporary preparations are easily made permanent by placing the slides on a block of dry ice and freezing[5] or by the use of more complicated apparatus[6]. The cover glass is removed while the slide is on the ice and then the preparation is placed in 95 per cent alcohol for 5 min. A drop of Euparal is added and a clean cover glass applied.

Method 2—The material is excised and then squashed by pressing between two slides placed crosswise on one another. Both these slides are immediately inverted and placed in a dish containing fixative. The excising and squashing must be carried out very quickly so that the material is in the fixative within a few seconds. The slide must be placed in the fixative in a horizontal position so that none of the material is washed off. Preparations can be made after 10 min but a longer time in the fixative is advantageous.

A drop of aceto-carmine is placed on the squashed material and a cover glass applied. This can be sealed or made into a permanent preparation as described in the previous method.

Method 3—The material is fixed and then placed in a mixture of equal quantities of 95 per cent alcohol and concentrated hydrochloric acid for 5–10 min[7]. This dissolves the pectic substances of the middle lamellae.

It is then transferred to Carnoy's fluid to harden the tissues which have been softened by the acid. A small piece of material is placed on a slide in a drop of aceto-carmine, then the same procedure adopted as for Method 1. The chromosomes in all aceto-carmine squashes are shown up more clearly if viewed through a green filter.

Aceto-orcein Stain

This can be used in the same way as aceto-carmine[8]. For some specimens this stain is preferable, as it does not stain the cytoplasm or the nucleoli and does not tend to overstain the chromosomes.

It is made up by dissolving 1 g orcein in 45 ml of hot glacial acetic acid, which is cooled and 55 ml of distilled water then added.

Squashes can also be stained with any of the cytological staining procedures and permanent mounts made. As the material adheres to the slide after being squashed, it can be transferred through the different reagents quite successfully provided it is handled carefully. The procedures are lengthy but worthwhile results can be obtained.

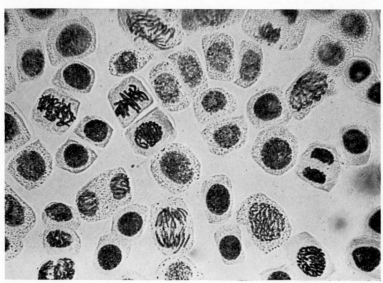

Figure 71. A squash preparation showing mitotic division in cells of onion root tip. Stained with aceto-orcein

The Feulgen Method

Leuco-basic fuchsin[9]—To make the stain, 1 g basic fuchsin should be dissolved in 200 ml of boiling glass-distilled water, the mixture shaken well and cooled to 50°C. It is then filtered and 30 ml N/1 HCl is added to the filtrate followed by 3 g potassium metabisulphite. This is shaken well and stored for 24 h in the dark and cold. To this is added 0·5 g +Norit or activated charcoal and the mixture shaken well for about 1 min before filtering quickly through coarse filter paper. This solution should be colourless and must be stored in a cool dark place.

After fixing the material, it is rinsed in water and hydrolysed in N/1 HCl in a water bath for 6–10 min at 60°C. It is then removed and stained in leuco-basic fuchsin for 2 h at the end of which it is transferred to water and rinsed several times.

The material is placed in a drop of 45 per cent acetic acid on a slide and a cover glass applied. The ball of the thumb should be used to press down upon the cover glass. The preparation is now heated gently. The cover glass and slide are separated by inverting in a dish of 45 per cent acetic acid, dehydrated in 95 per cent alcohol and mounted in Euparal.

Temporary preparations of squashes can be sealed with nail varnish[10].

SPECIAL STAINING METHODS

PREPARATIONS OF ALGAE

Live specimens are certainly the best to study, as good, permanent mounts of algae are difficult to obtain. They can be mounted in a drop of water on a slide, with a cover glass lowered carefully to avoid trapping any air bubbles. A very small drop of water should be used when mounting unicellular algae, otherwise, when the cover glass is placed in position, the algae will tend to float beyond the edges.

To prevent the preparation drying out, a little glycerol can be added to the water and the slide sealed with Gurr's Glyceel or with nail varnish[10]. Before sealing, any excess water must be wiped away from the edges of the cover glass.

Only a few threads of filamentous algae should be mounted on the slide and these should be cut out, never pulled from the sample, as this will damage the cells.

Semi-permanent preparations can be obtained by mounting in lactophenol which can be coloured with cotton blue to show up the cells.

If it is necessary to fix the algae, most specimens will keep their colour for 2–3 weeks in the dioxan fluid and they can be mounted in a drop of this temporarily.

When permanent preparations of filamentous algae are needed the following procedure may be used:

(1) Fix in a suitable fluid (see Chapter 2).
(2) Wash in water.
(3) Stain in Harris' haematoxylin.
(4) Wash in water.
(5) Differentiate if necessary in acidified water.
(6) Wash thoroughly in water.
(7) Dehydrate through a graded series of dioxan and water mixtures, 50, 75, 85, 90 and 95 per cent, allowing 30 min in each percentage.
(8) Pass into pure dioxan and allow to remain for at least 12 h. There should be another change of pure dioxan.

The filaments must not be pulled but cut with sharp scissors. The material can be placed in a solid watch glass and the stains and reagents are added and removed by using a pipette.

The filaments should then be cut into short lengths which can be mounted easily on a slide and mounted in a drop of Canada balsam dissolved in dioxan. This should be a very thin solution and more can be added to the preparation on the slide as the dioxan evaporates. When there is sufficient balsam on the slide, a cover glass is added.

Permanent preparations of unicellular algae can be obtained using the following method:

(1) Pipette a small drop of culture on to a slide.
(2) Fix by osmic acid fumes (see Chapter 2).
(3) Add a drop of 1 per cent aqueous crystal violet.
(4) Spread gently along the slide.
(5) Dry in a desiccator for 1–2 h.
(6) Flood slide with 1 per cent iodine in 2 per cent KI in 80 per cent alcohol.
(7) Rinse quickly with absolute alcohol twice.
(8) Complete destaining in benzyl alcohol.
(9) Clear in xylene and mount in Canada balsam.

PREPARATIONS OF FUNGI

Fresh sections of fleshy fungi or small structures can be mounted in distilled water but the preparations so viewed are not always clear.

A very good mountant for fungi is the Gelvatol fluid (p.138). Fresh material can be put straight into a drop of mountant on a slide and the cover glass applied. The fluid fixes the material and a permanent preparation results which shows up the structures very clearly. It is especially good for mounting zoospores. A little basic fuchsin dye added to the mountant will stain nuclear structures.

Semi-permanent preparations of fungal material can be obtained by mounting in lactophenol. The material can be shown up quite clearly by adding 0·05–0·1 per cent cotton blue to lactophenol. Chlorazol black can also be added to lactophenol and is a good stain for photographic purposes to show up hyphae and sporangia of fungi[11]. Enough dye is added to the lactophenol to produce the colour of Indian ink.

Methylene blue is a useful stain to show up some fungal material. It can be made up as a 0·02 per cent aqueous or alcoholic (70 per cent alcohol) solution. Alternatively, a little dye can be added to weak glycerine, lactophenol or Gelvatol.

To show up flagella, a drop of liquid containing zoospores should be placed on a slide and inverted over 1 per cent osmic acid. It is fixed in this vapour for 30 sec. A trace of gentian or crystal violet dye is added to the droplet containing the zoospores and a cover glass is placed in position.

Sections of fungi growing on leaves can be cut by supporting the piece of leaf material in pith or carrot.

A Method of Fixing and Staining Water Moulds

(1) Fix in Dioxan mixture p.89 for 18 h.
(2) Wash in distilled water.
(3) Stain in Harris' haematoxylin for 20 min.
(4) Wash in distilled water.
(5) Destain in acidified water.
(6) 'Blue' in tap water.
(7) Rinse in distilled water.
(8) Stain in a saturated aqueous solution of basic fuchsin for 2–5 min.
(9) Pass through a graded series of dioxan and water, 50, 75, 85, 90 and 95 per cent, allowing 30 min immersion in each percentage.
(10) Pass through three changes of pure dioxan.
(11) Mount in a drop of balsam made up in dioxan.

The whole procedure can be carried out in centrifuge tubes. After the prescribed time in each reagent, the specimens are centrifuged for 2 min at 2,500 r.p.m. The supernatant is discarded and the next reagent added.

BACTERIA

Preparations of Smears

It is very important that the slides and cover glasses should be chemically clean.

A drop of distilled water should be placed on a slide. A needle or wire loop should be flamed and a small quantity of material removed from the culture. This is placed in the drop of distilled water, spreading it out along the slide.

The slide is then warmed over a bunsen flame until the film dries and this is fixed by passing the slide through the flame several times.

Gram's Staining

Bacteria are described as being Gram-positive or Gram-negative according to whether or not they retain the violet stain. Gram-positive bacteria retain the violet stain. Gram-negative do not and are shown up with a counter stain.

If the bacteria have been treated with an acid or alkali before staining, the Gram's reaction is unreliable. Also, according to different techniques, the definition of the stain is variable. The following schedule has been suggested for standard results[12].

(1) Flood the slide with Hucker's crystal violet for 1 min.
(2) Wash the slide by dipping it several times in a beaker of tap water. This water must be changed frequently.
(3) Remove the water from the slide by rinsing it with Burke's iodine, then flood the slide with the iodine solution for 1 min.
(4) Wash for 5 sec in a beaker of water.
(5) Decolourize with 95 per cent alcohol for 1·5 min.
(6) Wash for 5 sec in a beaker of water.
(7) Remove the water from the slide by rinsing it with an aqueous 0·25 per cent solution of safranin. Flood the slide with the solution of safranin for 1 min.
(8) Wash for 5 sec in a beaker of water. Blot, air dry and examine the preparation.
(9) If a permanent mount is required, the preparation is thoroughly dried and mounted in Euparal or Canada balsam.

Hucker's Crystal Violet

Stock solution

2 g Crystal violet in 20 ml of 95 per cent alcohol

For use

Take 20 ml of the stock solution and add 80 ml of distilled water containing 1 per cent ammonium oxalate. This solution should be allowed to stand for 48 h before use. It is a stable solution and can be stored for months.

Burke's Iodine

Stock solution

Place 2 g potassium iodide into a mortar, add 1 g iodine and grind with a pestle. Add 1 ml of distilled water and grind again. Add a little more water and grind until the iodine and potassium iodide are in solution. Bring the total volume to 100 ml with distilled water.

For use

Dilute 1 part of the stock solution with 2 parts of distilled water.

Staining Method for Spores[13]

(1) Make smear and fix by passing through a flame several times.
(2) Stain with 5 per cent aqueous malachite green and heat the slide for 30 sec.
(3) Drain off stain and wash in running water for 30 sec.
(4) Counter-stain in 0·5 per cent aqueous safranin for 30 sec.
(5) Wash in water, dry and mount.

The spores are stained green.

Ziehl-Neelson's Carbol-Fuchsin

Saturated alcoholic basic fuchsin	10 ml
5 per cent aqueous carbolic acid	100 ml

This stain can be used for acid fast bacteria and spores.

STAINS AND STAINING TECHNIQUES

(1) After fixing the smear, flood the slide with carbol-fuchsin and heat for 5 min (do not boil).

(2) Wash in distilled water.

(3) Decolourize either in 95 per cent ethyl alcohol or 5 per cent aqueous sulphuric acid.

(4) Wash in water. The preparation should be a faint pink colour.

(5) Counter-stain with Loeffler's methylene blue. The time will vary with the species.

(6) Wash, dry and mount in balsam if a permanent preparation is required.

Indian Ink

Bacteria can be mixed with either Indian ink or nigrosin and then smeared on a slide. The bacteria are colourless and show up against a dark background. The film must be examined wet for the detection of capsules.

REFERENCES

[1]Stearn, A. E. and Stearn, E. W. (1930). 'The Mechanism of Staining Explained on a Chemical Basis. General Presentation.' *Stain Tech.* **5**, 17

[2]Conn, H. J. (1961). *Biological Stains*, 7th ed. U.S.A.; Commission on Standardization of Biological Stains

[3]Baker, J. R. (1958). *Principles of Biological Microtechnique*, 1st ed. London; Methuen

[4]Johansen, D. E. (1940). *Plant Microtechnique*, 1st ed. New York; McGraw-Hill

[5]Conger, A. D. and Fairchild, L. M. (1953). 'A Quick-freeze Method for Making Smear Slides Permanent.' *Stain Tech.* **28**, 281

[6]Jacobsen, P. (1965). 'An Improved Squash-Slide Freezer.' *Stain Tech.* **40**, 63–65

[7]Warmke, H. E. (1935). 'A Permanent Root Tip Smear Method.' *Stain Tech.* **10**, 101

[8]Lacour, L. (1941). 'Acetic-orcein. A New Stain Fixative for Chromosomes.' *Stain Tech.* **16**, 169

[9]Coleman, L. C. (1940). 'Preparation of leuco-basic Fuchsin for use in the Feulgen Reaction.' *Stain Tech.* **13**, 123

[10]Gerstel, D. U. (1953). 'Finger Nail Lacquer as a Sealing Medium for Cytological Squashes.' *Turtox News* **31**, 54

[11]Armitage, F. D. (1943). 'Further Uses for Chlorazal Black E and a New Stain for Botanical Sections.' *J.R. micr. Soc. Series III* **63**, 14

[12]Bartholomew, J. W. (1962). 'Variables Influencing Results and the Precise Definition of Steps in Gram Staining as a Means of Standardizing the Results Obtained.' *Stain Tech.* **37**, 139

[13]Schaeffer, A. B. and Fulton, M. (1933). 'A Simplified Method of Staining Endospores.' *Science* **77**, 194

BIBLIOGRAPHY

Darlington, C. D. and La Cour, L. F. (1960). *The Handling of Chromosomes*, 3rd ed. London; Allen and Unwin

CHAPTER 5

SPECIAL HISTOLOGICAL TECHNIQUES

MACERATIONS

The process of maceration is to separate the plant cells by dissolving away the true middle lamella which acts as a cementing layer.

Maceration by Ammonium Oxalate[1]

This is a useful method for non-woody material. Thin slivers of material, cut longitudinally, are placed in alcoholic HCl (1 part HCl:3 parts commercial alcohol) for 24 h or longer. They are then washed in distilled water and transferred to 0·5 per cent ammonium oxalate. The material should be mounted in this and the cover glass tapped gently to separate the elements.

Jeffrey's Method[2]

This is a good method for deciduous timbers.

Thin slivers of material are placed in a mixture of equal quantities of 10 per cent nitric acid and 10 per cent chromic acid contained in a Petri dish and left for 24 h. Slight heat hastens the process and the dishes can be left on top of an embedding oven, or similar source of heat, overnight. The slivers should then be washed thoroughly in water.

Franklin's Method[3]

This is an excellent method for any woody material.

Thin slivers of wood are cut longitudinally with a razor. When macerating a wood with large rays, cutting is best done from a radial longitudinal surface. The slivers of wood are placed in a flask containing equal parts hydrogen peroxide (20 vol.) and glacial acetic acid and boiled very slowly under a Liebig condenser. The bunsen flame should be as low as possible and the material is simmered until it becomes whitish in appearance. It can be tested any time during the operation by taking a small quantity and teasing it apart with mounted needles. The cells should fall apart readily at a touch.

WASHING MACERATIONS

Macerations can be washed by placing a No. 1 Whatman filter paper in a funnel supported in a wash bottle which has an outlet for excess water (*Figure 72*).

The macerated material in the macerating fluid is poured into the funnel and water allowed to drip through at a steady rate. The material should be washed for several hours and then the excess water drained off.

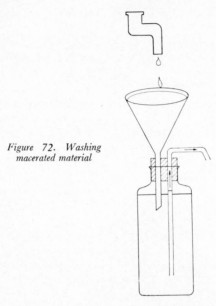

Figure 72. Washing macerated material

The macerated material is lifted off the filter paper with a spatula or section lifter and stored in distilled water to which a few drops of formalin have been added. Timber macerations can be successfully stored for several years.

MOUNTING

To prepare the material for microscopical examination, a very small quantity of the maceration is placed on a slide and gently teased out with two mounted needles. A drop of methylene blue and a drop of weak glycerin are added. A cover glass is lowered carefully and tapped gently to further disperse the cells. It is most important to take as small a quantity as possible for preparation on the slide, otherwise the elements obscure one another.

To make a permanent preparation, a little methylene blue can be added to Gurr's Water Mountant and the teased out material mounted in a drop of this mixture.

(a)   (b)

Figure 73. (a) *General maceration of apple;* (b) *isolated vessel element of apple. Both preparations are stained with Loeffler's methylene blue*

Sometimes for photographic or demonstration purposes it is advantageous to have a single element mounted under the cover glass. This is done by viewing the teased out material under the low power objective of the microscope, choosing the element required and, still viewing under the microscope, gently pushing the other elements away from the selected one with a pair of mounted needles. This can be a laborious task but is well worth while. It is easier to work with a small amount of material so that not much liquid is required on the slide. The excess liquid can be removed by just

171

touching it with the edge of a piece of filter paper. The macerated material must not be allowed to dry out, however. When the element is completely isolated, a drop of mountant and stain can be added and a cover glass applied. Gurr's Water Mountant coloured with methylene blue is ideal for this purpose as no dehydration is required to procure a permanent mount (*Figure 73*). If other techniques are employed it is advantageous to use an adhesive on the slide[4] to prevent loss of material.

The position of the single element should be marked on the cover glass.

MACERATION OF BOX LEAVES[1]

This method can be applied to other evergreen leaves, but box leaves are most successful as they are small in size.

To separate the layers of the leaf, the following method is employed using preserved material.

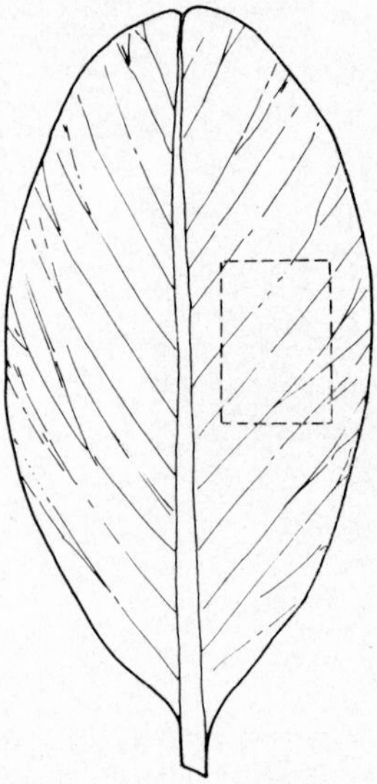

Figure 74. The marked area of the box leaf is the portion that is cut and mounted

(1) Warm the leaves in 8 per cent potassium hydroxide. Do not boil. Continue warming until the leaves swell, which takes at least 45 min, and sometimes much longer.
(2) Wash in running water for 2 h.
(3) Soak in 10 per cent hydrochloric acid overnight, or for at least several hours.
(4) Wash gently in running water.
(5) Store in 5 per cent formalin.

Mounting

A small square is cut out from the leaf between the mid-vein and the leaf margin see *Figure 74*.

This square of leaf material is floated in a watch glass containing water, when it will separate into three layers. These layers can be transferred with a paint brush to a slide and mounted in weak glycerin. Care should be taken to mount the two epidermal layers so that the outside surface is uppermost on the slide.

EPIDERMAL STRIPS

These can easily be taken from most fresh leaves, using a mounted needle which has been flattened as illustrated in *Figure 75*.

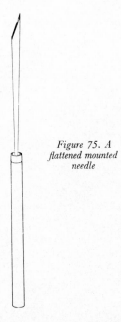

Figure 75. A flattened mounted needle

For examination of stomata and subsidiary cells, it is usually necessary to take a strip from the under side of the leaf. The edge of the epidermal layer is prised up with the tip of the needle, the flattened portion of the needle is slipped under the epidermal layer and the edge of the strip is lifted and pulled off with the fingers. It is sometimes easier to start by lifting the epidermal layer over a small vein and stripping from here. This should be done slowly to prevent the strip curling. If the strip curls badly, it can be corrected by supporting it with the thumb while stripping and letting it remain stretched out on either finger or thumb for a few seconds before placing it in a fixative. These strips can be fixed quickly in absolute alcohol for 10 min. If permanent preparations are required it is beneficial to fix in F.A.A. for a longer period, preferably overnight as this renders the chloroplasts colourless and facilitates staining.

Harris' haematoxylin is a good stain for epidermal strips while phenolic bismark brown shows up the cell walls and cytoplasm[5].

Phenolic Bismark Brown

Bismark brown	1 g
Phenol crystals	5 g
Distilled water	100 ml

The solution is mixed, allowed to stand for 1 h and then filtered. This solution is ready for use and will keep indefinitely.

A mixture of 2 parts Harris' haematoxylin and 1 part phenolic bismark brown gives an excellent, clear stain for both nuclei and cytoplasm of difficult material.

A suitable staining schedule is as follows:

(1) After fixing, place the epidermal strips in 70 per cent alcohol for 3 min.
(2) Place in distilled water for 3 min.
(3) Stain in mixture of Harris' haematoxylin and phenolic bismark brown (2:1) for 10–20 min.
(4) Rinse in tap water.
(5) Rinse in distilled water.
(6) Place in 70 per cent alcohol for 3 min.
(7) Rinse in two changes of absolute alcohol.
(8) Clear in methyl salicylate (oil of wintergreen).
(9) Mount in balsam.

Care must be taken not to retain too much methyl salicylate in the preparation.

When mounting, it is important to have the outer surface of the epidermal strip uppermost on the slide (*Figure 76*).

Epidermal Strips of Grasses

These are sometimes difficult to prepare without previous treatment. The leaves are cut at the base and the tip, and placed in boiling water to kill the cells. They are decolourized by boiling in a beaker of 70 per cent alcohol on a hot plate and then cleared in 88 per cent lactic acid[6].

Unwanted tissue can be scraped off and the epidermal strip inverted on a clean slide. The strip can be stained in lactophenol cotton blue and mounted in 88 per cent lactic acid. This method can be used for fresh or herbarium material.

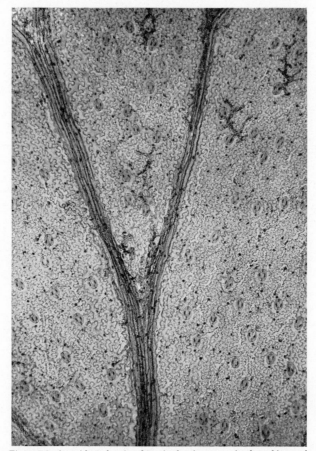

Figure 76. An epidermal strip of Pteris showing two veins branching and the stomata surrounded by their irregularly shaped subsidiary cells. The strip is stained in Harris' haematoxylin and phenolic bismark brown

Plastic Strips

Several methods have been devised, using colloidin and cellulose acetate solutions to procure strip impressions of leaves, but they are not altogether successful.

It has been suggested that Archer's liquid plastic can be used[7].

The leaves are washed in a mild detergent to remove any grime or grease, blotted dry and flooded with toluene. The liquid plastic is spread over the leaf with a piece of cardboard and allowed to dry thoroughly before being peeled off with tweezers and mounted.

Archer's Liquid Plastic

Toluene	720 ml
Methanol	180 ml
Ethyl cellulose	250 g
Dow Resin 276V-2	75 g

WHOLE MOUNTS OF MOSSES, LIVERWORTS AND FERN PROTHALLI

Gelvatol Method

This is the simplest way to procure permanent mounts of fresh material. The specimens are soaked in water, blotted and mounted in the Gelvatol mountant (see p. 138). This not only preserves but also clears the material. Depression slides, if available, can be used for mounting. Otherwise, a drop of mountant is placed on a $1/2$ in. square cover glass and the specimen orientated in it; a $7/8$ in. square cover glass is then placed carefully over the material and both cover slips are mounted on a slide with the larger one uppermost (*Figure 77*).

Figure 77. A whole mount of a fern prothallus showing the larger cover glass uppermost

Large specimens can be mounted in Gelvatol between 2 in. square cover glasses and, when set, projected from a lantern.

Stained Whole Mounts

After fixing in F.A.A. or F.P.A. the specimens can be stained in Harris' haematoxylin and counter-stained with fast green.

Sometimes it is necessary to clear the specimens before staining and this is done by immersing them in a saturated solution of chloral hydrate and heating if necessary. When clear, they should be washed in water before staining.

HERBARIUM MATERIAL

Small pieces of the material should be boiled for 5–10 min or until they sink. Obviously, care must be taken so that they are not boiled for longer than is necessary otherwise they will disintegrate.

With the material supported between two pieces of cork, sections of 18–22 μ can be cut on the sledge microtome.

For permanent mounts, the sections can be stained in a mixture of 80 per cent Safranin and 20 per cent matured Delafields Haematoxylin[8] for 2–6 hours. Care must be taken when using fairly high percentages of Delafields, as precipitation is likely to occur.

Destaining can be carried out in a Petri dish containing 50 per cent alcohol to which 2 or 3 drops of concentrated hydrochloric acid have been added.

Dehydrate and mount in the usual manner.

ARCHAEOLOGICAL MATERIAL

Compressed specimens, especially those from peat bogs, can be treated so that the material is expanded for identification[9].

After removal of loose soil or unwanted remains, the material should be cut into half-inch cubes and stored in commercial alcohol for 24 hours. This hardens them sufficiently so that they can be cut in the sledge microtome.

Thick sections of 30 μ or more are necessary otherwise they will disintegrate during further processing. They are placed in a Petri dish containing 50 per cent alcohol.

From the alcohol, the sections are transferred to water for a few minutes before being placed in a strong solution of sodium hypochlorite or domestic bleaching solution. The sections are allowed to remain in the sodium hypochlorite solution until they become completely bleached and have started to expand.

Further expansion will occur as they are washed carefully in several changes of water.

If necessary, each section can be placed on a slide in a drop of chlor-zinc-iodide and warmed gently for additional expansion. This process must be watched carefully otherwise the section will disintegrate.

Calcareous material—Small pieces of tissue which are impregnated with calcareous substances can be treated with dilute hydrochloric acid[10]. Preliminary tests should be carried out to ascertain what strength acid is required as this will vary with different material. Concentrations normally range between 3 and 10 per cent.

A smear of albumen on the slide will help to keep the tissue stable while it is irrigated with water to remove the acid. The tissue can be mounted in weak glycerin.

PEEL TECHNIQUE FOR FOSSILS

Impressions of fossils in rocks can be taken by this method. If the fossil is not visible, the rock must be cut with a special saw or ground with a coarse carborundum powder (grade 320 is suitable) until it can be seen. The steps are as follows:

(1) When the fossil is visible, the surface of the rock is ground until it is very smooth, using carborundum powder grade 600.

Grinding can be done on a piece of plate glass which must be washed thoroughly before using a finer grade of carborundum powder.

(2) The surface of the rock is then etched so that the fossil is exposed. Etching with hydrochloric acid removes some of the calcareous matter leaving the carbonaceous fossil material exposed. If the rock is composed of silica it is necessary to etch with hydrofluoric acid.

The piece of rock is placed, smooth side down into a dish of 10 per cent hydrochloric acid for 2–5 min. One side is lifted several times to allow the bubbles of gas to move away. Care must be taken when using commercial hydrofluoric acid as it causes severe burns. This acid must not be stored in glass bottles as it attacks the glass. Gutta percha or polythene bottles should be used. Specimens should be left from 30 sec to 2 min in the acid for etching.

(3) The specimen is rinsed in water, care being taken not to touch the etched surface.

(4) It is then left to dry thoroughly.

(5) Acetone is poured on to the etched surface and a piece of cellulose acetate paper[11] quickly placed in position.

(6) This is left to dry for about half an hour.

(7) When drying is complete, the cellulose acetate paper is peeled off and trimmed with a pair of scissors.

The peels can be placed in a book to flatten completely and are then mounted in Canada balsam on a slide.

GRINDING METHOD FOR PIECES OF NUT SHELL

A piece of shell is cut with a small saw from a part of the nut which is as flat as possible. One side is ground flat by rubbing it on glass paper, first using a coarse grade and finishing with a fine one. Attach the flat side of the piece of shell to a slide, using solid Canada balsam and melting it by heating. When set, the slide can be inverted over a sheet of glass paper and the second face ground down until there is only a thin section of shell left attached to the balsam. This is cleared in clove oil, a drop of balsam added and a cover glass applied.

GRINDING METHOD FOR FOSSIL FRAGMENTS[12]

The fossil fragment is ground with carborundum powders, instead of glass paper, but it is attached to the slide in the same way as a piece of nut shell. When preparing the second side, care must be taken not to grind too near to the fossil. The carborundum powder is washed away and the preparation dried. The slide and the balsam are covered with a protective coating of paraffin wax, leaving just the surface of the rock exposed. This is etched, washed thoroughly and the wax and excess balsam trimmed from the slide. The preparations can be examined under the microscope by reflected light.

EXTRACTION OF FOSSIL SPORES
(see Bibliography)

For the extraction of spores from highly carbonaceous rocks (e.g. coal, lignite) Schultze's solution is used (concentrated HNO_3 saturated with $KClO_3$) followed by washing, and the addition of a dilute alkali (a NH_3, KOH, $NaOH$ or Na_2CO_3 solution).

Peat needs less drastic treatment, and glacial acetic acid usually suffices to break down the non-spore components.

Rocks such as shale or clay are treated with commercial (approx. 30 per cent) hydrofluoric acid either hot or cold to break down and remove the clay and other siliceous material. This may be followed by the treatments above.

Spores may be concentrated (i.e. separated from the inorganic mineral particles) after such treatment by centrifuging the residue in a heavy liquid (e.g. bromoform diluted with one-fifth its volume of acetone. A saturated $ZnCl_2$ solution can also be used).

RADIOAUTOGRAPHS*

The stripping film technique of radioautography allows one to observe, at a sub-cellular level, the way in which substances, labelled with suitable radioisotopes, have been incorporated into intact living cells. The method is particularly valuable for following the synthesis of the nucleic acids and in the study of morphogenesis.

The method rests upon the ability of electrons, emitted by the decaying radioisotope in the labelled material, to cause ionization of grains of silver halide in a photographic emulsion. The material containing the radioisotope is sectioned, the sections are placed on a slide and the emulsion placed over them. The emulsion can be developed without it being detached from the slide, just as though it had been exposed to light. The distribution of the silver grains then shows where the electrons have impinged upon the film and hence the location of the radioactivity in the original material.

For detailed work involving high-powered microscopy, it is

* The introduction is written by J. Mackey and the rest of the technique summarized from an article which has been published by the *Journal of the Institute of Science Technology.*

advisable to use an isotope yielding electrons of a low energy. This ensures that the only ionization produced in the emulsion by the emitted electron will be close to the site of the radioactivity in the material.

The technique of radioautography was developed initially by Pelc[13]. If normal metabolic processes are to be investigated, it is essential that the specimen is alive when the radioisotope is introduced. The method varies with the nature of the specimen but, at a suitable stage in development, the radioactive substance is introduced.

Fixing, Embedding, Sectioning and Mounting

Care must be taken in choosing a fixative. It must penetrate rapidly but it must not destroy any cell substances which are likely to incorporate radioactive compounds.

Ordinary 50°C paraffin wax can be used for embedding. For small specimens, mycological rings $3/4$ in. in diameter placed on glass slides can be used as embedding chambers. A short line with an arrowhead in the middle is marked on the glass slide with a diamond pencil. The ring is placed over this line and, when the embedding chamber has been filled with molten wax, the object is orientated over the arrowhead. This can be clearly seen if a strong light source is placed below the slide. An imprint of the line and arrowhead is visible on the wax block when it is cast, thus allowing the block to be easily orientated on the block holder.

The thinness of the sections is important, otherwise, the electrons which are emitted from the lower part of the section are all absorbed in the material itself. If the blocks are cast with 50°C paraffin wax, they should be cut in a cold room at 4°C. The blocks should not be stored at this temperature, otherwise they will fail to cut properly.

Clean slides are dipped in a solution composed of 5·0 g gelatine and 0·5 g chrome alum, to 1 litre of distilled water and then placed in a rack to drain and dry.

The wax ribbons are cut and floated in a drop of distilled water on a prepared slide. A thick pre-heated slide is placed beneath the slide containing the wax ribbons so that the ribbons flatten out. The excess water is drained away and the slides are left to dry in a warm atmosphere for at least 24 h.

The wax is dissolved in xylene in the usual way and the slides are taken through a succession of diluted alcohols to distilled water.

Staining processes are usually carried out after the application of the film, but for a technique such as the Feulgen reaction where heat is applied this must be carried out before the application of the film.

Making and Processing Radioautographs

A Kodak safelight, Wratten Series I (red), can be used while cutting, stripping and processing the film[14].

The radioautographic plate is placed in a cutting frame, where it can be measured and the emulsion layer cut into eight pieces. These pieces are stripped off the glass backing slowly to prevent a flash of static electricity and then floated, emulsion side down, in a dish of boiled distilled water. The strips of film are allowed to remain on the water for several minutes after expanding. The glass dish and the water must be scrupulously clean, as dirt particles can easily be trapped between the emulsion and the specimen. A humid atmosphere reduces the hazard of a flash of static electricity and successful results are normally obtained if the box of plates is removed from the refrigerator 1–2 h before they are needed, to allow the film to soften slightly at room temperature.

A slide, containing the sectioned material, is slipped under the floating film and tilted, so that the long edge of one side of the slide touches the film. The film drapes itself over the specimen on the slide and most of the water drains away as the slide is lifted out of the water. The slides, with the pieces of film attached, are hung in a rack and thoroughly dried by a stream of cool air from an electric fan or a hairdryer.

The dried slides are stored in a slide box, which is made light proof by wrapping it in black polythene sheeting, sandwiched between two layers of brown paper. The box is then stored in a refrigerator for the exposure time. This may vary from 2 days to several weeks. It is sometimes necessary to develop test slides to find the correct time.

The film should be developed and processed at a working temperature of 15–18°C to prevent the film becoming detached from the slide during processing.

After fixing, the slides are washed in three changes of distilled water. They are then taken through a series of alcohols to 95 per cent alcohol and mounted in Euparal. Normal Euparal should be thinned out with Euparal essence, as a less viscid solution produces better results.

A control slide can be used to assess the background count as the working apparatus may exhibit a background count which is sufficient to upset the autoradiograph. A clean slide, without any sections attached, is treated in the same way as the other slides with true radioautographs.

181

RADIOAUTOGRAPHS FOR THE ELECTRON MICROSCOPE

The preparation and sectioning of labelled material is the same as for ordinary material which is to be studied in the electron microscope (see Chapters 2 and 3).

A coating technique is necessary, and it is very important that the single layer of emulsion should be as thin and as evenly distributed as possible.

Two methods of coating the material on the specimen grids have been described by Caro and Tubergen[15] and are quoted below.

Method 1

The preparation of the emulsion and the following procedures must be carried out in a dark room.

Several prepared grids are attached to a glass slide with Sellotape.

10 g of Ilford L-4 emulsion are melted in 20 ml of Pyrex distilled water in a beaker at 45°C for 15 min. During this time the emulsion should be stirred continuously and then it is placed in an ice bath for 2–3 min. After this it should be left at room temperature for 30 min. A platinum wire loop about 4 cm in diameter is dipped in the emulsion and withdrawn slowly. The film on the loop should be allowed to gel before it is touched on to the surface of the slide when it should fall on to the prepared grids and adhere.

Method 2

This method is more complicated but a more even film is produced. A 2 per cent solution of Difco agar in Pyrex distilled water is poured into a Petri dish to a depth of 0·5 cm and allowed to set. The solidified agar is cut out in rectangles 2 × 3 cm and placed on a clean glass slide with the surface which was in contact with the dish uppermost. The slides are warmed slightly for a few minutes to remove any surface moisture. The agar is then flooded with a 0·2 per cent solution of Parlodion in amyl acetate and the slides are left to dry in a vertical position.

The rest of the procedure must be carried out in a dark room.

The emulsion is prepared as for method 1. The film on the loop is applied to the collodion-agar surface without waiting for it to gel. The film which is formed is floated on Pyrex distilled water, emulsion side uppermost. The prepared specimen grids are brought up underneath the film and lifted out of the water.

BIBLIOGRAPHY

REFERENCES

[1]Priestly, J. H. and Scott, L. I. (1955). *Introduction to Botany*, 3rd ed. London; Longmans Green

[2]Jeffrey, E. C. (1917). *The Anatomy of Woody Plants*, 1st ed. Chicago; University of Chicago Press

[3]Franklin, G. L. (1946). 'A Rapid Method of Softening Wood for Microtome Sectioning.' *Trop. Woods* **88**, 35

[4]Stafford, H. J. and Heimsch, C. (1952). 'Mounting Macerated Plant Tissues with Adhesives. '*Stain Tech.* **27**, 197

[5]Blaydes, G. W. (1939). 'The Use of Bismark Brown in Some New Stain Schedules.' *Stain Tech.* **14**, 105

[6]Clarke, J. (1960). 'Preparation of Leaf Epidermis for Topographic Study.' *Stain Tech.* **35**, 35

[7]Sinclair, C. B. (1961). 'Surface Printing of Plant Leaves for Phylogenetic Studies.' *Stain Tech.* **36**, 299

[8]Cutler, D. F., from a thesis submitted to London University.

[9]Richardson, F. (1960). 'A Method of Reviving Sections of Compressed Wood from Archaeological Sites and Peat-bogs.' *Kew Bull.* **14**, 85–86

[10]Richardson, F. (1960). 'A Method of Examining Fossilized or Semifossilized Plant Tissues Impregnated with Calcareous Substances.' *Kew Bull.* **14**, 87

[11]Joy, K. W., Willis, A. J. and Lacey, W. S. (1956). 'A Rapid Cellulose Peel Technique in Paleobotany.' *Ann. Bot. N.S.* **20**, 635

[12]Walton, J. (1923). 'On a New Method of Investigating Fossil Plant Impressions or Incrustations.' *Ann. Bot., Lond.* **37**, 379

[13]Pelc, S. R. (1956). 'The Stripping Film Technique of Autoradiography.' *Int. J. appl. Rad. Isotopes*, **1**, 172

[14]Kodak Ltd., Leaflet obtained with each box of Autoradiographic Stripping Plates. London; Kodak

[15]Caro, L. G. and Van Tubergen, R. P. (1962). 'High-Resolution Autoradiography.' *J. Cell Biol.* **15**, 173

BIBLIOGRAPHY

Brown, C. A. (1960). *Palynological Techniques*. Baton Rouge, La.; Brown

CHAPTER 6

SOME USEFUL TESTS FOR
BIOLOGICALLY IMPORTANT SUBSTANCES

CELL WALLS

TESTS FOR CELLULOSE

Iodine in KI

Potassium iodide	2 g
Iodine	1 g
Distilled water	100 ml

The potassium iodide is dissolved in as little water as possible and then the iodine is dissolved. The solution is made up to 100 ml with distilled water.

Iodine in KI gives a yellow colouration to cellulose.

Iodine and Sulphuric Acid

The material is mounted in a dilute solution of iodine in KI and irrigated with 70 per cent sulphuric acid. Considerable swelling takes place and cellulose walls take on a bright blue colour.

Chlor-zinc-iodide

(A)	Zinc chloride	20 g
	Distilled water	8·5 ml

Dissolve the zinc chloride in the water and cool.

(B)	Potassium iodide	1·0 g
	Iodine	0·5 g
	Distilled water	20·0 ml

Add B to A drop by drop until a precipitate of iodine forms.

There may be some swelling and cellulose is coloured violet.

TESTS FOR LIGNIN

Phloroglucinol and Hydrochloric Acid

The preparation on a slide is flooded with a 1 per cent solution of phloroglucinol in commercial alcohol for 1–2 min. The phloroglucinol is drained off and a few drops of concentrated hydrochloric acid added. Lignified tissue will be coloured red. The acid should be

184

drained off as soon as a red colouration appears and the preparation mounted in a solution of weak glycerin (see p. 137).

Aniline Sulphate or Chloride

A saturated aqueous solution of either aniline sulphate or aniline chloride is made up and a few drops of hydrochloric acid are added. Lignified walls are stained bright yellow.

TESTS FOR SUBERIZED AND CUTINIZED CELL WALLS

Sudan Blue

Use a 0·1 per cent solution in equal parts of glycerol and alcohol.

The preparation on the slide is flooded with Sudan blue and warmed until the liquid is just about to boil. It is then washed with alcohol and mounted in weak glycerin (see p. 137).

Concentrated Sulphuric Acid

Suberized and cutinized membranes are insoluble in sulphuric acid.

CELL CONTENTS

TEST FOR STARCH

Iodine in KI (see p. 184).

The starch grains will show a dark blue to black colour.

TESTS FOR CARBOHYDRATES

Fehling's Reaction for Reducing Sugars

Fehling's solution—(A) Dissolve 34·6 g of copper sulphate in 500 ml distilled water.

(B) Dissolve 175 g of sodium potassium tartrate (Rochelle salt) and 50 g sodium hydroxide in 500 ml distilled water.

Method—Prior to use, equal quantities of solutions A and B are mixed. To 3 or 4 ml of the solution to be tested, 1 ml of complete reagent is added and heated to boiling. A bright red precipitate will show the presence of reducing sugars such as glucose and fructose.

Sucrose will give a positive reaction with Fehling's solution if first hydrolysed by boiling with a few ml of dilute hydrochloric acid.

Benedict's Test for Reducing Sugars

Benedict's solution—(A) Dissolve 173 g sodium citrate and 90 g sodium carbonate in 600 ml of water. Use heat if necessary.

(B) Dissolve 17·3 g of cupric sulphate in about 150 ml of water. Mix solutions A and B and make up to 1 litre to form final solution which will keep indefinitely.

Method—To 5 ml of Benedict's solution, 2 ml of test solution are added, mixed thoroughly and heated in a water bath full of boiling water for 5 min. An orange precipitate indicates the presence of reducing sugars.

Foulger's Test for Fructose and Sucrose

Foulger's solution—Take 40 g of urea and dissolve in 80 ml 40 per cent sulphuric acid. Add 2 g of stannous chloride and boil the mixture till clear. Cool and make up to 100 ml with 40 per cent sulphuric acid. Take 1 ml of Foulger's solution and add a few drops of the solution under test. Boil gently for 1 min and allow to cool. A blue colouration indicates fructose or sucrose.

Although a specific test for fructose this reagent will give an indication of the presence of other substances.

A green or amethyst colour indicates glucose, maltose, lactose or starch. A yellow colour indicates pentoses.

Test for Inulin

Small cubes of the material, for example dahlia tuber, are placed in absolute alcohol for at least 48 h. A section is cut and viewed under a microscope. Characteristic sphaerocrystals will be seen in the cells (*Figure 78*). These crystals can be dissolved by placing the section in a few drops of warm water.

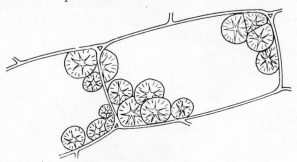

Figure 78. Sphaerocrystals of inulin in cells of dahlia tuber

TESTS FOR PROTEINS

Proteins in general coagulate upon heating or upon the addition of alcohol. They are also precipitated by the addition of a few ml of 10 per cent trichloroacetic acid. Before carrying out the following colour reaction, it is wise to test the experimental solution by

186

warming a little in a test tube, adding a few drops of ethanol or a few ml of trichloroacetic acid and checking for coagulation or precipitation.

The following colour reactions of proteins are dependent, not upon the protein itself, but upon its constituents.

For example, the mercuric nitrite test and the xanthoproteic test give a reaction which depends upon the aromatic amino acids contained in the protein molecule. The Sakaguchi test requires the presence of the amino acid arginine. The biuret test requires the presence of two peptide linkages to give a positive reaction. Ninhydrin also gives a positive reaction with protein because of the constituent amino acids.

Millon's Reagent (Mercuric nitrite test)

Millon's reagent—Dissolve 10 ml mercury in 188 ml concentrated nitric acid. The solution is heated carefully, preferably in a fume cupboard. When dissolved, the solution is added to 200 ml of distilled water. Since this reagent does not keep for any length of time it is better to prepare only a small quantity.

Method—To 1 ml of the solution under test 1 ml of Millon's reagent is added and the mixture boiled for 1 min. A red precipitate indicates the presence of protein.

Xanthoproteic Test

Add 1 ml of concentrated nitric acid to 3 ml of solution under test. If the solution contains protein in some form, a white precipitate will form at this stage. It should be boiled for 1 min. The precipitate will turn yellow and dissolve, or partially dissolve to give a yellow solution. It should then be cooled and excess 0·880 ammonia added. The yellow colouration will deepen into orange.

The Ninhydrin Reaction

Dissolve 0·2 g ninhydrin (Indane-trione hydrate) in 100 ml water.

Method—To 3 ml of the solution under test, 5 or 6 drops of ninhydrin reagent are added and the mixture heated. A blue colouration indicates the presence of α-amino acids. Ninhydrin reagent is unstable and will only keep for 2 days.

Biuret Reaction

(A) 5 per cent sodium hydroxide: take 5 g of sodium hydroxide pellets, and dissolve in 20 ml distilled water. Cool and make up to 100 ml.

(B) 1 per cent copper sulphate: Take 1 g of copper sulphate and dissolve in a little distilled water. Make up to 100 ml.

Method—To 3 ml of the solution to be tested, 3 ml of A and 1 drop of B are added. A pink or violet colouration indicates the presence of proteoses or peptones.

Sakaguchi Test

(A) 5 per cent sodium hydroxide (prepared as for biuret reaction).
(B) 1 per cent α-naphthol: take 1 g α-naphthol, and dissolve in a little commercial alcohol. Make up to 100 ml with alcohol.
(C) 10 per cent sodium hypochlorite.

Method—To 3 ml of solution under test, 1 ml of A and 2 drops of B are added. These are well mixed and 1 drop of C is added and mixed. A red colouration indicates the presence of arginine.

This test is a good general test for protein as arginine is a basic amino acid found in all proteins.

Test for Nitrite

Greiss-Ilosvay solutions—Prepare 300 ml of 30 per cent acetic acid by diluting 90 ml glacial acetic acid to 300 ml with distilled water.
(A) Take 1·12 g of sulphanilic acid and dissolve in 150 ml 30 per cent acetic acid.
(B) Take 0·1 g α-napthylamine and boil for 10 min with 20 ml water. Pour the clear liquid from the violet residue and make up to 150 ml with 30 per cent acetic acid.
Store solution B in a dark bottle.

Method—Just before testing, equal quantities of solutions A and B are mixed. To 1 ml of solution to be tested, 1 ml of the mixed reagents is added. A deep red colouration indicates the presence of nitrite.

Test for Nitrate

Snell's reagent—(1) Heat 1 litre of nitrogen-free sulphuric acid with 2 g ammonium chloride to 180°C and maintain the temperature for 1 h. (2) Add 100 mg diphenylamine to 800 ml of distilled water. Slowly add the litre of prepared acid, cooling between each addition of acid. (3) When cool pour into Pyrex glass stoppered bottles and add 6 g ammonium chloride to each litre of mixture.

Method—To 1 ml of solution to be tested add 3–4 ml of Snell's reagent (the reagent must always be in excess of the liquid to be tested). The slow development of a blue colouration indicates the presence of nitrate. If the colour develops rapidly nitrite is present. Nitrites can be removed by boiling vigorously with dilute sulphuric acid. After this treatment tests may be made again for nitrate.

Nessler Reaction. (For Ammonia)

Stock Nessler solution—Dissolve 75 g KI in 50 ml of warm distilled water; then add 100 g of mercuric iodide and stir. Dilute with water to about 500 ml. Filter and make up to 1 litre.

Sodium hydroxide solution (10 per cent)—Dissolve 10 g sodium hydroxide in 30 ml distilled water, cool and make up to 100 ml.

Method—Before testing the experimental solution, the above reagents should be mixed as follows. To 30 ml stock Nessler solution, 20 ml 10 per cent sodium hydroxide solution is added and the mixture diluted with distilled water to 100 ml. To 2 ml of this mixed reagent 3 ml of the solution under test is added. The development of a deep yellow to orange colour indicates the presence of ammonia. This test is very sensitive and should be carried out using freshly prepared reagent in an atmosphere completely free from extraneous ammonia.

TESTS FOR FATTY SUBSTANCES

The Sudan stains are the most widely used for detection of fatty substances.

Sudan blue—(see test for suberized and cutinized cell walls).

Sudan black—A saturated solution of the stain in 70 per cent alcohol is made up. Sudan III and IV, which are the older stains for fats, are also made up in 70 per cent alcohol.

TESTS FOR SILICA BODIES

Sections are taken from 50 or 70 per cent alcohol and placed in carbolic acid (phenol). (Enough water is added to the carbolic acid crystals so that they deliquesce.) A pink colouration will be seen if silica is present.

Polarized light (pp. 29, 30) can also be used. Silica does not shine when viewed between crossed polars.

BIBLIOGRAPHY

Casselman, W. G. B. (1959). *Histochemical Technique*, 1st ed. London; Methuen

Cole, S. W. (1942). *Practical Physiological Chemistry*, 9th ed. Cambridge; Heffer

Day, A. R. and Joullié, M. M. (1960). *Organic Chemistry*, 1st ed. U.S.A.; Van Nostrand Inc.

Jensen, W. A. (1962). *Botanical Histochemistry*, 1st ed. San Francisco; Freeman

CHAPTER 7

CARE OF PLANTS AND AQUARIA

INTRODUCTION

GENERAL MAINTENANCE OF A GREENHOUSE

Ventilation

The optimum temperature, at which any plant will make most satisfactory growth, varies with the individual specimen concerned. Ventilation and shading enable the temperature to be kept near the optimum.

Ventilators should always be opened gradually and before the temperature is allowed to get too high. Draughts should be avoided and ventilation should be kept at a minimum in bad weather, as violent fluctuations in temperature weaken the plant. At night, ventilators must be closed before there is any rapid drop in temperature.

When plants are growing quickly, plenty of moisture is necessary in the atmosphere. On a hot dry day, when ventilation is necessary, the floor and benches of the greenhouse should be damped down with water. This should not be done, however, if the temperature is low, as it encourages fungoid diseases.

When plants are flowering or fruits ripening, a drier atmosphere may be required and, if the weather is suitable, some ventilators can be left open slightly at night.

Shading

This can be carried out by using blinds or by applying a solution of Summer Cloud to the roof of the greenhouse. This shading cuts out the damaging rays of the sun and allows the temperature of the house to be more easily regulated. Shading must be done early in the summer before the heat of the sun becomes too intense.

Cleanliness

This is most important and all dead or badly diseased plants should be removed from the greenhouse at once.

If there is staging in the house it must be cleaned, especially when it is covered with grit. The grit should be removed from the staging occasionally, and washed. The floor must be swept regularly and everything taken into the house must be clean, including flower pots and seed boxes.

The greenhouse should be spring cleaned annually by washing down all the glass and paintwork. The latter should be washed with Teepol as this clears any virus infections.

Fumigation

This is sometimes necessary to control pests in the greenhouse. Most fumigation is carried out by producing fumes from various chemicals but there are aerosols on the market which produce a mist from a liquid.

Small canisters of D.D.T. and B.H.C. can be placed on the floor of the greenhouse and lighted. The cubic area of the house should be calculated in order to judge the number of canisters required.

D.D.T. is used as a general fumigant for caterpillars. B.H.C. controls aphides and white fly, but it should not be used in a house where there are seedlings which have been newly pricked off. Instructions on the canisters should be carried out explicitly.

A specified amount of calcium cyanide powder can be sprinkled on the floor of the greenhouse and left to absorb the moisture either from the soil or the atmosphere. When the powder comes in contact with water, hydrocyanic gas is given off. This gas kills aphides, capsids, thrips and white fly. It is safe to use with the majority of plants but is extremely poisonous to human beings.

A safe method of fumigation for the control of aphides and thrips is by using nicotine. Special shreds or cones can be ignited and left to smoulder, or special liquid nicotine can be vaporized over a small spirit lamp.

The greenhouse must be kept tightly closed for about 12 h after fumigation to allow the trapped fumes to kill the pests. Any cracks around ventilators and doors should be plugged or covered with damp sacks. A dry, warm evening is usually the most convenient time to fumigate, and the doors should be locked to prevent anyone entering the house. The following morning the ventilators should be opened to clear the fumes before anyone is allowed to work in the house.

FLOWER POTS

Earthenware flower pots are baked on trays or casts. The smaller the pot, the larger the number which can be baked at one time, so a small pot has a high cast number and a large pot has a low cast number. Flower pots can be described either by their cast number or by the inside diameter of the pot (Table 6).

New pots should always be soaked in water before using.

TABLE 6
Popular sizes of flower pots

No. of pots to a cast	Inside diameter (in.)	Outside depth (in.)
72 Thimble	$1\frac{1}{2}$	2
72 Medium	2	3
72 Thumb	$2\frac{1}{2}$	3
60 Small	3	$3\frac{1}{4}$
60 Medium	$3\frac{1}{2}$	$3\frac{1}{2}$
60 Large	$3\frac{3}{4}$	4
54	$4-4\frac{1}{2}$	$4\frac{1}{2}$
48	$4\frac{3}{4}$	$4\frac{3}{4}$
40	$5-5\frac{1}{2}$	$5-5\frac{1}{2}$
32	$6\frac{1}{4}$	$6\frac{1}{4}$

COMPOSTS

Formulae for composts have been devised from work carried out at the John Innes Horticultural Institution. Composts made up to these specifications can be purchased from any reliable horticultural stockist.

Compost for Seed Sowing

2 parts by bulk medium loam (sterilized).
1 part by bulk horticultural peat (or sterilized leaf mould).
1 part by bulk coarse silver sand.
$1\frac{1}{2}$ oz. superphosphate ⎫ per bushel of the above mixture.
$^3/_4$ oz. chalk ⎭

Compost for Potting (J.I.P.1)

7 parts by bulk medium loam (sterilized).
3 parts by bulk horticultural peat (or sterilized leaf mould).
2 parts by bulk coarse silver sand.
$^1/_4$ lb. John Innes Base ⎫ per bushel of the above mixture.
$^3/_4$ oz. ground chalk ⎭

John Innes Base can be bought ready mixed. It consists of:
2 parts by weight hoof and horn meal $^1/_8$ in. grist.
2 parts by weight superphosphate.
1 part by weight sulphate of potash.

The ground chalk can be omitted from the mixture if the plants to be potted are 'lime hating'.

When mixing one's own compost, the loam and peat must be sieved, but not through too fine a mesh, otherwise the compost will clog. The sieved loam is spread out a few inches thick and covered first with the peat, then the sand and finally the fertilizer see *Figure 79*.

The heap of compost to be mixed should be flat and not conical in shape. This flat heap is cut through in sections and turned with a spade until the whole pile has been turned. The procedure is then repeated two or three times until the compost is thoroughly mixed.

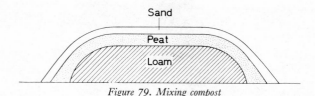

Figure 79. Mixing compost

Vermiculite

This can be used for germinating seedlings and striking cuttings. It is also a clean medium for plants which are needed for experiments. Vermiculite has no nutrient value and, if the plants are to remain growing in it, a general fertilizer must be added.

Before using, the vermiculite should be soaked in water and then allowed to drain.

Sterilization

Steam is the most effective method of soil sterilization and unlike baking, does not impair the physical condition of the soil.

Small electrical sterilizers are on the market and from these a mains current can be passed through metal plates to the soil.

A simple method of sterilizing soil is to suspend a small sack half full of soil over a few inches of boiling water in a domestic boiler. The water must be kept boiling fast, as the temperature of the soil must be raised quickly to about 200°F and allowed to remain at this temperature for 20 min.

Sterilization can also be carried out by watering the soil with chemicals. Formalin is considered to be the most efficient. 1 pt. of formalin is used to 6 gal. of water.

The soil is spread out, watered with the diluted formalin and covered with sacks so that the fumes are trapped. After 48 h the sacks can be removed. The soil is left until all trace of the formalin has disappeared.

SEEDS

Conditions necessary for Germination

Water supply—All seeds need to absorb water and some need to absorb as much as half their own weight before germination can begin, so a sufficient quantity of water must be available.

Temperature—Some seeds will germinate at only a few degrees above freezing point, e.g. broad beans and peas, but others such as cucumbers will not germinate below about 12°C. Tropical plants need a much higher temperature before germination will take place. It is necessary to provide a suitable temperature for the particular seeds being grown, but this does not mean that it should be too high. The optimum temperature for germination of most garden seeds is between 25° and 30°C.

Oxygen—All germinating seeds need oxygen for respiration, so there must be sufficient fresh air available.

Darkness—Is not essential for germination, except in a few cases, e.g. onions and delphiniums. Most seeds will germinate successfully in either darkness or light.

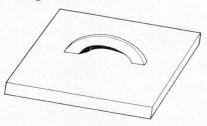

Figure 80. A presser

Method of Sowing

Seeds may be sown in shallow pans or boxes using John Innes seed compost (p. 192) or vermiculite (p. 193).

Boxes—Seed boxes can be wiped clean with a piece of rough sacking or washed with water and allowed to dry thoroughly before being used.

A presser is needed to make the soil firm when the seed box is being filled. A presser consists of a flat piece of wood about 1/2-in. thick which fits the inside of a seed box. It has a handle attached for ease of working (*Figure 80*).

The bottom of the seed box is covered with a layer of leaves or other coarse material for drainage and then it is filled two-thirds full with the prepared compost which is made firm with the tips of the fingers. More compost is added and levelled to the top of the seed box with the edge of the presser. The presser is then placed face down so that $1/2$ in. is left between the surface of the soil and the top of the box. A sprinkling of sand is then added.

The compost in the box is watered, using a fine rose on the watering can, and then left to drain.

The seed is sown thinly and is covered with a little sieved compost. This is also made firm with the presser.

Pans—The pans should be washed and thoroughly dried before being used. A large piece of broken flower pot is placed over the drainage hole or holes and smaller pieces are added to cover the bottom of the pan. These crocks are covered with a thin layer of rough material and then the required compost is added. This is made firm with a circular presser.

The seed should be sown thinly, covered with sieved compost and gently made firm with the presser. The pan should be stood in a little water and allowed to remain until the surface of the soil becomes damp. When this stage is reached the pan is removed from the water and allowed to drain. After draining, the pan is covered with a sheet of glass which should be wiped dry and turned over each day.

Pots—Large seeds such as beans are sown in flower pots. The pots should be thoroughly cleaned and crocked as for pans. Each pot is two-thirds filled with compost which is lightly pressed firm with the fingers. The beans are sown, covered with compost which is made firm again. Beans can be sown singly in 60's, or several to a pot when using 48's. Flower pots can be used for small seeds which are to be pricked out and, if this is the case, the pots should be half filled with crocks to ensure good drainage.

Seeds of peas and beans germinate more rapidly if they are soaked in water before sowing. The seed coats of lupins and sweet peas can be pricked with a pin or rasped with a nail file to permit easier absorption of water. In both cases, care must be taken to avoid damaging the embryonic root and shoot.

Pricking Out

The seedlings can be pricked out as soon as they are large enough to handle. This stage is usually reached when the first pair of true leaves develop.

The boxes are prepared and filled as for seed sowing using John Innes potting compost No.1. A standard size seed box takes 6 rows of 8 or 10 seedlings.

A small wooden dibber (*Figure 81*) is necessary and this can be used to mark out the position of the rows along the length and breadth of the box (*Figure 82*).

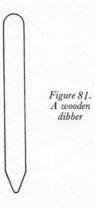

Figure 81.
A wooden
dibber

Each seedling is held by a leaf between the first finger and the thumb, and the roots are lowered into the hole made with the dibber. While still supporting the seedling, the hole is closed by gently pressing the soil on one side with the side of the dibber (*Figure 83*).

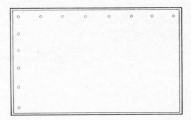

Figure 82. Diagram of the top of a seed box showing positions marked for the seedlings

This pressure must not be applied too near the stem as this is easily crushed. For the same reason, seedlings must never be handled except by their leaves.

After pricking out, the seedlings should be watered using a fine rose on the can.

Seedlings can be pricked out singly into small 60 pots in the same manner. As with boxes, a $1/2$-in. gap should be left between the soil and the top of the pot for watering. Only the tips of the fingers should be used for pressing the soil in the pot, never the thumbs, as too much pressure will be exerted.

196

Damping off

This is a disease caused by several fungi and it affects many plants in the seedling stage. The seedlings are attacked at ground level and collapse.

It is advisable to take preventative measures such as the following:

(1) Sterilization of all soil boxes and pots. Cleanliness of staging and greenhouse.
(2) By watering the soil which is to be used for pricking out and potting, with Cheshunt compound at the rate of 1 oz. to 2 gal. of water or by watering the soil and boxes with a dilute solution of permanganate of potash in water.
(3) Making sure that there is adequate ventilation and no overcrowding of the plants.

Figure 83. Pricking out a seedling into a flower pot

CARE OF ESTABLISHED PLANTS IN THE LABORATORY AND GREENHOUSE

General Conditions

Plants which are grown in the laboratory must get enough light and they should be placed in a position where they are not in a draught or in danger from gas fumes.

Watering

Pot plants should only be watered when they are dry, but they should not be allowed to dry out so that a gap is left between the ball of soil and the sides of the pot. The soil level should be $1/2$ in. from the top of the pot and this gap should be filled with water. This amount of water will be sufficient to drain right through the pot. Little dribbles of water must not be given, as, while the surface of the soil may be kept quite wet, the water does not always penetrate to the bottom of the pot.

To ascertain whether or not large pot plants need watering, the pots can be tapped with a cotton reel fixed to the end of a cane. If the tapping produces a ringing sound then watering is necessary but, if there is only a dull thud, the plant has no need of any more water.

The leaves of plants should not be watered when they are in full sun as they will be scorched.

Feeding

All established plants growing in pots need feeding and should be given a top dressing from time to time, particularly just before flowering.

Clay's fertilizer is a good general fertilizer and can be given weekly at the rate of one level teaspoonful per 48 pot. This should be given before watering.

Re-potting

When the plant roots start to form a mat around the ball of soil inside the pot, the plant needs re-potting. This stage is usually reached when the roots are visible through the hole in the bottom of the pot. John Innes potting compost can be used.

The pots must be clean. If dirty pots are used the roots adhere to the sides of the pot and are damaged when the plant is turned out.

Re-potting should be carried out through several stages using slightly larger pots each time. A plant must never be removed from a very small pot and re-potted in a final stage pot in one operation, otherwise poor results will be obtained. The roots often fail to find enough air in the new, thick ball of soil, which holds more water than the roots can absorb. Plants in 2-in. pots should be re-potted into 4-in. pots.

The pots are crocked and a little well-rotted manure or coarse material is added. This is covered by a little compost which should not be too wet. A good test is to take a handful of the soil, squeeze it and then open the hand again. The ball of soil should fall apart. If it remains in a solid lump then the soil is too wet. Bone dry compost must never be used.

Plants which are dry should be watered about 15 min before re-potting.

To remove the plant, turn the pot upside down and tap the edge of the pot on the bench. Support the ball of soil containing the plant in one hand (*Figure 84*).

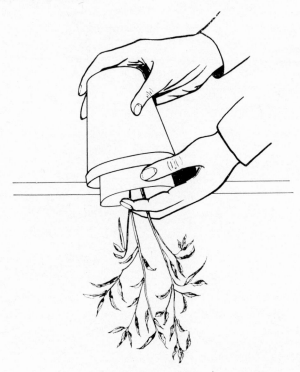

Figure 84. Removing the plant from the pot prior to re-potting

Place the plant in the prepared pot and add fresh compost round the sides. This compost is rammed down into position with a spatulate piece of wood (*Figure 85*).

The new compost should cover the old ball of soil, but the final level must still be $1/2$ in. down from the top of the pot to allow for watering.

When the plant has been re-potted, the rim of the pot should be held in both hands and the pot tapped on the bench twisting it round slightly at the same time. This levels and loosens the surface of the soil.

Wilting—Causes and Remedies

Wilting means that the plant loses more water than it can absorb. This can be caused by:

(1) Insufficient moisture in the atmosphere surrounding the plant. For plants in greenhouses this can be remedied by damping the floor and the staging. Plants growing outside can be sprayed in the evening.

(2) Strong sunshine and strong drying winds cause the plant to wilt. Where it is possible the plants should be shaded from the sun and protected from the wind.

(3) Lack of moisture at the roots is a common cause of wilting.

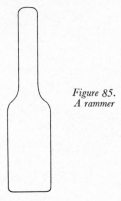

Figure 85.
A rammer

The plants must be watered and, if possible, a surface mulch applied. Grass cuttings can be used for this purpose, or any other material which will hold moisture and prevent the surface of the soil from drying out.

There are definite wilt diseases, and drooping may be brought about by fungal infection or insect pests.

General Unhealthiness in Plants

This is often caused by a deficiency or an excess of certain materials.

Bad drainage and overwatering are common causes of the foliage turning yellow, as the supply of nitrogen to the plant is checked.

FERNS AND FERN PROTHALLI

Fern prothalli are best grown in well crocked pans or pots. The pots are filled to within an inch of the top with sterilized loam and a sprinkling of brick dust is applied to the surface. Soak the pots in water until the surface of the loam becomes damp, and then drain them.

The spores are sown thinly and the pots are covered with a piece of glass which is wiped free of condensation each day. Stand each pot in a saucer of water, in a shady part of a warm greenhouse. If the spores are being germinated in a laboratory, the pot must be covered with a bell jar.

When the prothalli appear, they can be pricked off into small pots using equal parts of loam, leaf mould and sand. If fertilization takes place, these fern prothalli will grow into young ferns and should be kept in a moist, warm atmosphere.

If the ferns are kept in a greenhouse this must be shaded, as the direct sun will scorch the fronds. In hot dry weather the floor and staging should be damped down with water but the foliage of most ferns must not be splashed with water otherwise they will be scorched.

Old fronds of maiden hair fern can be cut just as the new ones begin to appear as they are sometimes difficult to remove later owing to the dense growth of the plant. Normally, however, ferns should not have their foliage cut until it becomes unsightly (in the case of the evergreen varieties) or dead (in the case of the deciduous varieties).

When ferns are grown in the laboratory they must be kept out of draughts. A hot dry atmosphere is also injurious, especially where bunsen or other gas burners are used. Tepid water should be used for watering and a damp atmosphere can be created by standing a container of water near the plant. Potted ferns must never be allowed to stand in saucers of water as this causes the soil to become waterlogged; the air supply to the roots is cut off and they begin to rot.

MARCHANTIA AND LUNULARIA

These two liverworts can be successfully grown on ashes in a cold frame or under the staging of a cool greenhouse. They do not like excessive heat.

SOME METHODS OF PROPAGATION

Besides propagation by seed, there are various methods of vegetative propagation used to obtain plants which are replicas of their parents, in a short space of time.

Stem Cuttings

These can be taken from the majority of plants. Softwood cuttings are best cut transversely or at a slight angle just below a node. The lower leaves are then carefully removed (*Figure 86*). A sharp knife is essential for taking cuttings of any plant.

Figure 86. Stem cutting of a geranium

The cuttings may be rooted in sand, sandy soil or in vermiculite. Boxes or pots can be used but pots are preferable. The cuttings are inserted in the sand around the edge of the pot as this stimulates root formation.

A hormone solution or powder can be used to encourage and hasten root formation. The cut end of the stem is soaked in the solution or dipped in the powder, before inserting the cutting in the pot.

Leaf Cuttings

Some plants such as *Begonia rex* can be propagated by their leaves. Cuts are made across the main veins and the leaves are laid on a compost consisting of equal parts sand and leaf mould. Boxes are more convenient than pots for leaf cuttings and should be left to stand in a warm place.

Root Cuttings

Some plants having fleshy roots may be propagated by cutting a portion of the root (*Figure 87*) and inserting it in a box of sandy compost.

202

Layering

Border carnations and some shrubs can be propagated by layering, which is done by pegging down the stem on to sandy soil. This is done while the stem is still attached to the parent plant. This method is also used for plants which are difficult to propagate by seed or cuttings.

Strawberry runners may be layered into small pots which are sunk into the ground up to their rims (*Figure 88*).

Division

Many hardy perennials and rock plants can be divided easily into smaller pieces.

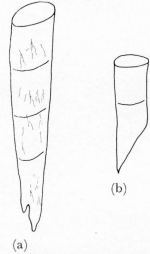

(a)

(b)

Figure 87. (a) Root of Anchusa; (b) prepared root cutting

ARTIFICIAL POLLINATION

Pollination is simply the transference of the pollen grains from the anthers to the stigma. The pollen grains are usually carried by the wind or by insects. Some plants are self pollinated, violets for example, but with the majority of plants cross pollination is necessary. This is because, either the male and female organs are on different plants or, if they are on the same plant: (*a*) the pollen is produced before the stigma is receptive, (*b*) the stigma is receptive before the pollen or (*c*) the stamens are produced below the stigma.

If plants are grown in a laboratory or greenhouse where there is less likelihood of pollination occurring, they can be artificially pollinated.

Figure 88. Strawberry runner layered into a small flower pot whilst still attached to the parent plant

The pollen can be removed from the anthers by touching them with a soft brush and then touching the stigma of another flower. For a large number of open flowers such as peach or nectarine blossom, a rabbit's foot attached to the end of a cane is used.

Artificial pollination is also used to produce new varieties of plants. The parent plants must be carefully selected. One, perhaps, for the colour of the flower and the other for a vigorous growth. A number of flowers on plant No. 1 are selected just before they open. The flowers of plant No. 1 are carefully opened out and the anthers are removed. Care must be taken that none of the pollen touches the stigma. Using a camel-hair brush, some of the pollen is removed from the anthers of plant No. 2 and transferred to the stigma of the flowers of plant No. 1. After the flowers of plant No. 1 have been pollinated in this manner they are tied up in a paper bag to prevent insects bringing pollen from other plants.

Artificial pollination is not always successful in producing new varieties and is usually carried out on plants where the anthers and stigmas are easily reached.

COLLECTION AND STORAGE OF SEEDS

Seeds must not be collected too soon. They must be allowed to ripen before they are collected.

Dry conditions are necessary for the collection of seeds and the seed heads also need to be dry. After they are cut they should be placed in a glass jar and exposed to the sun for a few days, or left in a sunny window to make quite sure that the seeds are fully ripened and dry.

Seeds from plants which have an ejection dispersal mechanism are sometimes difficult to obtain when they are ripe. A paper bag should be tied round the seed head when it begins to swell so that the seeds will not be lost as they ripen.

Before storing, the debris of the seed head must be removed from the seeds either by sieving or by blowing. This latter method can be used for heavier seeds.

A handful of seeds and debris is taken and gently blown until all the light debris has been removed.

Seeds should be stored in packets or in tins provided that suitable precautions are taken to exclude moisture. The packets must be labelled clearly with the name of the seeds and the date of collection.

AQUARIA

The tank chosen should not be too tall in relation to its surface area. The larger the surface area, the more oxygen will be made available to its inhabitants. A large tank has the advantage that it does not have rapid temperature fluctuations.

Unheated tanks can be left open or have a dust cover fitted a few inches above the top of the tank.

Heated tanks should be covered. This helps to control the temperature, the evaporation of the water, and prevents the fish jumping out.

Before setting up the tank it must be sterilized by washing the glass with strong, salt water or by filling it with a deep red solution of potassium permanganate. It must then be rinsed very thoroughly with clean water.

Sand or fine gravel may be used in the bottom of the tank. Builders sand should not be used as the fine particles pack very close together and it is difficult to clean them. The particles of gravel must not be too large otherwise debris and unwanted pieces of food are trapped between them. The sand and gravel can be sterilized in boiling water and placed in the tank to a depth of $2-2^1/2$ in.

The tank should be half filled with water before any plants are introduced. This can be done by placing a sheet of polythene on the sand or gravel and pouring the water on to it gently.

The polythene will rise with the level of the water and prevent the water from disturbing the sand. Very hard tap water can be boiled and cooled before using. It should be decanted carefully.

Plants can be sterilized in a very weak solution of permanganate of potash for 10 min. Before planting, they should be washed in water and examined for traces of filamentous algae, which if introduced into a tank will spread very rapidly.

Most plants are happier if there are not too many different species in one tank and they must not be overcrowded.

After planting, the tank is completely filled with water, and a watering can is useful for this purpose as it disperses the water and prevents the plants from being uprooted.

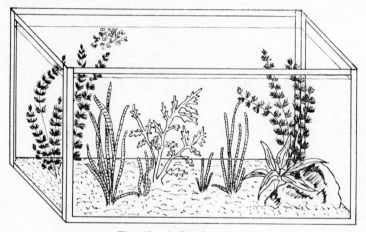

Figure 89. A planted aquarium

The planted tank (*Figure 89*) must have as much daylight as possible but not direct sunlight as this encourages unicellular algae. The tank can be shaded but this must be done with care as the plants need an adequate amount of light.

Where it is necessary to use artificial light, the bulb or bulbs should be as near the surface of the water as is practicable.

In heated tanks, the electrical heater must not be buried in the sand, as lime is deposited on the outside and its heat value is reduced. The best place for a single heater is in the centre of the tank.

When the tank has been planted it should be left for about a week before any fish are introduced.

It is very important that there is no overcrowding of the fish.

Sometimes, in heated tanks, it is necessary to aerate artificially but this must not be carried out continuously, otherwise the fish will become dependent on this means of obtaining oxygen.

It is necessary to aerate artificially when a tank is overcrowded. This can be done by using a small, electrically operated air pump. The rubber tubing is inserted through the top of the tank and the end of the tubing should reach nearly to the bottom of the tank.

Cloudy water is caused through the tank or sand being dirty, usually through excessive organic matter. This means that the tank must be completely drained and cleaned.

To keep the tank clean, all uneaten food particles or other debris should be removed regularly by siphoning. The end of the siphon tube is held about $3/4$ in. above the level of the sand and moved along the tank so that the whole surface area is covered. The $3/4$-in. clearance prevents the sand being sucked into the tube.

Any scum on the surface of the water hinders the supply of oxygen and should be removed by lifting it off with a sheet of blotting paper.

Algae can be scraped off the sides of the tank with a safety razor blade or with a special scraper.

Plants

Valisneria—This plant is a good oxygenator and invaluable in a heated tank, or a tank that is in a warm atmosphere. Care should be taken not to cover the crown with sand when planting.

Valisneria spiralis and *Valisneria torta* are two common species of *Valisneria*, the latter species being the smaller.

Sagittaria—This plant also does well in a tropical tank but can be grown quite successfully in a cool tank.

Myriophyllum—This plant looks lovely in the water and can provide protection for the young fish or spawn. It does best in a heated tank.

Ceratophyllum—This plant is similar in appearance to *Myriophyllum* but is best grown in a cool tank. The pieces of *Ceratophyllum* should be weighted down in the tank with small pieces of lead.

Ceratophyllum is also useful for providing cover for young fish.

Cryptocoryne—This plant does not like direct sunlight and actually prefers some shade.

Floating Plants

Lemna minor (duckweed)—A small amount of duckweed is beneficial in an aquarium. It does not seem to prevent oxygen being absorbed but it does shade the tank.

207

Azolla—This plant prefers warmth and it is a very pretty one to have growing on the surface of a tank.

Salvinia—This plant grows best in slightly acid water and prefers some heat. It is not a good oxygenator.

Riccia—This plant is a good oxygenator but it should not be allowed to form too thick a mat. It is very useful to provide cover for young fish or spawn.

Snails

These should not be kept in an aquarium when the fish are spawning but otherwise they are good scavengers.

Fish

It should always be remembered when introducing fish into a tank that overcrowding is harmful. For details of fish, breeding habits and diseases see the bibliography.

BIBLIOGRAPHY

Hellyer, A. G. L. (1954). *The Encyclopaedia of Garden Work and Terms*, 1st ed. London; Collingridge

King, E. J. (1950). *The Propagation of Plants*, 1st ed. London; Hutchinson

Wright, R. C. M. (1955). *Plant Propagation*, 1st ed. London; Ward & Lock

Mellen, I. M. and Lander, R. J. (1936). *1001 Questions Answered about your Aquarium*, Reprinted 1951. London; Harrap

Marshall, T. H. (1955). *Exotic Fishkeeping, Plants and Snails*, 1st ed. Mitcham, Surrey; Saturn Press

Gohm, D. (1952). *Tropical Fish in the Home*, 1st ed. London; Pearson

CHAPTER 8

MUSEUM AND HERBARIUM WORK

INTRODUCTION

All material collected for museum and herbarium work must be typical specimens, in good condition and should be preserved as soon as possible after collection. Small plants should be collected whole, although this is impracticable with larger specimens where only parts of the plant can be obtained. When collections are made from large flowering plants, a selection of flowers or fruit is obtained, plus some leaves from the top, middle and basal portions of the plant. In plants where the flowers are produced before the leaves it is necessary to collect at different times to procure both.

Collections of ferns should preferably contain fertile fronds and also pieces of rhizome.

With fungi it is wise to note the colour and odour at collection time, as these are changed by preservation. Also, some note should be made of any host plants, and samples brought back for identification.

PRESERVATION

LIQUID METHODS

Before preservation, all specimens must be clean and any particles of soil should be washed away gently in water, using a soft brush.

It is sometimes necessary to bleach specimens containing gummy substances because, if this is not done, the liquid which surrounds them will become dark, rendering the preparations useless for display purposes. Certainly all specimens should have a preliminary immersion in the preservative for two or three days, before finally being placed in the museum jar.

One advantage of liquid preservation is that it preserves the form of the specimen, provided the correct solution is used, but it is important to remember that when mounting, the relative positions of different parts of the plant must be preserved, for example the angle between the stem and leaves.

Herbaceous plants should have a preservative with an alcohol base, as penetration is rapid and the outward shape is set before the plant becomes flaccid. Succulent plants containing large quantities of water in their cells, however, should have a preservative with a formalin base, which means that penetration is much slower than with the use of alcohol and there is less risk of the cells contracting.

For preservation in alcohol, the solutions can range from 70–95 per cent and in formalin, solutions from 2–5 per cent. It must be remembered that these are extreme preservatives and often it is necessary to have a general one containing both alcohol and formalin.

A good general formula consists of the following:

> 15 parts commercial alcohol
> 10 parts distilled water
> 1 part commercial formalin
> 1 part glacial acetic acid

Various formulae containing copper salts have been used to try and preserve the green colouring of the plants. Two of these methods are mentioned here, but although a measure of success is obtained, it is not possible to retain natural colouration in all specimens.

1. Copper sulphate can be added to any of the formalin alcohol mixtures[1].

Copper sulphate	0·2	g
Distilled water	60	ml
95 per cent ethyl alcohol	36	ml
Commercial formalin	4	ml

Specimens should be immersed in this solution for 3–4 days before being transferred to an ordinary formalin alcohol solution in a museum jar. The reaction can be hastened by expelling the air from the specimens. This formula is not suitable for algae which contain excess carbonates in their cells because a precipitate is formed. For marine algae, sea water should be substituted for the distilled water. After fixing, the addition of 5–10 per cent glycerol to the preservative prevents evaporation from the museum jar.

2. Uranium nitrate may also be used[2].

50 per cent alcohol	90	ml
Commercial formalin	5	ml
Glycerol	2·5	ml
Glacial acetic acid	2·5	ml
Copper chloride	10	g
Uranium nitrate	1·5	g

The specimens should be immersed in the preservative from 3–10 days before being transferred to ordinary F.A.A. solutions.

For blue-green algae, 10 g of copper acetate should be substituted for the copper chloride and uranium nitrate in the solution.

Natural green colouration of various algae has been very successfully preserved for 2–3 weeks by immersion in the dioxan solution given on p. 89.

Colours of flowers cannot be preserved successfully by liquid methods but flowering specimens are quite successfully dried by heat. Good results of colour retention in flowers have been obtained by several people who have packed them in polythene bags while fresh and then placed them in a deep freeze until required. This method enables the flowers to be examined at room temperature and to retain their colour for several hours after being brought out of the deep freeze.

The preservation of fungi is not usually successful by liquid means although preliminary soaking and then drying has been found successful[3]. The fungi are soaked in a mixture containing 2 parts commercial formalin and 1 part liquid phenol. After soaking, the specimens are superficially dried with blotting paper and suspended over strong ammonia. The time varies from a few hours to a day according to the size of the specimen. After this treatment they should set quite solid and not shrivel on drying. They can be handled as museum specimens or used for class material after soaking in water. Impregnated specimens should not be kept in glass topped boxes as the phenoluro-tropin compounds attack glass.

Museum Jars

Museum jars with flat sides should be used if possible as viewing is clearer and there is no distortion as there is with cylindrical jars. Various sizes of museum jars having one polished side are available, these have ground glass lids to fit.

Perspex jars are useful and the lids can be sealed with Perspex dissolved in chloroform.

Mounting

When a suitable jar for the specimen has been selected, a background plate is cut to fit into the jar. This plate must be high enough to prevent movement after the jar is sealed, and should preferably be cut from black or milk glass to show up the specimen when mounted.

The specimen can be tied or stuck to the plate. If it is tied, the piece of glass is laid in a trough containing a little water. The specimen is then laid upon the glass and secured by tying with a thin thread of the same colour as the glass. The arrangement of the specimen is important and the final touching up can be done with a glass rod or piece of wire after the plate has been set in position and the jar filled with preservative.

When sticking the specimen on to the plate, a gum should be used which is not soluble in the preservative.

Sealing

There are two methods of sealing the jars: the lid can be smeared round the edge with Vaseline, placed on the jar and bound into position with glued strips of paper or the lid can be permanently sealed by the use of a cement.

There are numerous recipes for cements but a good one is the Stockholm tar formula. This cement is prepared by stirring Stockholm tar into red lead until it becomes chocolate in colour and paste-like in consistency. It hardens rapidly and only the amount required should be mixed.

DRY METHODS

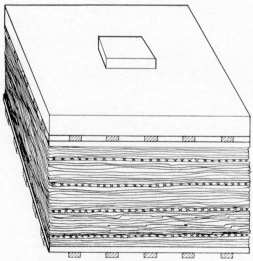

Figure 90. A pile of drying papers containing specimens compressed by a weight on the top

Flowering Plants

The plant, or parts of a plant, should be arranged on sheets of drying paper or newspaper and each sheet covered with muslin or greaseproof paper to prevent the specimen adhering to the next sheet.

Care must be taken in arrangement of the specimen so that essential features are not obscured. Pressing can be carried out in several ways but a useful method is to place the pile of drying papers containing the plants on to a wooden framework, with another wooden frame on the top of the pile. A coverweight is placed upon this and, as the material dries, the pile is compressed (*Figure 90*). The wooden frames can easily be made by nailing $^3/_4 \times ^1/_4$-in. battens as illustrated in *Figure 91*.

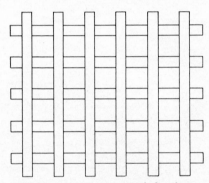

Figure 91. A wooden frame made from battens

This method allows for a circulation of air and an even pressure the whole time.

Two straps can be used to hold the pile together instead of using the coverweight but these must be tightened as the plants dry. The drying paper should be changed daily and the specimens examined for fungal growth.

Drying by heat, providing there is a good circulation of air, is one of the best ways of preserving the colour of the plant. If a special oven is not available, an airing cupboard or a radiator is quite an adequate source of heat, always remembering that the straps on the press must be tightened frequently and the papers changed.

There are several types of presses for collection in the field. The simplest is just a cover with ties containing drying paper. The one described here has two leaves of heavy wire mesh reinforced with metal round the edges and has three single-leaved springs which exert pressure when the press is closed (*Figure 92*).

Awkward material, with thick succulent stems, can be split so that only half the stem is pressed. If still bulky, padding can be inserted around the specimen between the sheets of drying paper to enable even pressure to be maintained.

Spiny material may have to have one or two pieces removed with secateurs to facilitate pressing.

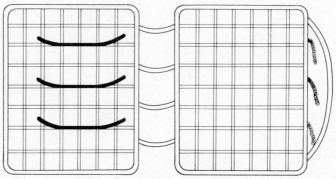

Figure 92. A metal plant press

Fleshy fruits can be scooped out and packed with absorbent material which should be changed several times. Smaller fruits can be pricked so that the juice is absorbed by the drying paper but they must not have heavy pressure applied as this will crush them.

Conifers

When dried normally, conifers very easily lose their needles. To overcome this difficulty the specimen is placed on a sheet of cotton wool about 1/2-in. thick and covered with a sheet of heavy celluloid[4]. The celluloid sheet is stapled so that it is in permanent contact with the specimen and the cotton wool backing. Before placing on the sheet of cotton wool the specimen should be flattened in a press overnight.

Ferns

These are pressed in a similar manner to flowering plants. Parts of tree ferns are dried and stored in boxes.

Mosses and Liverworts

These are also dried and pressed in the same way as flowering plants. Tufts of small mosses are opened out to allow all the features to be seen and then they are pressed.

Fungi

As with flowering plants it is most important to have a good circulation of air when drying fungi. Drying by heat, coupled with good ventilation, helps to dry the specimen rapidly thus preserving the colour. This may be done in an oven at a moderate temperature, or over a radiator until the fungi are quite dry and probably brittle. If this first drying operation is not carefully carried out, the specimens may take up atmospheric moisture after pressing.

As the specimens cannot be pressed in a brittle state, they are placed in a moist chamber[5] and allowed to become pliable. This moist chamber can be made by placing a bell jar over a trough containing a little water, with a raised shelf in it for supporting the specimen (*Figure 93*).

Figure 93. A moist chamber for fungi

When sufficiently pliable the specimens are taken from the moist chamber, placed between sheets of drying paper and pressed carefully so that the shape and structure are preserved.

Algae

To prepare small aquatic plants and algae for drying, a sheet of glass or perforated zinc is covered with a sheet of thin paper such as flimsy duplicating paper, and placed in shallow water in a dish or sink. The specimens are then floated out in the water, above the paper-covered sheet of zinc which is slowly raised from one end so that the specimens adhere to the paper. While they are still wet, any necessary arranging can be carried out using a soft brush. Another sheet of thin paper is then placed over the specimens and pressed so

215

that the excess water is removed. The two sheets of paper containing the specimens are removed from the zinc sheet and placed in a press. The paper can be changed after a few hours and, if the top sheet is removed each time, the specimens will remain firmly fixed to the bottom sheet when they are dry. Several changes of paper are necessary and the whole procedure takes a few days.

PRESENTATION

Arranging and Mounting

Flowering plants—Normally one single plant (or parts of a single plant) is arranged on each herbarium sheet. Specimens with reasonably sized leaves can be pasted and stuck on to the paper, care being taken to clean off any excess paste. More delicate specimens are placed on a pasted sheet.

Strips of linen with an adhesive backing are cut and used to secure the plant more permanently. These strips are placed over the thickest portion of the stem, taking care not to obscure any features (*see Figure 94*). Gummed paper strips may also be used but not Sellotape as the edges collect dirt so readily.

Conifers—The edges of the cotton wool and celluloid mount are bound with masking tape and fixed to a herbarium sheet.

Ferns—These are mounted in the same way as flowering plants except that larger herbarium sheets are used for the very large specimens.

Mosses and liverworts—These are pasted on to the sheets and in the case of smaller mosses the pressed tuft is secured by a narrow linen strip.

Fungi—Small fungi are best mounted in polythene envelopes as this prevents spore drift from one specimen to another. The top of the envelope is attached to the herbarium sheet. By using this method both sides of the specimen can be viewed. Large fleshy fungi and bracket fungi are dried and stored in plastic or glass topped boxes.

Rust and smuts—These are preserved on their host leaves, which are pressed and dried in the same way as flowering plants but a number of specimens are pasted on one herbarium sheet.

Spots or lichens on twigs—These are dried without pressing and the split twig attached to the sheet by an adhesive strip.

Algae—The paper on which the alga has been dried is trimmed and pasted on to the herbarium sheet. Crustaceous algae and some seaweeds are stored in boxes after drying.

Labelling

Labels on herbarium sheets should contain the following information: Generic and specific names, vernacular name, family name, locality where found, habitat, altitude and any other notes of interest. Also the name of the collector, date of collection and finally the herbarium number. If the label is stuck in the left-hand bottom corner of the sheet it is less likely to be continually fingered.

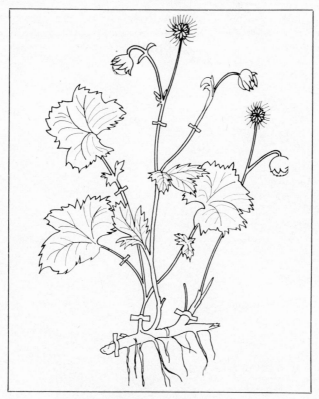

Figure 94. A specimen mounted on a herbarium sheet

When they are labelled, the herbarium sheets are placed in brown paper folders and a number of these are held together in a stiffer folder bearing the name of the group of plants on the outside.

Labels of two different colours are used to distinguish British from foreign specimens. Herbarium folders are normally indexed in family order but they can be indexed alphabetically.

Preservation

Herbarium specimens may be eaten by various insects and need regular examination.

Repellants such as napthalene can be used.

MAPS AND DRAWINGS

Reproduction of maps and drawings, of the same size as the original, is effected quite simply by tracing but if the reproduction is to be larger than the original the following method can be used. Half-inch squares are drawn on a sheet of tracing paper and the outline of the original drawing is traced. A sheet of drawing paper, which is large enough to take the enlarged drawing, is also marked out in squares with a pencil. To enlarge the original four times the squares should be 1 in. If an enlargement is needed twice the size of the original then the squares should be $3/4$ in. The larger squares on the drawing paper are filled with the same lines that are found in each of the smaller squares of the traced original. The lines of the finished drawing can be inked in and when the ink is dry the pencilled squares can be rubbed out.

A pantograph can be used to copy drawings to the same scale or to produce enlarged or reduced copies which are in exact proportion to the original.

A Rapidograph variant pen is very useful for inking in drawings and an attachment can be obtained for using with a compass. A Rapidograph vario-script can be used for stencilling. Uno pens are used with the special stencils provided.

LABELS AND PLACARDS

For display purposes these should be made from stiff white paper or cardboard and the lettering spaced centrally and evenly.

Stencils can be used for making labels and placards. Letraset instant lettering can also be used. Sheets of letters and numbers can be obtained which are placed face down on to the card or label. The back of the letter is rubbed over with a pencil or ballpoint pen.

REFERENCES

[1]Blaydes, G. W. (1937). 'Preserving the Natural Colour of Green Plants.' *Science* **85**, 126

[2]Keefe, A. M. (1926). 'A Preserving Fluid for Green Plants.' *Science* **64**, 331

[3]Ewart, A. J. (1933). 'On the Preservation of Fungi.' *Ann. Bot., Lond.* **47**, 579

[4]Reeder, J. R. (1955). 'Another Method for Preparing Herbarium Specimens of Picea and Tsuga.' *Trop. Woods* **102**, 46

[5]British Museum (Natural History) (1957). *Instructions for Collectors, No. 10*, 6th ed. London; British Museum

CHAPTER 9

CULTURE

INTRODUCTION

Culturing is the technique whereby whole organisms or single cells may be grown in the laboratory. Obviously it is important to try to simulate the organism's optimum habitat. Observation of the organism in its natural habitat is a useful guide to determine the conditions necessary for its growth. The most important conditions to be considered are temperature, humidity, pH, substrate, and the need for, or absence of, light. It is not possible for any one person to investigate the habitats and peculiarities of all the organisms with which they may come in contact but the culture worker has a valuable ally in the library. These two chapters will cover the various aspects of culture work with regard to (*a*) the lower photosynthetic plants; the algae, bryophytes and pteridophytes and (*b*) the non-photosynthetic plants; the fungi, with a brief mention of bacteria.

NECESSARY CONDITIONS AND APPARATUS

Some organisms are difficult to culture and it may be several months before sufficient growth occurs for work to be carried out. It is essential, therefore, that any faster growing organisms are not present on, or in, the culture media, otherwise they will overgrow the slower culture. To prevent this situation occurring, aseptic techniques should be used throughout all operations concerning culturable organisms. This means that before inoculation, all apparatus, media and glassware, etc., must be sterile. Also, the very act of inoculation and any subsequent operations should be carried out in a sterile room or hood to prevent contamination of the sterile apparatus by unsterile air. All inoculating needles, bottles of water, etc., should be sterilized before use and the necks of flasks and tubes should be flamed in the bunsen, after the removal and before replacement of the plug, screw cap etc.

Sterile inoculating hoods can be made quite easily and *Figure 95* shows a suggested plan, but, better than a hood, is an inoculating

219

chamber or room. The sterile room should have a glass or similar bench surface, gas and electric points, stool, air conditioning (sterile air of course), ultra-violet (u.v.) lamp for sterilizing the room before use, normal light source, window and warning lights outside the room to show when the u.v. lamp is on, or to denote that the room is being used.

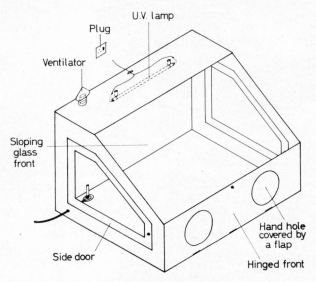

Figure 95. An inoculating hood

Before using the room or hood, it should be sterilized for at least 20 min by the u.v. lamp. To help maintain sterile conditions, a laboratory coat should be sterilized in the room at the same time. It is better if the laboratory coat is permanently installed in the inoculating room. Before the room is used the u.v. lamp must be switched off, as u.v. rays are harmful to the eyes and may cause cancer of the skin. The use of a bunsen incorporating a pilot jet is to be preferred to the normal type of bunsen (see p. 3).

The glass apparatus likely to be found in a culture laboratory will include, apart from the normal equipment, conical flasks to 5 litres capacity, assorted stoppered bottles, assorted screw-capped bottles, vials, test tubes, boiling tubes, pipettes, measuring cylinders, aeration flasks, Petri dishes, Roux bottles and penicillin flasks (*see Figure 96 a* and *b*).

Large conical flasks are used primarily for media making and occasionally for media storage, in which case they are plugged with cotton wool.

Assorted stoppered bottles are useful for the storage of reagents, stains and stock solutions, etc. It should be noted that new glassware contains insoluble salts (calcium phosphate, etc.) and must be washed in dilute hydrochloric acid (10 per cent), then well rinsed in tap water and finally rinsed in distilled water.

Screw-capped bottles may be used as alternatives to glass-stoppered bottles, although their primary use is for the storage of media. These bottles should range from $1/2$ dram vials having a capacity of 1·75 ml, to large bottles capable of holding 2 litres.

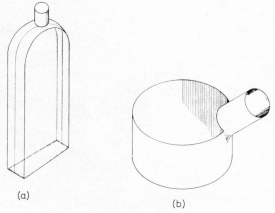

(a) (b)

Figure 96. (a) A Roux Bottle; a (b) penicillin flask

The universal containers in $1/2$ oz. and 1 oz. sizes can be used for the storage of measured volumes of liquid media, or suspending fluids, and for slopes of solid media. The screw caps on these bottles will prevent evaporation of liquid media. The screw caps supplied with the bottles, in some ranges, are interchangeable. The washers can be made of either rubber or cork lined with foil. The rubber washer seems to be the better as it stays in the cap, while the cork type has an infuriating habit of either falling out or turning over, so that the foil is against the cap instead of the bottle.

Test tubes and boiling tubes are used for slopes of solid media, volumes of liquid media and suspending fluids. The fact that cotton wool plugs are required, allows for the full circulation of air (filtered free of contaminating organisms by the cotton wool) so enabling the respiration of cultured organisms to proceed naturally.

Aeration flasks (*Figure 97 a* and *b*) have a bubbler or sintered glass disc fitted inside them which is connected to an air supply by glass tubing. Each flask also has a side arm to serve as an air outlet. A sterile cotton wool filter should be attached to the side arm to prevent possible contamination of the media. Alternatively the air can be sterilized by filtration.

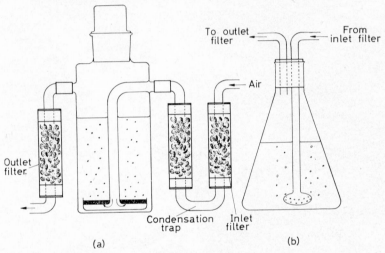

Figure 97. (*a*) *Aeration flask with sintered glass bubbler with appropriate filters connected;* (*b*) *conical flask with an all-glass bubbler*

Petri dishes (generally termed 'plates') are by far the most useful containers for culturing organisms as they give a large surface area for a small volume of media. They consist of two shallow glass dishes, one fitting over the other.

Sterile disposable Petri dishes can be obtained from some manufacturers, e.g. Oxoid Co., Ltd. After use, the dishes are sterilized to kill all cultures grown in them and then disposed of in the normal way. A limited service is also provided of ready poured media in sterile disposable dishes.

In order to keep pace with the work in progress, it is essential to label the plates, tubes, etc., with the culture, type of media, and the date. For this purpose a number of commercial products have been produced.

222

Glassware can be marked permanently by:

(1) Scratching through the glaze of the glass either with a diamond pencil or a glass knife.

(2) Using fusible glazes or dyes, e.g. 'Rejafix'. These need firing for the recommended time at the required temperature.

Temporary marking of glassware and the labelling of Petri dishes can be carried out by using any of the following:

(1) Gummed labels—these are not recommended.

(2) Self-adhesive labels.

(3) Chinagraph wax pencils—a variety of different colours are available.

(4) Felt tipped pens—coloured inks available.

(5) Rapidograph drawing pens.

(6) Indian ink used with an ordinary or a mapping pen.

Non-toxic vegetable and cotton dyes can be incorporated in the medium and used in conjunction with a colour code to denote specific media or solutions. They must not be used where a coloured pigment is likely to be produced by the organism, as the dye may mask the colour; this could lead to false identification and therefore mis-classification.

Freeze-dried cultures (see pp. 282-285) normally have the name of the culture, date and type of medium written on a piece of paper, which is sterilized inside the vial before the culture is added.

STERILIZATION

Any person hoping to produce high quality culture work must fully appreciate all the aspects of sterilization. Sterilization is the killing of all living organisms and their spores, so that there is no fear of the contamination of pure cultures due to unsterile apparatus or media. Although the methods of producing sterile conditions are numerous, all are based on one of the following: heat, either wet or dry; filtration; chemical action; or radiation.

WET HEAT

It should be noted that the sterilization times quoted only apply to the holding period at the specific temperature. The times do not include the warming up or cooling down periods.

The cytoplasm of an organism when in contact with hot water or steam will be coagulated or denatured, thus killing the organism.

The simplest form of wet heat sterilization is carried out by using boiling water. Instruments such as scalpels, needles, agar cutters, dishes, slides, syringes, rubber bungs, and tubing may all be sterilized in this fashion. It is necessary to boil the articles for at least 10 min by which time all vegetative forms, and some, though not all, of the sporing organisms will be dead; some bacterial spores can resist boiling for several hours before they are killed. This method is convenient for quickness (test tubes may be sterilized in this manner if required urgently) or when other methods are not available, but it will not give absolute sterility.

Where hard water is encountered it is advisable to use distilled water, as hard water may leave a deposit of 'fur' on the treated apparatus.

By lowering or raising the pH of the water, the killing time for a specific organism can be shortened.

The apparatus is removed from the boiling water with forceps, so these also must be sterile. The most convenient method is to immerse them in a disinfectant solution (an example of chemical action). If the articles are not used immediately after sterilization, they should be placed in a sterile container. Koch's method of sterilization is carried out in a 'steamer' and can take either of two forms:

(1) Single exposure for 40–70 min.

(2) Intermittent exposure or Tyndallization.

Single exposure—Exposure of unsterile articles to pure steam at 100°C for 40–70 min will kill the majority of organisms. Warming-up periods of 20 min are necessary for small volumes of about 150 ml. Larger volumes, in excess of 4 litres, may require some 50 min to reach a temperature of 100°C.

These times should be added to the exposure times in order to obtain the total period required to achieve sterility. A few of the thermophylic bacteria (i.e. those bacteria which normally grow at temperatures above 50°C) may not be killed by this method but the majority of culturable organisms have an optimum growth temperature of less than 50°C, so incubation at lower temperatures will prevent the growth of the thermophyles.

Intermittent steaming—This method is either called Koch's method of sterilization or Tyndallization. It involves steaming at 100°C for 20–30 min on each of three successive days. The principle of this method is quite simple: steaming on the first day will kill all the vegetative forms of life but not the spores. Before the second day, some of the spores will germinate, producing vegetative forms and these are subsequently killed during the second steaming. The remainder of the spores should germinate before the third steaming when they also will be killed.

This method will kill most of the organisms liable to cause contamination. Some of the anaerobic bacterial spores may not germinate under aerobic conditions, and if the organism to be cultivated requires anaerobic conditions, then contamination may be expected but for normal purposes the media should be sufficiently sterile.

These methods of sterilization are not satisfactory for glassware, etc. Their principle use is for the sterilization of thermolabile substances (i.e. those substances liable to breakdown due to excessive heating), particularly those unstable above 100°C. Gelatine is often sterilized by these methods, as subjection to excessive heat prevents the gelatine setting.

Sterilization by Increased Pressure

At normal atmospheric pressure water will boil and produce steam when it is heated at 100°C. By increasing the pressure, a higher temperature is required to make the water boil, therefore the temperature of the steam produced will be increased.

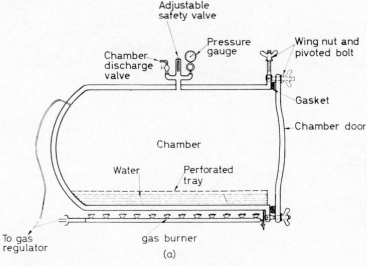

Figure 98. (a) Non-jacketed autoclave (cont.)

Thus a wet heat method of sterilization at a temperature above 100°C is possible. The apparatus used is known as an autoclave which, in the smaller size, resembles a large pressure cooker which itself can be used to sterilize small items. It is important to note that the temperature achieved at a certain pressure depends on the amount of air mixed with the steam. Only pure steam will produce the maximum temperature at a particular pressure.

An autoclave may be simple, steam jacketed, manual or automatic.

Simple autoclave—This consists of a gun-metal cylinder, closed at one end by a hinged door also made of gun-metal. Between the cylinder and the door is a gasket seal, capable of withstanding high temperatures. This cylinder may be in a vertical or a horizontal position (as shown in *Figure 98a*). Inside the barrel is a perforated tray on which the articles to be sterilized are placed. Below this tray, water is boiled by gas or electricity to produce the steam.

Also incorporated in the apparatus is a pressure gauge which measures the pressure in lb./in.^{2} above atmospheric pressure, a steam outlet operated by a tap, and a safety valve that may be pre-set to any safe pressure. Usually, this is regarded as 10°C above the highest pressure required for general use. To use the autoclave the following steps should be carried out.

(1) Check that the volume of water in the autoclave is sufficient.
(2) Check the safety valve setting.
(3) Load the autoclave with the articles to be sterilized.
    These should be sparsely packed to allow for the full circulation of the steam.
(4) Open the steam outlet.
(5) Shut the door and secure it by the bolts. These bolts should be tightened evenly and in order diagonally.
(6) Set the automatic pressure setting, if there is one fitted.
(7) Light the gas or switch on the immersion heater.
(8) Allow the water to boil. Shut the steam outlet when a continuous stream of pure steam is emitted. This can be tested by running a length of tubing from the steam outlet into cold water, the steam will condense, while air will bubble through. When all bubbling has ceased the steam being emitted is pure.
(9) When the required pressure is reached, regulate the amount of heat so that a steady pressure is maintained. (This is unnecessary if an automatic device is fitted). Then start the timing.
(10) When the articles have been at the necessary pressure for the correct length of time, switch off the heat and allow to cool.
(11) When the gauge registers zero, open the steam outlet.

It is dangerous to open the valve before zero is reached. Apart from this, the liquid contents will boil and any cotton wool plugs will be saturated, which means that bacteria can contaminate the medium by gaining entrance through the moisture film.

Also, if a vacuum is allowed to develop and the valve then opened, the sudden inrush of air will cause loose fitting plugs to be forced into the container. Moisture will be removed from the medium if it is kept under vacuum for any length of time.

(12) Allow to cool further before opening the door and removing the now sterile contents. This additional cooling is essential. The pressure in the autoclave may be atmospheric but any bulk liquids will not have had time to cool down to below 100°C and may still be superheated (i.e. having a temperature above 100°C). In this condition a slight knock may cause them to boil.

Some of the later, simple autoclaves are operated by mains steam and this eliminates the need to boil water for the generation of steam.

Steam-jacketed autoclave—It is not practicable to manufacture the simple type of autoclave in large sizes, owing to the loss of heat that occurs from the surface of the autoclave barrel. To overcome this dissipation of heat, large autoclaves have a steam jacket surrounding the barrel (*see Figure 98b*). This jacket is filled with steam at the same

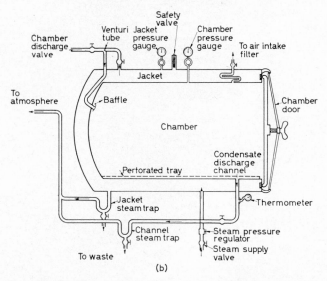

Figure 98. (b) Steam-jacketed autoclave showing a system for vacuum drying

temperature and pressure as the steam in the barrel. These autoclaves are usually operated by mains steam, or by steam generated by means other than in the autoclave itself. The steam lines must have condensation traps fitted to collect condensed steam, thus preventing the steam from becoming waterlogged. As mentioned previously, saturated steam will cause cotton wool plugs to become soaked, thus facilitating the entry of bacteria, etc. Alternatively, steam which is superheated will cause excess evaporation from the media and this will cause the concentration of media constituents.

Generally, steam is allowed to circulate through the jacket continuously and at a predetermined pressure. When the jacket has attained the working temperature, the articles to be sterilized are loaded into the autoclave. The door is then shut, securely locked or bolted into position and the discharge outlet in the bottom of the barrel checked to ensure that it is open. The majority of jacketed autoclaves are automatic in operation and the discharge outlet is thermostatically controlled. It will remain open until the predetermined temperature is reached when it will close. During sterilization, any drop in temperature due to condensation, etc., will cause the outlet to open. This allows the condensation to go to waste and enables fresh steam to enter the barrel so that the required temperature is maintained. Steam is allowed to enter from the jacket via the baffle at the back of the barrel. When the required temperature is reached, the discharge outlet valve will close, and the timing for the holding period is started. At the end of the holding period, the supply of steam to the barrel is stopped thus allowing the temperature to drop. Some of the modern autoclaves have a device built in, which enables sterile air to enter the barrel at a pressure slightly below that of the jacket. This facilitates cooling and prevents the boiling of any liquids. When the pressure becomes atmospheric, the door can be opened and the articles removed.

Material to be autoclaved should be placed in a suitable container, e.g. Petri dish canisters, biscuit tins, etc. If a rigid container is unsuitable the item or items may be wrapped in brown paper, Kraft paper or aluminium foil. Nylon bags are available which may be sealed with autoclavable tape. These bags are impermeable to bacteria, etc. but still allow steam to enter thus ensuring sterility.

TABLE 7

Moist heat		Dry heat	
Temperature	Sterilizing time*	Temperature	Sterilizing time
100°C	20 hours	120°C	8 hours
110°C	2½ hours	140°C	2½ hours
115°C	50 min	160°C	1 hour
121°C	15 min	170°C	40 min
125°C	6½ min	180°C	20 min
130°C	2½ min		

*These times are the minimum sterilizing periods for resistant spores of thermophylic bacteria.
(After Mackie and McCartney, 1960. See Bibliography)

The autoclavable indicator tape serves as a useful guide to ensure that articles have been sterilized. A number of types are available but most show a colour change on exposure to steam above 115°C. The tape may be marked to denote the date, the contents of the container, etc.

It is important to note that stoppers of bottles should be left slightly open, except when very small bottles with small amounts of liquid are used. Cotton wool plugs should be loosely covered with either Kraft paper or aluminium foil to prevent condensation wetting the plugs. As liquids expand when they are heated (e.g. water expands at 40 ml/l. at boiling point) bottles should not be filled to more than 75 per cent of their total volume.

DRY HEAT STERILIZATION

Flaming

Flaming is an essential part of aseptic techniques. It consists of passing the mouths and necks of flasks, tubes and bottles through a bunsen flame until they are hot but not red hot. Slides, cover slips, micro scalpels, cork borers and agar cutters, etc., may also be sterilized by this method.

Red Heat

This involves heating the article until it is red hot. A bunsen burner is the most convenient source of heat. Inoculating needles, scraping wires and points of forceps, etc., are usually sterilized in this way.

Oven

This consists of a thermostatically controlled chamber heated either by electricity or by gas. Ideally, the chamber should be fitted with a fan to enable even distribution of heat. Glassware which is to be sterilized should be perfectly dry, otherwise it is likely to crack in the oven. Wet glassware may be dried in a drying oven at 90–100°C before it is placed in a sterilizing oven. The thermostat is adjusted to the required temperature and the sterilizing oven switched on. The holding period is timed from the moment when the pre-set temperature is attained. For most items, a temperature of 160°C for 1 h is quite sufficient. Some substances, such as oils, fats and powders, take a long time to reach this temperature and it is advisable, therefore, to extend the holding period to 2–3 h.

Flasks, tubes, pipettes and bottles, etc., should be plugged with cotton wool stoppers before sterilization.

Sealed glass vials containing crystals which change colour above a certain temperature are a useful check on whether an article has been efficiently sterilized. They are known as Brown's indicator tubes.

FILTRATION

Sterilization is effected by passing the unsterile liquid through a bacteria-stopping filter. Any bacteria present in the liquid cannot pass through this filter so a sterile filtrate is obtained providing the filter and the receiving vessel are sterile before use. The filters in common use are the Berkefeld, Chamberland, Seitz, Gradacol and various membrane filters.

Berkefeld filters—These are made from kieselguhr and have rather a coarse appearance. They are produced in three grades, V—coarse, N—normal or medium, and W—fine. The filter used for sterilization purposes is V. Although this filter will prevent the passage of bacteria, it will allow the majority of viruses to pass through.

Chamberland filters—These filters are manufactured from unglazed porcelain and will stop all but the smallest viruses from passing through to the filtrate. The grades commonly used are 'L1a' 'L2' and 'L3' which correspond to the Berkefeld V, N and W respectively. The filter L1 (coarse) is often used as a clarifying filter but is of no use for sterilization purposes.

Seitz filters—These filters consist of a metal or glass holder containing a compound asbestos pad. The pads, which are used once and then discarded, are graded as 'Normal K' and 'Special EK'. The Normal K and Special EK pads are bacteria-stopping filters. British pads are now made and are graded as GS (equivalent to EK) and FCB (equivalent to K). These can be obtained from A. Gallenkamp & Co. Ltd.

Membrane filters—These filters are available in a range of pore sizes and are prepared from collodion (Gradacol filters) or cellulose esters (Millipore and Gelman filters). Their construction is such that approximately 80 per cent of the surface consists of uniformly fine pores of the size quoted. Some types are available with grid markings and they can be obtained in disc form to fit special holders similar to Seitz filters. One very useful holder is the syringe adaptor allowing the filtrate to be sterilized. Some grades of membrane filters are marketed in sheet form.

Other filters—The 3/5 grade of sintered glass filter is sometimes used and consists of a fine No. 5 filter supported by a coarser filter No. 3. They are extremely delicate and easily damaged, particularly by extremes of temperature.

Methods of Using Filters (for example Seitz filter)

Negative pressure is usually employed to increase the rate of filtration and this can be effected by using a water or mechanical vacuum pump. The Seitz filter is connected by a rubber bung to a filtration flask, which is a thick-walled conical flask possessing a side arm. A cotton wool filter is attached to the side arm and the whole apparatus wrapped in aluminium foil or Kraft paper. It is then sterilized in an autoclave for 20 min at 20 lb./in.² When required for use, the wrapping is removed and the sterile cotton wool filter attached to the vacuum pump by pressure tubing. The unsterile liquid is poured into the Seitz filter and a slight negative pressure allowed to develop. As filtration proceeds, the negative pressure may be increased but it is not advisable to use a high

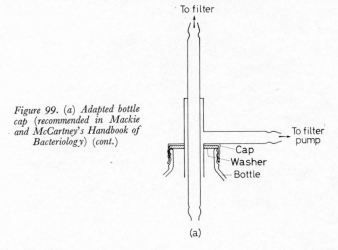

Figure 99. (a) Adapted bottle cap (recommended in Mackie and McCartney's Handbook of Bacteriology) (cont.)

(a)

vacuum, as small particles may be forced into the pores of the filter thus preventing further filtration.

A disadvantage with using a filtration flask as a collection vessel, is that the liquid, after sterilization, has to be transferred to another sterile container for storage. This operation is likely to cause contamination of the filtrate. It may be overcome by adapting a bottle cap.

The adapted cap (*see Figure 99a*) consists of an inner piece of stainless steel tubing, surrounded by an outer jacket also of stainless steel and from this outer jacket projects a side arm. A hole is made in the cap to accommodate the tubing and a rubber washer is fitted inside the cap to ensure a gas-tight seal. The filter is attached to the metal tubing by pressure tubing. This system is very convenient because the large range of screw capped bottles have only a few different sizes of cap. Thus the filter unit may accommodate more than one size of bottle. When the unit is sterilized, prior to use, a number of similar sized caps are sterilized in a plugged glass tube. After filtration, the unit is removed and, after flaming, replaced with a sterile cap.

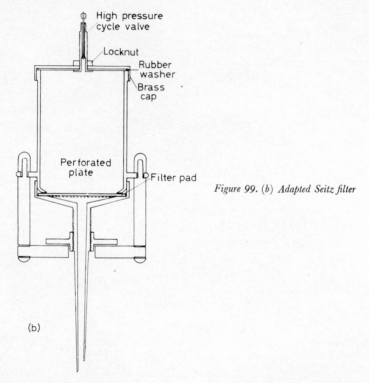

High pressure cycle valve

Locknut

Rubber washer

Brass cap

Perforated plate

Filter pad

Figure 99. (b) Adapted Seitz filter

(b)

A standard metal Seitz filter can be adapted so that it can be used with positive pressure (*see Figure 99b*). A brass ring is sweated on to the upper rim of the filter and then threaded on a lathe. A cap, also made of brass, is fashioned to fit the threaded rim. The centre of the cap is drilled to take a standard high pressure cycle valve which is then bolted into place. A rubber washer inside the cap acts as an air-seal.

To use this filter, the liquid is poured into the top reservoir and the cap screwed into place. A few pumps with a cycle pump is usually sufficient to give a gentle pressure and filtration then takes place. The filtrate is collected in a sterile bottle and then, after removal of the filter, it is stoppered with a sterile screw cap or a sterile cotton wool plug.

CHEMICAL STERILIZATION

The most common method of chemical sterilization is the use of antiseptics such as Lysol or cresol; 3 per cent solutions of these antiseptics are excellent for sterilization purposes. Instruments, used slides, Petri dishes containing cultures, and any other used apparatus may be immersed in these solutions to ensure killing and sterility. Benches may be swabbed down with these solutions either to kill spilt cultures, or to sterilize a bench prior to use, as in an inoculating room or hood.

Chloroform or toluene can be used to keep stock solutions free from contamination. The solution is sterilized by adding chloroform or toluene until a layer approximately $1/4$ in. deep is formed in the bottle. The whole is shaken and then stored. When required for use, the stock solution is added to the media which is then sterilized in the normal way. The heat produced during sterilization will cause the chloroform or toluene to evaporate.

Mercuric chloride in a concentration of 0.1 per cent is occasionally used as a disinfectant but it is more commonly used for the preservation of herbarium material from bacterial, fungal or insect attack.

Aqueous solutions of calcium hypochlorite ($0.5–1$ per cent) can be used to sterilize seeds before sowing. Bryophyte spores, when obtained from a contaminated stock, may also be sterilized in a like manner thus ensuring a pure culture.

Alcohol is not a true sterilizing agent but it is often useful as a quick method of sterilizing inoculating needles, spreaders or scrapers. These instruments are stored in 95 per cent alcohol (95 per cent alcohol has a better killing power than absolute alcohol) and when required for use, the alcohol is burned-off. (Whether the sterilization is due to the heat produced by the burning of the alcohol, or by the storage, is open to question.)

IRRADIATION BY ULTRA-VIOLET LIGHT

Ultra-violet light of a certain wavelength is lethal to living organisms and is used to sterilize air, rooms, hoods or apparatus. It is important to remember that light will only travel in straight lines, therefore the under surfaces of benches, etc., will not be sterilized. An exposure of one hour is usually quite sufficient. Plate glass will absorb u.v. light thus preventing sterilization. The optimum wavelength for killing is 2,600 Å.

A few examples of the methods of sterilizing common articles and substances are given below.

Oils, Fats, Greases

These should be placed in shallow layers in suitable containers, e.g. large conical flasks, and sterilized in an oven at 160°C for 2–3 h. They should not be autoclaved or steamed because they are impervious to moisture, therefore the conditions of moist heat do not apply.

Powders

These should be placed in shallow layers in a similar manner to fats and sterilized at 160°C for 2–3 h. The majority of powders, even if water soluble, will not allow steam to pass through them and in any case powders are usually required dry.

Glassware

Articles may be autoclaved, boiled, steamed, or, when dry, oven sterilized. Petri dishes should be oven sterilized and, if a canister or a biscuit tin is not available, they should be wrapped singly in brown paper or Kraft paper. Pipettes should be plugged at the mouthpiece end and placed in canisters or wrapped in Kraft paper. They should be autoclaved for 30 min at 15 lb./in.^{2} (121°C) or alternatively, they can be placed in an oven at 160°C for 1 h.

Media

If the media is able to withstand the temperature, it should be autoclaved at 121°C for at least 15 min. Some media constituents, e.g. serum, sugars and some vitamins, break down under heat and should therefore be sterilized differently. To prevent caramelization, glucose agar media may be sterilized at a lower pressure of 12 lb./in.^{2} for 15 min or glucose liquid can be filtered through a bacteria stopping filter. Vitamins and serum can also be sterilized by filtration. Gelatine may be sterilized by Tyndallization. Glucose and phosphates must not be autoclaved together, as a complex substance is formed which will precipitate on cooling. If it is essential to use an autoclave, the glucose must be sterilized separately and added to the media afterwards under aseptic conditions.

Dung bottles, for the growth of some fungi, are best autoclaved at 20 lb./in.² pressure for 1 h. This may seem rather a long time but it has been found that these bottles became contaminated within a few days if sterilized for a shorter period at a lower pressure.

Filters

These should be loosely assembled and completely wrapped in foil or Kraft paper before autoclaving for 45 min at 121°C (15 lb./in.²) or 30 min at 20 lb./in.².

MEDIA PREPARATION

All the media constituents should be of an analytical grade. Unless otherwise quoted under the separate media headings, the technique for preparing media is as follows:

Liquid Media

The constituents are dissolved, in the order given, in almost the total volume of distilled water; any pH adjustment is then made by the addition of hydrochloric acid or sodium hydroxide and the volume made up to that specified by the addition of distilled water. The medium is then dispensed, or left as it is in the vessel, and autoclaved at 15 lb./in.² (121°C) for 15 min, unless mentioned otherwise. It can be converted to solid media by the addition of the correct amount of agar or gelatin.

It should be noted that autoclaving may produce a further pH change, therefore it is advisable to check the pH both before and after sterilization. An allowance can then be made in the amount of acid or alkali added before sterilization.

Solid Media

The constituents are dissolved in the order given but in only two-thirds of the total volume of water. The other third of distilled water is used to make up the agar. The agar is heated in a steamer or water bath and, when it has completely dissolved, the other constituents in the remainder of the water are added. After dispensing, the medium is autoclaved as for the liquid medium.

Alternatively, the constituents and then the agar can be added to the distilled water. This mixture is allowed to soak for at least 20 min when it will then be ready for autoclaving. For volumes of media larger than 500 ml (in any one vessel), it is advisable to increase the steaming period when autoclaving. This is to allow the larger volume of liquid to attain the higher temperature more rapidly.

The percentage of agar which is used depends on the quality but it is usually between 1–2 per cent, e.g. Japanese agar–2 per cent, Oxoid Ion agar 0·8–1·0 per cent, Difco Bacto agar 1·0–1·5 per cent. The agar concentrations quoted in the media lists are as for Japanese agar.

Gelatin is rarely used except in some aspects of bacteriological work when it is used in concentrations of 12–20 per cent (15 per cent is most commonly used). Media containing gelatin should be clarified before sterilization by adding a beaten egg white, shaking vigorously and then filtering through paper pulp or a Whatman 541 filter paper.

Dispensing of Media

Small amounts (1–5 ml) can be dispensed by using one of the semi-automatic syringes such as the Record all-glass syringe (manufactured by Chance) which has a removable duo-valve assembly fitted in place of a hypodermic needle. The B.D. Cornwall pipetting outfit is similar and comprises an automatic Luer lok syringe with a duovalve assembly. The piston is spring loaded for automatic return and the volume can be pre-set. The valve assembly allows the liquid, or molten medium, to be sucked into the barrel when the plunger is lifted. On pressing the plunger, the medium is squirted through a nozzle into the test tube. The valve is connected to the source of the medium by polythene, or similar tubing.

For volumes of media in tubes, etc., where accuracy is not required, the media may be dispensed from a large funnel supported in a retort stand. A short length of rubber tubing carrying a glass nozzle is attached to the bottom of the funnel. The medium is poured into the funnel and the flow from the nozzle is regulated by a pinch clip fitted on to the rubber tubing. The medium is dispensed into the tubes to a predetermined mark.

For laboratories where large numbers of tubes of medium are required, it is worthwhile to invest in an automatic filler such as that devised by T. H. Ayling (supplied by R. B. Turner and Co., London or by Astell Laboratory Service Co. Ltd., London, S.E.6). This consists of a 7 in. diameter glass funnel attached to a three-way stopcock by rubber tubing (polythene or silicone tubing may be preferred by some workers, and it is a simple matter to change from the rubber tubing). The stopcock is attached to an all-glass syringe. Syringes of differing capacities are available although the 15 ml by 0·5 ml capacity syringe is the one that is commonly used. The barrel is connected to the stopcock by a metal screw fitting. The plunger is hollow so that it may be lifted by quite low pressures. The syringe and funnel are clamped to a retort stand so that the funnel is about 18 in. higher than the syringe. The medium is placed in the funnel and the stopcock switched to allow the medium to flow into the syringe barrel. As it does so, the plunger is lifted by the medium until it comes in contact with a screw (which is adjustable to allow any volume to fill the syringe). When the syringe barrel is full, the handle of the stopcock is turned and the media delivered into the receptacle by pressure from the weight of the plunger. A motorized and fully automatic form of dispenser is the Griffin Voluspence which has interchangeable syringes giving volumes of 0–1, 0–5 or 0–10 ml. It is manufactured by Griffin and George, Wembley, U.K.

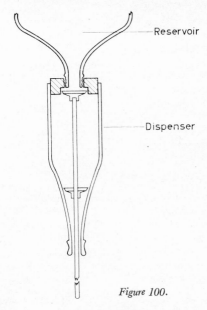

Reservoir

Dispenser

Figure 100.

Larger volumes, e.g. 100 ml, are best measured in a graduated cylinder. G. E. Dunning[1] of the Chemistry Department, University College, London has devised a simple media dispenser with a delivery volume of 100 ml. It consists of a Pepsicola bottle, with its base removed, as a measure and a winchester as a reservoir. A glass rod, two suction pads and a rubber bung complete the apparatus (*Figure 100*). The distance between the pads is adjusted to give the correct volume. Accuracy for 100 ml is ± 1 per cent.

237

Solid media may be allowed to set with the tubes either in a vertical or in a sloped position. Test tubes for 'stab' cultures are filled with solid medium to a depth of about 3 in. and the agar is allowed to set with the tubes in a vertical position. Slopes or slants are formed by placing 5 ml of medium in each standard test tube (15 × 150 mm). The tubes are placed in a sloping position on the bench to produce a large surface area of medium. This is best carried out by supporting the neck of the tubes about 1 in. from the horizontal position. After cooling, the tubes are stored in a vertical position until they are required. This is to stop any condensation from flowing along the tube to the plug, which, if it is allowed to become damp, will considerably increase the chance of contamination.

Penicillin flasks or Roux bottles can be used to produce agar 'slopes' having a very large surface area. They are mainly used when large amounts of culture or spores are required.

Solid media for plates are dispensed in volumes up to 500 ml, preferably in stoppered media bottles, although conical flasks, stoppered with cotton wool plugs, may be used if the medium is to be used shortly after sterilization.

Cotton Wool Plugs

The making of cotton wool plugs is a laborious task and one that is often skimped. However, if the plugs are firm and well made they can be used more than once. Non-absorbent cotton wool should be used, as it does not become so damp during autoclaving. Wet plugs are one of the commonest causes of contamination because bacteria are able to move through the moisture film and reach the medium. There are two good methods of making plugs. The first is convenient for plugs less than 25 mm diameter. The second method is quicker but is only really suitable for plugs over 25 mm diameter.

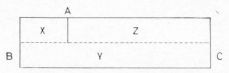

Figure 101. Plan for making a cotton wool plug

A thin strip of the cotton wool, twice as wide and about eight times as long as the required plug, is torn off the roll. The thickness of the last part of the strip should taper to nothing; the reason for this will become apparent during the actual making of a plug. As shown in *Figure 101* a tear is made down the line A, and X is folded on to Y. Beginning at B, the cotton wool is rolled tightly towards C, until just past A. Z is then folded on to Y and rolling continued towards C. Any rough edges can be neatened by folding them in towards the centre of the plug. The taper in thickness at C, allows the last strands of cotton wool to blend into the plug, thus preventing the wool from unrolling. Experience is required in order to judge the thickness of the cotton wool required for different sizes of plugs.

The second method begins in the same way. The strip of cotton wool is prepared as before and then rolled towards the taper; this rolling should not be too tight. The wool is blended as before so that the roll is twice the length of the plug required. The roll is then folded in half and inserted into the flask or tube.

Some machines are available which automatically plug test tubes with cotton wool string. Upwards of 2,000 tubes per hour can be plugged if all the tubes are of a standard size.

Caps

Pressed anodized aluminium caps are available from a number of manufacturers, e.g. Oxoid Co., Ltd., and can be obtained in a variety of colours and sizes. Although suitable for short term work, the seal to the tube is not good enough to prevent the evaporation of water from the medium.

Rubber caps of the Subaseal type may be used but owing to their impervious nature tend to allow toxic by-products of respiration to accumulate to an inhibitory level.

Polyurethane Foam Plugs

Some laboratory suppliers stock plugs constructed from foam polyurethane. They can be autoclaved for a limited number of times and can be obtained in a number of different sizes and colours. The cost of these plugs is very reasonable.

Types of Media

Specifications for various media are given in the following pages and Table 8 gives a summary of the type of media and temperature required for different organisms.

Natural Media—Under suitable conditions some organisms will develop on almost any foodstuff or liquid if exposed to the atmosphere.

Damp bread, rotten apples, beetroot and cheese will almost certainly produce the growths of some fungi, e.g. *Mucor*, *Rhizopus*, *Aspergillus* and *Penicillium*.

239

A few algae, generally single-celled flagellates, will develop in tap water if left in a suitable light.

Bacteria abound on all substances but not normally in a form visible to the naked eye.

TABLE 8

Organism	Media	Temperature
Bacteria		
Cocci	Nutrient broth/agar	37°
Staphylococci	Nutrient broth/agar, Blood agar	37°
Streptococci	Nutrient broth/agar, Blood agar	37°
Salmonella	Nutrient broth/agar	37°
Coliforms	Nutrient broth/agar	37°
Algae		
Chlorophyceae	Soil extract+mineral salt solution; also solid media	15–18°
Cyanophyceae	Nitrogen free media	15–18°
	Nitrogen fixing media	
Pteridophytes	Moore's Medium	15–18°
Fungi		
Phycomycetes	Potato, prune, malt Y.P.S.S., etc.	28–30°
Ascomycetes	Cellulose, oatmeal, malt, Y.P.S.S., etc.	24°
Basidiomycetes	Malt agar, Y.P.S.S., dung	25–37°
Fungi Imperfecti	Oatmeal, malt, Y.P.S.S., etc.	25–37°
Yeast	Y.E.P. Pasteur solution	25°

N.B. It must be noted that not all the organisms are able to grow on all the media quoted.

PTERIDOPHYTE MEDIA

Moore's Medium (modified by P. R. Bell. U.C. London)

Ammonium nitrate	0·5	g
Magnesium sulphate	0·2	g
Potassium phosphate (K_2HPO_4)	0·2	g
Calcium chloride	0·1	g
Ribose	0·01	g
Glass-distilled water	to 1000	ml
Ferric citrate solution (0·1 g/100 ml)	2·0	ml
Trace element solution	1·0–2·0	ml

Solidified by addition of 1·5 per cent Difco Bacto agar.

ALGAL MEDIA

Chu No. 10

Calcium nitrate $(Ca(NO_3)_2)$	0·04	g
Potassium phosphate (K_2HPO_4)	0·01 or 0·005	g
Magnesium sulphate $(MgSO_4.7H_2O)$	0·025	g
Sodium carbonate (Na_2CO_3)	0·02	g
Sodium silicate $(NaSiO_3)$	0·025	g
Ferric chloride $(FeCl_3)$	0·0008	g
Glass-distilled water	to 1000	ml

Plus trace elements if required.

Benecke's Solution

Calcium nitrate	0·5 g
Magnesium sulphate	0·1 g
Potassium phosphate (KH_2PO_4)	0·2 g
Ferric chloride	Trace only
Glass-distilled water	to 1000 ml

Kratz and Myer's Medium
(For non-nitrogen fixing Cyanophyceae)

Sodium citrate	0·2	g
Ferric sulphate	0·005	g
Magnesium sulphate	0·25	g
Potassium nitrate	1·0	g
Calcium nitrate	0·025	g
Potassium phosphate (K_2HPO_4)	1·0	g
Glass-distilled water	to 1000	ml

Plus trace elements if required.

Allen and Arnold's Medium
(For nitrogen-fixing algae—e.g. Anabaena)

Magnesium sulphate $(MgSO_4.7H_2O)$	0·0246 g
Calcium chloride	0·0554 g
Sodium chloride	0·2360 g
Potassium phosphate (K_2HPO_4)	0·3482 g
Glass-distilled water	to 1000 ml

Knop's Solution (modified)

Potassium nitrate	0·01	g
Calcium nitrate	0·001	g
Potassium phosphate (K_2HPO_4)	0·002	g
Magnesium sulphate	0·001	g
Ferric chloride	0·00001	g
Glass-distilled water	to 1000	ml

Plus trace elements if required.

Soil Extract

Garden soil (not clay)	**500 g**
Tap water	1000 ml

The mixture is autoclaved at 15 lb./in.^{2} for 2 h, cooled and allowed to settle. It is then decanted and filtered until clear. This is the stock solution.

The stock solution is diluted with glass-distilled water to give concentrations of from 5 to 35 per cent. To each dilution 1 ml of a 5 per cent solution of aqueous potassium nitrate is added to each 100 ml of liquid.

PUTREFACTION MEDIA

From 1 to 5 wheat or barley grains are placed in a test tube and covered with soil to a depth of 3–5 cm. Tap water is added to within 4 cm of the rim of the tube which is plugged with cotton wool, placed in a cold steam chamber and the temperature increased to 100°C. This is kept at boiling point for at least 3 h, then allowed to cool. Inoculation can be carried out any time from 1 to 10 days.

Foyen's Erd-Schreiber Marine Medium (1934)

Sodium nitrate	0·001 g	
di-Sodium hydrogen phosphate (Na$_2$HPO$_4$)	0·002 g	
Soil extract	5·0	ml
Sea water	100	ml

Artificial Sea Water

Sodium chloride	0·3	g
Magnesium chloride	0·04	g
Potassium chloride	0·1	g
Magnesium sulphate	0·05	g
Calcium sulphate	0·01	g
Sodium nitrate	0·001	g
Potassium phosphate	0·0001	g
Tap water	1000	ml

If glass-distilled water is used a little calcium carbonate should be added.

Trace Element Solution (Hoagland and Snyder A–Z sol.)

Lithium chloride	0·0278 g
Copper sulphate	0·0556 g
Zinc sulphate	0·0556 g
Boric acid	0·6110 g
Aluminium sulphate	0·0556 g
Stannous chloride	0·0278 g
Manganese chloride	0·3889 g
Nickel sulphate	0·0556 g
Cobalt nitrate	0·0556 g
Titanium oxide	0·0556 g
Potassium iodide	0·0278 g
Potassium bromide	0·0278 g
Glass-distilled water	1000 ml

When required add 1 ml of this solution to 1 litre of medium.

FUNGAL MEDIA

Prune Agar

About 25 prunes are boiled for 1 h in less than 1 litre of water. The liquid is poured off and made up to 1,000 ml with distilled water. After adding 25 g of agar and heating in a water bath until melted, it is filtered and autoclaved.

Potato Agar

250 g of peeled potatoes are chopped into small pieces and gently boiled in water for 30 min. This is allowed to cool and settle, then the fluid is decanted and the supernatant made up to 1000 ml. 25 g of agar is added, dissolved and then autoclaved.

Corn Meal Agar

Corn (maize) meal	300·0 g
Distilled water	1000 ml

The mixture is boiled for 15 min, the supernatant decanted, 2 per cent agar added and autoclaved (pH 6·8).

Malt Agar

Malt extract ('treacle' or powder)	20·0 g
Agar	15·0 or 20·0 g
Distilled water	1000 ml

The malt is dissolved in some of the water, and the agar in the remainder. When melted, it is mixed and autoclaved. (pH 5·4 approximately.)

Dung Agar

About 500 g of partially dried horse, cow or rabbit dung is soaked in cold water for 3 days. The supernatant is decanted and diluted to a straw colour before adding 2 per cent agar and autoclaving.

Brown's Agar

D. Glucose	2·0	g
L-Asparagine	2·0	g
Potassium phosphate (K_3PO_4)	1·23	g
Magnesium sulphate	0·75	g
Agar	15·0	g
Distilled water	to 1000	ml

Barnes' Agar

Potassium phosphate	1·0 g
Ammonium nitrate	1·0 g
Potassium nitrate	1·0 g
Glucose	1·0 g
Agar	25·0 g
Distilled water	to 1000 ml

Czapek-Dox Agar

Sucrose (glucose for Mucoraceae)	30·0 g
Sodium nitrate	2·0 g
Potassium phosphate (K_2HPO_4)	1·0 g
Magnesium sulphate	0·5 g
Potassium chloride	0·5 g
Ferrous sulphate	0·01 g
Agar	15·0 g
Distilled water	to 1000 ml

Pasteur's Solution—modified

Potassium phosphate (KH_2PO_4)	1·0 g
Calcium phosphate ($CaHPO_4$)	0·1 g
Magnesium sulphate	0·1 g
Ammonia tartrate	5·0 g
Glucose	75·0 g
Distilled water	to 1000 ml

Shaker's Medium

Yeast extract	10·0 g
Peptone (Commercial bacteriological)	20·0 g
Glucose	20·0 g
Distilled water	to 1000 ml

Can be solidified by addition of 15–20·0 g agar. This does not require any pH adjustment.

Vegetable Juice Agar

Vegetable juice V.8. Dilute by 66 per cent with distilled water. Add 1·5 per cent agar and sterilize by autoclaving.

Oatmeal Medium

Porridge oats	60·0 g
Distilled water	1000 ml

The mixture is autoclaved for 15 min at 5 lb./in.². It is then filtered through a fine metal sieve and the supernatant made up to 1000 ml. 1·5 per cent agar is added and sterilized by autoclaving for 25 min at 15 lb./in.².

Wheat Grain Medium

Boiled half wheat grains in a dish containing 2–3 in. of boiled sterile water serve as a suitable medium for some of the water fungi, e.g. Saprolegniaceae.

Boiled wheat grains can be stored in 30 per cent alcohol until required but should be washed well before use.

An infected wheat grain is a suitable inoculum.

Cellulose Yeast Extract Medium

Yeast extract	4·0 g
Macerated filter paper	12·0 g
Agar	24·0 g
Tap water	1000 ml

Y.P.S.S. Medium

Yeast extract	4·0 g
Soluble starch	15·0 g
Potassium phosphate (K_2HPO_4)	1·0 g
Magnesium sulphate	0·5 g
Agar	20·0 g
Distilled water	1000 ml

Y.E.P. Medium

Glucose	20·0 g
Yeast extract	10·0 g
Peptone (Bacto)	20·0 g
Distilled Water to	1000 ml
Add Agar for solid medium	15–20 g

BACTERIAL MEDIA

Hay infusion Broth

This broth normally yields a culture of *Bacillus subtilis*, although other organisms will be present.

Pour hot water on to chopped hay, then filter through muslin and cover the liquor to exclude dust. Leave at room temperature until turbidity denotes a bacterial population.

Nutrient Broth

Commercial bacteriological peptone	10·0 g
Meat extract (Lab–Lemco)	10·0 g
Sodium chloride	5·0 g
Tap water	1000 ml

Solution can be aided by brief heating in a water bath or steamer. It should be cooled and the pH adjusted to 7·2–7·4. It can then be filtered if required.

Nutrient Agar

Nutrient broth	1000·0 ml
Agar	20·0 g

Nutrient Gelatin

Nutrient broth	1000·0 ml
Gelatin	150·0 g

Blood Agar and Serum Agar

Nutrient agar is melted and cooled to 55°C ready for pouring into plates. To this is added 5–10 per cent sterile blood (normally horse blood) or 10 per cent sterile uncoagulated serum.

MacConkey's Bile-Salt Neutral Red Lactose Agar

Peptone (commercial)	20·0 g
Sodium taurocholate (commercial)	5·0 g
Tap water	900 ml
Agar	20·0 g

Heat may be required to dissolve the first two constituents. When they have dissolved, the agar should be added and dissolved in a water bath, steamer or autoclave. It should then be filtered or the white of an egg used to clear the medium. After adjusting to pH 7·5 approximately 7·0 ml of fresh 1 per cent aqueous solution of neutral red indicator should be added. The medium should become reddish-brown. (If pink, sodium hydroxide should be added until the colour changes.) It is then sterilized by steaming, cooled and 100 ml of a sterile 10 per cent aqueous solution of lactose added before sterilizing by intermittent steaming (Koch's method of sterilization).

READY PREPARED MEDIA

Some companies, such as Oxoid, produce ready prepared media and dehydrated media. These are very useful when only small volumes of media are required. For bulk media, the cost may be too high.

Instructions for preparing the media are supplied on request by the manufacturers.

BIBLIOGRAPHY

REFERENCE

[1]Dunning, G. E. (1965). 'A Suitable Liquid Dispenser.' *J. Sci. Technol.* **11**, 28–30

BIBLIOGRAPHY

Bernhardt, E. (1946). 'Time Saving in the Preparation of Corn-meal Agar and in the Identification of Yeast-like Fungi.' *Mycologia* **38**, 228

Bold, H. C. (1942). 'The Cultivation of Algae.' *Bot. Rev.* **8**, 69-139

Grossowicz, N. and Kaplan, D. (1946). 'Chemical Sterilization of Bacteriological Media by Means of Mercuric Oxycyanide and the Subsequent Inactivation of the Mercury by Thioglycolate.' *Science* **105**, 237

Mackie and McCartney (1960). *Handbook of Bacteriology*, 10th ed. Ed. by R. Cruickshank. Edinburgh; Livingstone

MacLean, R. C. and Cook, W. R. I. (1958). *Plant Science Formulae.* London; Macmillan

Pringsheim, E. G. (1946). *Pure Cultures of the Algae*, 1st ed. Cambridge; University Press

— (1961). *The Oxoid Manual*, 2nd ed. London; Oxo Ltd.

Snyder, W. C. and Hansen, H. N. (1946). 'Control of Culture Mites by Cigarette Paper Barriers.' *Mycologia* **38**, 455

CHAPTER 10

CULTURE TECHNIQUES

PREPARATION

POURING OF MEDIA FOR GENERAL USE

Ideally, solid media should be poured immediately after sterilization, although bulk media in flasks may be stored for short periods provided that the cotton wool plugs are covered with sterile Kraft paper or foil. Media in bottles may be stored for several months if the screw caps are screwed down tightly.

(a)

Figure 102. Pouring medium: (a) unscrewing the bottle cap with the little finger of the right hand (cont.)

Solid media that has been stored should be heated in a water bath at 100°C until the agar becomes molten. The temperature should be

allowed to drop to 45°C before pouring to reduce excessive condensation. (Molten agar begins to set at about 39°C but after solidifying
will remain solid to about 85°C.) Media which are to be poured
immediately after autoclaving should likewise be allowed to cool to
45°C. To pour into plates, the following procedure should be adopted.
The u.v. lamp in the inoculating chamber is switched on for 20 min
prior to use in order to sterilize the bench top and the air. If an
inoculating chamber is not available, the bench top must be wiped
over with a damp cloth or with 95 per cent alcohol to remove any

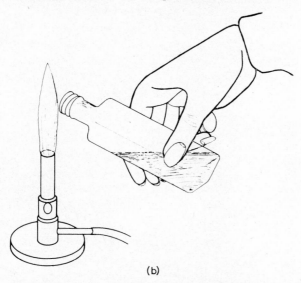

(b)

*Figure 102. (b) Flaming the neck of the bottle—note the bottle cap still held by the
little finger (cont.)*

dust, etc. The plates can be arranged singly or in stacks of three. The
stopper is removed from the media container with the little finger of
the right hand (for a right-handed person) and the container transferred to the same hand after passing the neck and mouth through
the bunsen flame. The lid of the dish is lifted on one side sufficiently
to admit the mouth of the container and then the required volume of
medium is poured into the plate (*see Figure 102*). The lid is replaced
immediately. When dealing with plates in stacks of three (or four
depending upon the size of the hand), the left hand is placed over the
pile so as to grip the lid of the bottom dish and also to hold the upper
plates. The medium is poured and the lid replaced. The lid of the

middle dish is lifted with the top plate and so on until the stack is completed. Care must be taken to ensure that only the lid of a plate is lifted. Occasionally, a base sticks in the lid, with the result that the

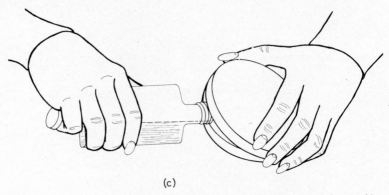

(c)

Figure 102. (c) The lid of the plate is lifted sufficiently to allow the medium to be poured into the Petri dish

medium is poured on the lid of the dish beneath. The stacks of plates should be labelled and it is a good plan to label the top plate of each pile immediately after pouring.

Layer Plates

These are plates containing two different media, one super-imposed upon the other (*see Figure 103a*).

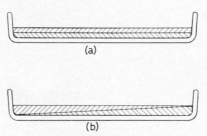

Figure 103. (a) Section through a layer plate; (b) section through a gradient plate

The first medium is poured and allowed to cool. When this has set, the second layer is poured over the first. The plate is then labelled (e.g. X over Y).

250

Gradient Plates

These are similar to layer plates but each layer has a tapered thickness thus producing a gradient of concentration of, for example, an antibiotic. A measured volume of medium (generally an aliquot of 10 ml) in a test tube or bottle is poured into a plate which is inclined until one side of the medium is just touching the edge of the dish. The plate is left in this position to cool. When the medium has set, the dish is placed on a flat surface and a similar measured volume of the second medium is poured on the first one at the 'thin side' (*see Figure 103b*). When this has set also, the plate should be clearly labelled to denote the position of the gradient (not on the lid of the dish but on the bottom). It is useful to incorporate an artificial dye into one of the media as this will show the gradient quite clearly.

Assay Plates

For antibiotics or drug assay, the plates of media are poured as for normal plates. However, dishes for antigen–antibody reactions, such as testing the specificity of pollens against known antisera, must contain a perfectly clear agar so that precipitation bands will be seen clearly. Agar may be cleared in the following way[1].

A 1 per cent agar suspension is made up and melted to obtain even mixing by heating in a water bath at 100°C. When molten, 1 per cent sodium azide is added followed by 0·75 per cent of a mixture of equal parts bentonite and Celite 'Hyflo-Super Cel'. This should be shaken vigorously. A constant temperature of 60°C should be maintained overnight in order to allow the clearing agents to settle. The following morning the mixture is re-suspended by gentle inversion and allowed to settle. When the mixture has cleared, the agar is decanted and filtered through a Whatman's No. 541 filter paper. This is hastened if the temperature of the agar is brought to 100°C in a water bath prior to filtering. It is advisable to filter the agar in a steamer.

Drying of Plates

When suspensions are to be plated out, the media must be 'dried' so as to absorb any fluid. Plates may be dried by placing the lid, face down, on an incubator shelf and inverting the dish so that it 'leans' on the lid (*see Figure 104*). The incubator is set at a temperature of between 37°C and 55°C and must not have a fan working as the air currents are likely to carry dust particles on to the surface of the drying plates, thus causing contamination of the medium. A plate is 'dry' when the surface appears matt instead of shiny and this usually takes about 2 h at 37°C or 45 min at 55°C.

Figure 104. Drying a plate

INOCULATION

Needles

A comprehensive selection of needles should be available so that a variety of different inoculations can be made with the minimum of bother.

Wire loops are made of Nichrome or Eureka wire of No. 24 s.w.g. A length of wire about 3 in. long is fashioned into a loop which has an internal diameter of 2–4 mm at one end. The other end is inserted into a holder. This can be done by fusing the end of the wire into a glass rod, or by clamping it into a metal holder with a screw grip at the end.

A straight wire is made from the same material as the loop and can be about 3 in. in length. Occasionally, a straight wire about 5 in. long is useful and, in this case, a thicker wire will give more rigidity.

For lighter work, particularly for inoculating fungi, a needle made from 0·3 mm tungsten wire is useful. This wire is inserted into a slit cut in the end of a length of aluminium welding rod. The needle should not be longer than 1¹/₂ in. otherwise it will be too flexible. It may be sharpened to a point by placing the end, at an oblique angle, into molten sodium nitrite contained in an old tin lid. This is placed on a tripod over a bunsen. Care should be taken to ensure that the wire does not become red-hot, or the reaction will become too rapid. When a successful point has been obtained, the excess nitrite must be removed from the needle, otherwise the beads of nitrite will dissolve the tungsten wire when it is passed through a bunsen flame. *Figure 105* shows various types of inoculating tools.

Pipettes

Graduated pipettes of 1, 2, 5, 10, and 25 ml capacity are commonly used for inoculation purposes. These should be made of hard glass, such as Pyrex, so that they may be sterilized repeatedly by dry heat.

Pasteur, or capillary pipettes are very useful in pure culture techniques and can be made from 6 in. lengths of glass tubing having an internal diameter of 4–5 mm. These lengths are plugged at each end with non-absorbent cotton wool, bundled together and wrapped

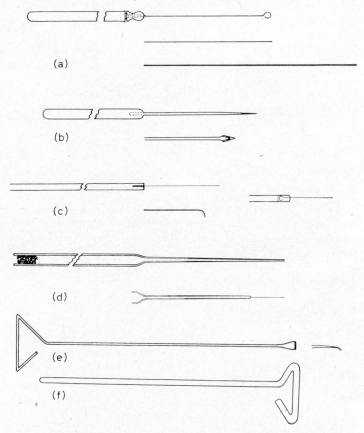

Figure 105. Inoculating tools: (a) metal holder with a loop, straight wire and 'deep-stab' wire; (b) wooden holder with ordinary dissecting needle and microscalpel; (c) aluminium rod with tungsten needles; (d) Pasteur pipettes; (e) scraping wire (Nichrome); (f) glass spreader

in foil or Kraft paper before autoclaving at 15 lb./in.^{2} for 20 min. When required for use, a length of the sterile tubing is removed from the wrapping and rotated in the flame of a small fish-tail or a bats-wing burner until it is 'floppy', when the two ends are pulled apart.

If pulled apart immediately after heating, a very narrow thin-walled pipette is obtained. However, if a few seconds elapse before pulling, a wider capillary is formed which has thicker walls. With practice, pipettes can be made which have different capillary sizes and wall thicknesses. To part the two pipettes formed in this manner, the capillary is heated in the middle and sealed. When needed the sealed tip is broken off and lightly flamed.

Alternatively, these pipettes may be made from unsterilized tubing and placed in a glass tube or a pipette canister and then autoclaved.

When a very narrow capillary is required, one of the Pasteur pipettes is reheated and drawn out to the desired size.

Miscellaneous

All types of metal dissecting scalpels and needles are useful for cutting tenacious cultures.

Haemacytometers

In some aspects of culture work, such as the preparation of suspensions for dilution and plating, it is essential to know the number of organisms/ml of suspension. Suspensions can be counted on a special slide called a haemacytometer. As its name implies, the special

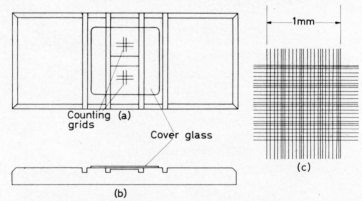

Figure 106. (a) Plan of a double-celled haemacytometer; (b) side view; (c) grid

slide was first devised for counting blood cells. The Thoma or Neubauer slide is commonly used and consists of a chamber exactly 0·1 mm deep. In this is engraved a 1 mm square sub-divided into 16 main squares, each of which is further divided into 25 smaller squares (*see Figure 106*). Thus each haemacytometer grid is 0·1 mm deep and has 400 small squares contained in 1 mm².

To use the haemacytometer, a drop of suspension is placed on the grid and the special cover glass placed into position, ensuring that no air bubbles are trapped between the grid and the cover glass. The cover glass is slid backwards and forwards until coloured rings are seen between the slide and the cover glass. These rings (Newton's rings) occur when two surfaces are in very close contact. The num-

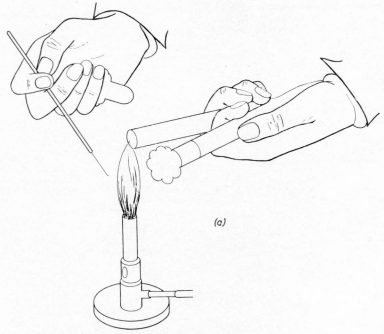

Figure 107.'Subbing' from tube to tube: (a) flaming of needle and the mouth of the old tube (note that the cotton wool plug is held by the little finger of the right hand) (cont.)

ber of cells covering the grid are then counted. To calculate the number of cells/ml, the number of cells present on the grid is multiplied by a factor of 10,000 (10^4). This factor is the number of grids in one ml. As the grid is 0·1 mm deep, 10 of these are required to make 1 mm³, but there are 1,000 mm³ in one ml, therefore 1 mm³ × 1,000 = 1 ml. Thus the grid × 10 × 1,000 (i.e. 10^4) gives the number of cells/ml.

The Fuchs Rosenthal haemacytometers are also available which have a total grid area of 16 mm² and a grid depth of 0·2 mm. Each millimetre square is divided into 16 smaller squares. All that is necessary to obtain the number of cells in one ml is to count the 16 small squares of 1 mm², multiply by 5 to convert to 1 mm³ followed by a further multiplication by 1,000.

SUB-CULTURING

Sub-culturing, or 'subbing', is a method of transferring a culture from one medium to another. Cultures in general use are kept on slopes or on plates of medium and should be subbed regularly to prevent depletion of the medium constituents. The task of subbing, particularly from one tube to another, can be difficult for the inexperienced but the following schedule should be a useful guide.

The old tube is held between the second and third fingers of the left hand with the palm uppermost and the bottom of the tube supported by the palm of the hand. The tube of fresh medium is similarly held but between the thumb and first finger (*see Figure 107a*). The needle is held in the right hand.

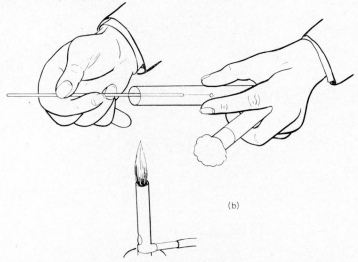

(b)

Figure 107. (b) The left hand has been rotated through 90 degrees—the inoculum is being placed in the fresh tube

The needle, or loop, and as much of the holder as is possible, is flamed in a bunsen. The plug of the old tube is removed by the little finger of the right hand and the mouth of the tube lightly flamed, care being taken to prevent the plug in the other tube from catching alight. The cool sterile needle is lowered immediately into the tube and an inoculum removed. After removal of the inoculum from the tube, the latter is again flamed and the plug replaced. If the hand is rotated through 90 degrees, the tube of fresh medium becomes accessible. The plug is removed as before, the tube flamed and the inoculum carefully placed on the surface of the medium. After withdrawal of the needle, the tube is flamed and the plug replaced.

The inoculum depends on the type of organism and can be any of the following: asexual spores, an agar block containing actively growing cells, or cells picked, or scraped, from the surface of the culture. It is important not to forget to label the fresh slope or plate with the name of the culture, type of medium and the date of inoculation.

Inoculation of dung bottles is carried out by using either the heterokaryon derived from the mated cultures or by a suspension of sexual spores.

PTERIDOPHYTES

Any organism collected from the wild will be contaminated with bacteria and fungi, etc. It is essential, therefore, to obtain the required organism in pure culture.

PURE CULTURE

Pteridophytes are best collected as spores, as this increases the chances of obtaining a pure culture. The spores should be collected aseptically and placed in a sterile centrifuge tube containing a sterile solution of a wetting agent at a concentration of 10^{-5}. Tween 80 (manufactured by Shell Chemical Co. Ltd.) is a good wetting agent, as it helps the spore to absorb moisture by lowering the surface tension of the suspending fluid. The spores are centrifuged, the supernatant removed and replaced by tap water, which is allowed to remain overnight. This time lapse allows any fungal spores to germinate and the fern spores to be coated with a thin layer of calcium carbonate. This coating protects the spores in subsequent operations. The following morning the suspension is centrifuged and the supernatant is again removed. The spores are now treated with a $0 \cdot 5$–$1 \cdot 0$ per cent solution of calcium hypochlorite (bleach), which kills the germinated fungal spores and most of the bacterial contaminants. After 5 min, the treated spores are washed in sterile tap water and then in sterile distilled water by centrifugation. The sterile spores are plated on to solid Moore's medium (see p. 240) in Petri dishes and are then incubated. Incubation can take place, at room temperature, under a bank of six fluorescent tubes.

When the spores have germinated and have produced the fern prothalli, these can be isolated. A small piece of the medium containing the prothallus is removed with a sterile needle, and transferred to a slope of Moore's medium. The cotton wool plugs of the individual tubes should be covered with pieces of polythene sheet, secured with elastic bands. These polythene caps help to prevent loss of moisture from the medium while still allowing the passage of air.

The tubes are best laid in racks with the flat surface of the slope uppermost and incubated as previously mentioned.

The growth of the fern prothalli provides a useful source of photosynthetic differentiated tissue.

Mature ferns are not normally grown in the laboratory under strict pure culture conditions and therefore do not come into the scope of this chapter.

ALGAE

In many aspects of algal work, a pure culture is unnecessary and therefore a certain amount of tedious work can be avoided. It is essential, however, to have an unialgal culture. This is a culture consisting of a single species of alga and is a useful starting point from which to obtain a pure culture. Unialgal cultures are also known as preparative cultures. They are not necessarily free from bacteria.

PREPARATIVE CULTURES

During the greater part of their life history, algae are contaminated by adhering bacteria. The preparative culture is used to enable the alga to establish itself in a medium that is unfavourable to bacteria. Thus the high ratio of bacteria to alga is reversed.

The majority of the common algae, such as are used in schools, colleges, etc., for demonstration purposes, may be obtained from one of the supply units. These cultures can be regarded as preparative cultures. If a specific alga is not available from these sources it will have to be obtained either from a research group using the organism, or from the wild. Isolating a species of alga from the wild poses a number of problems, particularly if the organism only grows in small numbers. It is essential to know the following information before a successful search can be attempted; its habitat, morphology, and, to a lesser degree, its physiology. Having selected a hopeful area and collected the normally prolific algal flora by means of glass hooks, fine mesh nets, etc., the next step is to attempt cultivation. It is advisable to inoculate a number of different media, preferably inorganic media, so as to give the required alga the greatest chance to grow. After inoculation, the media should be incubated under conditions that are favourable to the particular organism. If it is suspected that the latter requires organic substances, in addition to the basic inorganic medium, then either a soil and water medium or a putrefaction medium can be used. Alternatively, a basic inorganic medium can be supplemented with an organic material such as cheese, malt extract, peptone, etc. Primary inoculation is best carried out in a liquid medium. After suitable incubation and microscopic examination, the alga may be isolated by plating and dilution techniques.

Plating Technique

A solid medium which is suitable for the specific alga is prepared and held at a temperature of 45°C prior to pouring. It is best contained, in a sterile condition, in plugged test tubes as aliquots of 10 ml into which 1 ml of the liquid culture is pipetted. The medium is then shaken and poured into a sterile Petri dish. If the liquid culture is very densely populated, it is advisable to dilute the culture to such a degree that the individual organisms are sufficiently separated to ensure that an isolated colony is formed. When sufficient growth has occurred to enable the colony to be easily visible to the eye, it can be carefully removed by cutting it out of the agar and transferring it to fresh medium.

Dilution Technique

This is an adaptation of the bacteriological technique whereby a known volume of liquid contains a known number of cells; for example, a suspension of individual cells may be counted on a haemacytometer slide (see p. 254) and the number of cells/ml calculated.

If the suspension contained 10^6 cells/ml and this is diluted by one-tenth (1 ml of suspension plus 9 ml of water, or 1 drop of suspension plus 9 drops of water), it will result in the new suspension containing 10^5 cells/ml; similarly, a hundredth dilution (1:99) of the second suspension will produce a suspension having 10^3 cells/ml.

When diluting a suspension of algae, a complication occurs, because not all algae exist in a unicellular state. Vigorous shaking of a filamentous alga results in the production of a number of fragments and it is these fragments that are counted with any individual cells that are present. The idea is to produce a suspension so that a certain volume (ideally less than 1 ml but more than 0·2 ml) contains very few algal cells and fragments, preferably only one cell or fragment. This predetermined volume is then pipetted into a tube of liquid medium. It is essential to set up a large number of tubes, as some tubes will not contain any algal cells while others will have more than one.

Dilution, in conjunction with centrifugation, is a useful method of reducing the bacterial population. This is very important in the plating technique and is a good example of combining techniques to overcome some culture problems. If a suspension which is to be used for plating has a bacterial population far in excess of the algal population, it is essential to reduce the number of bacteria so that the algae have a chance to grow without too much competition from the unwanted bacteria. The method is as follows. The laws regarding the settling rate of a particle, state that a particle which is larger and denser than another will settle at a faster rate. This principle can be used to separate algae and bacteria. The suspension of algae and bacteria is poured into a sterile centrifuge tube and lightly centrifuged so that the algae settle and the bacteria remain in suspension. The supernatant is removed with a sterile Pasteur pipette and discarded. Sterile water is added to the precipitate and well mixed by shaking. The operation is then repeated some three or four times before plating in the usual way. It is essential to use a sterile Pasteur pipette each time the supernatant is removed.

It is as well to note that some of the flagellates, which are classified with the algae, cannot exist in a healthy state in the absence of bacteria.

PURE CULTURES

Having established a unialgal culture, the next step is to obtain the alga in a bacteria-free state, thus producing a true, pure culture.

The majority of workers have evolved their own techniques for the purification of algal cultures but these are generally adaptations of the following methods.

Plating

This technique was discussed in the preceding section but, as such, has only a limited application. Variations can widen the scope quite considerably. The great disadvantage of mixing the culture with the agar is that not all algae are able to grow below the agar surface, probably due to the lack of available CO_2. By plating the organisms on to the surface of the agar, where CO_2 is available from the atmosphere, more algae are likely to grow. Any bacteria which are present in the algal suspension will develop visible colonies on the solid medium. This, at first sight, may seem a disadvantage but at least they can be seen, carefully cut out and placed in a solution of disinfectant. Very motile bacteria, however, are a problem but some consolation may be gained from the knowledge that the bacteria would still spread even if they were mixed in with the agar. To a certain extent the use of a 4 per cent or a 6 per cent agar will limit the spreading of motile bacteria. It must be realized that algae take a long time to develop into sizeable colonies and that bacteria and fungi take only a short period to become established; therefore it is very important that strict aseptic techniques are used throughout.

There are three common methods by which an agar plate may be surface inoculated with a suspension; spraying, spreading and streaking.

Spraying—Spraying the algal suspension on to the surface of the medium is simple but rather a nuisance. The sprayer consists of two glass tubes, set at right angles to each other, which are held in position by a metal clip[2]. The horizontal tube is drawn out to a fine jet which finishes half-way across the top open-end of the vertical tube. The unit must be autoclaved before it is used. The vertical tube is placed in a narrow test tube, which should be almost full of the suspension, and the horizontal tube (this must contain a cotton wool filter which should be put into place before sterilization) is connected to an air supply. The pressure of air will produce a fine spray which is directed over the surface of the plate. The plate of medium should be dried (see p. 253) before spraying which must be carried out so that only a very fine film is formed.

Spreading—This method is regarded by a number of algologists as being a very inefficient technique. Although this may be the case with some algae it can be quite successful with others. If the plate of medium has been well dried before use, so that the agar will absorb about 0·5 ml of water quite quickly, there is no reason why the technique should not be used. About 0·5 ml of a suitable suspension is pipetted on to the agar and quickly spread over the surface with a piece of sterile glass rod bent at a right-angle about 1 in. from one end. The rod may be sterilized by flaming, after immersion in 95 per cent alcohol.

Streaking—This is another technique that has been borrowed from the bacteriologist. It is quite straightforward if approached in a light-handed fashion. A loopful of suspension is rubbed lightly over the surface of the plate in a succession of flattened Z's (see p. 280). The principle is that the cells or fragments are gradually separated from each other in each successive streak. Alternatively, a straight wire, a sterile brush, or a piece of sterile cotton wool wrapped round a piece of wood may be used.

Pipetting

This is a means of removing contaminating bacteria by a series of washings in sterile water.

Many algae have stages in their life-cycle which are relatively free from adhering bacteria. It is these stages that offer the greatest chance of success; for example, motile spores (zoospores) or spores formed within the cells or in cysts.

Healthily growing algae can often be induced to form zoospores by changing the nature of the medium, for example from a solid to a liquid medium, or from a slightly exhausted medium to a fresh one. If a test is performed which shows the existence of flagellate spores (which are usually phototactic), these can be seen as a green zone on the side of the vessel nearest the light. Cultures in test tubes form a green vertical line in the centre of the tube where the light is concentrated. Careful observation will suggest the best period to collect the spores for washing.

Cysts or cells can be squashed between sterile slides to liberate the bacteria-free cells and spores. It is advisable to wash the cysts, etc., before squashing.

Algae which do not form any bacteria-free stages may also be washed and, indeed, it is often the only way of producing a pure culture, but extreme patience is required before success is accomplished.

The pipettes used for this technique need to have a very fine capillary and can be made from Pasteur pipettes as described previously.

A short piece of rubber tubing, plugged with a length of glass rod, should be used to act as a teat because a standard rubber teat is not strong enough to overcome the extreme capillary action. It is as well to sterilize a number of Pasteur pipettes at the same time and, when required, these can be converted into algal washing pipettes.

Sterile flat-bottomed watchglasses are also required and these are best sterilized individually in Petri dishes. A piece of wire shaped into a triangle is a good support for ordinary watchglasses and helps to prevent them tipping over or moving during subsequent operations. Into each sterile watchglass is placed 1 ml of sterile, glass-distilled water. The zoospores or algal cells are removed from the suspension with one of the capillary pipettes. This is easily performed under a stereo microscope. The pipette is placed into the suspension so that capillary action sucks the cell into the pipette and, by repeating this action, a selection of algal cells are obtained. The improvised teat is pressed to expel the contents of the pipette into the sterile water of one of the watchglasses and the operation is then repeated. After some 8 or 9 washings, the cells should be free from bacteria. Between each washing, the pipette should be redrawn so as to render it sterile, thus one pipette should suffice for the whole operation. After washing, the individual spores or cells are inoculated into tubes containing a suitable liquid medium, or on to plates of solid media from which an unialgal, bacteria-free culture will develop.

A method of inducing an algal culture to produce motile spores is as follows: the preparative suspension is coated on to a 0·2 per cent Knop's solution solidified with 1 per cent agar. Bacterial colonies will develop first and after a few weeks the algal colonies will be visible. By wedging the lid of the dish and leaving it slightly open for a few days, the colonies will tend to become dry. Removal of the dry algal colonies to narrow tubes of sterile water should result in the liberation of zoospores.

DRUG RESISTANCE

It has been shown by a number of people that some bacteriostatic and fungicidal compounds do not affect certain algae. Thus a further method of obtaining a pure culture of certain algae has been developed.

Some of the Myxophyceae are resistant to anisomycin, nystatin and actidione[3] whereas members of the Chlorophyceae and Bacillariaceae are sensitive (nystatin is insoluble in water so it should be used as a suspension). The Myxophyceae are sensitive to bacitracin, although other algae are resistant, therefore, by culturing an alga, contaminated with blue–green algae, on a media containing bacitracin, the contaminants should be severely inhibited allowing a pure culture to develop. Further references for these techniques are quoted in the bibliography.

GROWTH MOVEMENTS

Some of the algae exhibit creeping movements and these movements often free an alga of bacterial contamination. The alga is inoculated on to a plate of solid medium and incubated; periodically a sub-culture is taken from the growing tip and subbed on to fresh medium. The sub-cultures may themselves have to be re-isolated before success is achieved.

BULK CULTURES

Normally algae are grown on solid media in large test tubes or Petri dishes. Occasionally, large numbers of algae are required, and, for this purpose, culture vessels such as penicillin flasks or Roux bottles are useful. Large glass tanks can also be used so long as they can be sterilized effectively and maintained in a sterile condition. When large volumes of liquid media are used, a difficulty arises concerning the availability of carbon dioxide. Penicillin flasks and Roux bottles may be aerated, or a mechanical shaker can be used which does give a certain amount of aeration. The larger tanks should be aerated by passing a stream of carbon dioxide through the liquid medium (see p. 222).

Marine cultures must be grown in a sea-water medium. Some algae will only grow in natural sea water but the majority can be grown in synthetic sea water (see p. 242). The addition of a small amount of natural sea water to the synthetic medium is often sufficient to bring about a recovery of an unhealthy culture.

INCUBATION

The majority of algae grow at a temperature of about 15–20°C and, as these temperatures approximate an average room temperature, algae only need the correct type and amount of light in order to grow healthily in the laboratory.

The light source can be natural and cultures placed in the north window of the laboratory will receive indirect sunlight. Cultures should never be grown in direct sunlight unless protection is available.

Protection should take the form of a glass tank filled with water; this is to absorb harmful u.v. rays and, to a certain extent, heat. Where natural light is not available artificial light can be used so long as the heat generated is prevented from reaching the culture. Fluorescent tubes give a good source of cool light and they can be arranged vertically in a circle of five or six tubes. The cultures can be placed in spring clips on a frame surrounding the tubes, with the surface of the agar slope facing the lights and about 15 in. away from them.

STOCK CULTURES

Stock cultures are those maintained as a ready source of inocula. A methodical worker will keep a book in which dates, types of media and observations covering the entire collection of stock cultures are regularly recorded. Algae are best kept on solid media, as contamination is usually more easily seen and sub-culturing is less troublesome than when done from liquid media. Experience will show the frequency of sub-culturing required to keep stocks healthy. As a general rule, the stock cultures should be sub-cultured less frequently than those in everyday use; this is to reduce the possibility of natural mutations or changes from taking place.

The freshly inoculated culture is grown under optimum conditions to give approximately half the maximum growth and then transferred to a cool situation with less light; this tends to reduce metabolism and growth rate. All cultures should be in duplicate and at different stages of development. Thus loss of the current culture does not mean loss of the particular species, as a second one is available.

Some cultures which will not grow readily on agar should be kept in liquid media, or even grown by a soil and water culture, from which they may be freed from bacteria before use.

Cultures which are able to withstand long periods before sub-culturing should have the plugs of the test tubes covered with polythene to prevent desiccation while still allowing the passage of air for respiration and photosynthesis.

Occasionally, a culture will show an apparent difference, or appear unhealthy due to too frequent sub-culturing on agar. This may be overcome by culturing the alga in a soil and water culture and then sub-culturing back on to agar. Individual cultures should be labelled with the type, code number and date of culture and should also be recorded in the laboratory book.

FUNGI

Except for a few instances, the cultivation of fungi in the laboratory is far easier than the cultivation of algae. Owing to their greater growth rate, most fungi are easily purified of bacterial contamination. Also, the majority of fungi are abundant spore producers and these spores give the worker a good chance of producing a pure culture.

If a sample of soil is suspended in sterile water, shaken, and the heavy particles allowed to settle before it is plated out on to a malt extract agar, a variety of fungi will appear after suitable incubation. By gently removing a few spores from one of the resulting colonies and transferring them to a suitable medium it is very likely that a pure culture will be the result.

The growth rate of an organism is important in obtaining a pure culture. If a mixture of a slow and a fast growing culture is inoculated on to a solid medium and then incubated, the faster growing culture can be taken from the edge of the colony freed from the other organism.

The pure culture techniques for yeast are basically the same as for bacteria. The yeast media used should not be allowed to become exhausted as starvation causes ascus formation. Yeast normally undergoes asexual reproduction by budding but exhausted media causes sexual reproduction and therefore ascus formation.

The two most important aspects of fungal pure culture have only been briefly mentioned. Full details for these techniques will be given in the ensuing pages.

Raper's Glass Ring

The isolation of fungi from bacterial contamination can often be achieved by using Raper's Glass Ring.

The glass ring which is used has a diameter of about 15 mm and three short legs attached to the base. The ring is sterilized and placed in the centre of a Petri dish. A suitable medium is poured into the dish so that the level is just above the legs of the ring (*see Figure 108*).

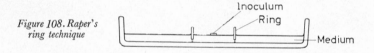

Figure 108. Raper's ring technique

The contaminated, or impure culture is inoculated into the centre of the ring. As the colony develops, the hyphae grow under the ring leaving the bacteria behind on the surface of the agar inside the ring. A block of agar containing bacteria-free hyphae can then be transferred to a slope of fresh medium and incubated. This should produce a pure culture.

Tip Isolation

As mentioned previously, it is relatively easy to isolate a fast-growing culture from a slow-growing one but it is not quite so easy to separate two cultures growing at the same rate. By using a low-power dissecting microscope and fine pointed needles, the growing tips of each of the cultures may be removed and transferred to separate tubes of sloped media and incubated. A high number of failures may be experienced and it is important, therefore, to isolate as many individual tips as possible to ensure success.

Selective Media

This method can only be used when the required fungus is able to grow on a medium where the other contaminating fungi cannot. This is best shown by using a single species having a number of mutants deficient in some nutritional requirement (those unable to synthesize amino acids etc., from the basic inorganic salts provided in the minimal medium) and a 'wild' type (one that can convert the inorganic salts in the minimal medium into its nutritional requirements). Thus, a mixed culture of mutants, each requiring a different substance, can be separated from each other by inoculating minimal medium, which has been supplemented with one of the required substances, with the mixed culture. The only culture able to grow will be the one whose additional substance was provided by the supplemented medium. *Figure 110* (*a, b* and *c*) demonstrates this principle.

Spores

Plating—A suspension of fungal spores in a solution of a wetting agent (10^{-5} concentration) is counted on a haemacytometer slide and then diluted to give a density of approximately 2,500 spores/ml. This final dilution is plated on to a solid medium to give a concentration of about 750 spores on each plate. The reasonably high density of spores plated is due to the inviability of the majority of spores and also to make isolation easier under the microscope.

After germination has taken place, the individual spores may be cut out on small blocks of agar and transferred to fresh medium. From these should arise a number of pure cultures.

The use of a wetting agent is to be preferred to water as it reduces the surface tension and allows the absorption of moisture by the dry spores; the conidia of the Ascomycetes are rather warty in appearance and this means that air is trapped around the spore. This trapped air prevents contact with the suspending water and thus there is no absorption of water by the spore. By using a wetting agent, the surface tension is lowered and this helps to prevent the air being trapped.

Streaking—This technique is the same as that described for algae (see pp. 261-262) and is particularly useful when purifying budding yeasts. The suspension of contaminated yeast cells is streaked over a plate of suitable medium and incubated. The growth of the yeast on solid medium resembles that of many bacteria and it is therefore advisable to take a smear of a possible yeast colony and observe it under the microscope. If the smear is satisfactory, the colony from which the smear was taken can then be inoculated on to fresh medium.

Sub-culturing—The use of spores as a means of sub-culturing an organism is very popular, particularly among workers using the Ascomycetes. It is important to inoculate while the Petri dish is held upside down as this prevents the spores falling off the inoculating needle and thereby causing scattered colonies to appear all over the plates.

Some of the fungi shed their spores by some form of propulsion and this habit can be used as a means of purifying the particular fungus from bacterial or other fungal contaminants. An example of a fungus that exhibits this form of spore dispersal is *Ascobolus*, one of the Ascomycetes. *Ascobolus* shoots its spores towards the light so, if a sterile slide is placed in the lid of an inverted Petri dish containing an actively growing culture and the dish is placed in an incubator with a source of illumination underneath it, the spores will be shed on to the slide. The collected spores can then be placed on to a dish of fresh sterile medium and incubated. The resulting colonies should be free from the contaminants.

INCUBATION

Fungi, depending on their type, can be grown at temperatures ranging from 15° to 37°C. Light is not essential except in a few cases, such as the shedding of *Ascobolus* spores, or fruit body production (toadstool) in the Basidiomycetes, etc.

Incubation is best carried out in an incubator that can be thermostatically controlled (see Chapter 1). The use of a controlled incubator means that conditions can be repeated exactly and this is important when carrying out research work.

The best temperature for growing a particular species is determined from studies of the organism's environment, for example the Basidiomycetes which grow on dung heaps are likely to prefer a high temperature, while species inhabiting the ground in fields, etc., will probably grow best at a lower temperature.

SPECIAL TECHNIQUES

Mating

The production of sexual spores is accomplished by mating two appropriate strains. A number of incompatibility systems have been evolved to help prevent constant in-breeding. To appreciate the full meaning of incompatibility the worker must be conversant with a few technical terms.

A homothallic organism is one that can undergo self-reproduction, i.e. it is self-fertile. A heterothallic organism must be cross fertilized, as it is self-sterile. Homothallic fungi are present in all of the groups. The heterothallic forms are also common throughout the groups of fungi. The type of incompatibility system can be one of three forms, simple, bi-polar or tetra-polar.

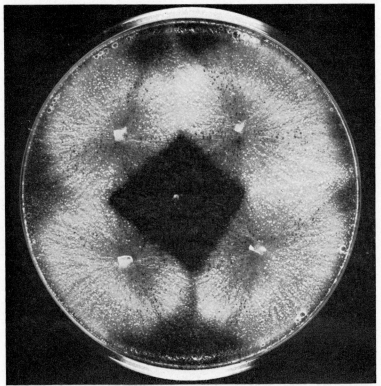

Figure 109. (a) Mated Sordaria spp.—a black strain is crossed with a white strain, the small black and white spots show perithecia formation (cont.)

Simple—This, the two-allele system, is determined by a single gene which has two alleles. In order that a successful mating can occur the two strains must have different alleles. Generally the two mating types are termed plus $(+)$ and minus $(-)$ and the alleles a and α.

Bi-polar—This system also employs a single gene, designated A, but the number of alleles is not limited to two. For successful mating the two strains must have different alleles. The alleles are given numbers in order to simplify the classification, i.e. A_1, A_2, A_3, A_4, etc. Therefore a strain A_1 is compatible with a strain A_2 but incompatible with a strain A_1.

Tetra-polar—This is the most complicated of the fungal incompatibility systems and involves two genes denoted as A and B. As in the

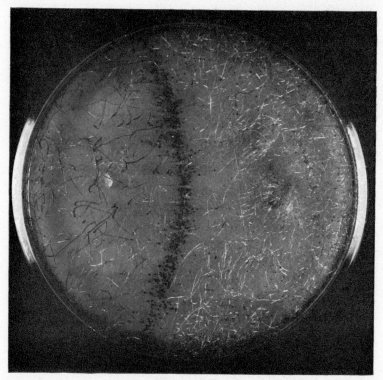

Figure 109. (b) A cross between two phycomycetes—dense black line across the plate shows formation of zygospores (cont.)

bi-polar system the two strains must have different alleles, not only of the A gene but of the B gene as well. Again, the alleles are given numbers A_1, A_2, A_3 and B_1, B_2, B_3, etc. Thus a strain $A_1 B_1$ can only mate with one differing in both the A and B numbers.

In order to produce sexual spores of the homothallic fungi, it is only necessary to inoculate the fungus on to solid medium and then

270

incubate. This will produce spores which have a genotype exactly the same as the parent strain. If crossed strains are required, it is necessary to inoculate one of the strains in the centre of the Petri dish and to place inocula from the other strain in a square around the central inoculum, about mid-way between the centre and the edge of the plate. On incubation the two strains will meet and fuse. Along

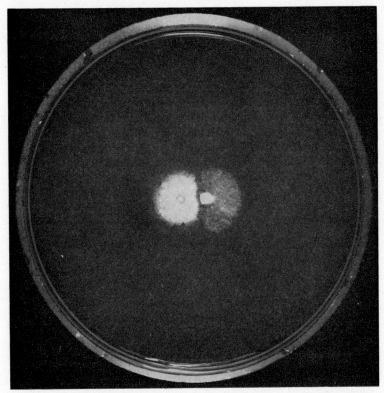

Figure 109. (c.1) Incompatible mating between two strains of Coprinus lagopus having common A.B. alleles (cont.)

these lines of fusion the perithecia and hence the sexual spores, will be produced (*see Figure 109a*). Not all of the spores produced will be the result of fusion between the two different strains, as some self reproduction will occur. To identify the spores and to check that an actual cross has occurred, the spores must be analysed and compared with the original parents. If the two parent strains are noticed in the progeny of the cross then it can be said that cross-reproduction has occurred.

The heterothallic fungi must be cross-mated before sexual spores are produced. A plus and a minus strain are inoculated about 1 in. apart on solid medium and incubated. Along the line of fusion will arise the sexual spores (*see Figure 109b*). Similarly the two strains

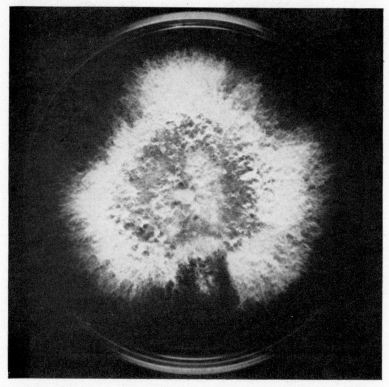

Figure 109. (c.2) Compatible mating of C. lagopus showing dikaryon formation

having different *A* alleles are inoculated 1 in. apart and incubated. The tetra-polar system of the higher fungi, for example Basidiomycetes, does not allow for the immediate production of sexual spores, as an interim stage occurs. This stage is the heterokaryon (the dikaryon in *C. lagopus*), which consists of one mycelium containing the nuclei of the two parental strains. It is from this stage that the fruit body (toadstool) develops. To produce the heterokaryon, the two strains are inoculated in the centre of a plate of solid medium so that they are almost touching. After suitable incubation, the heterokaryon will be seen as a faster growing part of the colony (*see Figure 109c, 1 & 2*). Microscopic investigation is essential to confirm that a heterokaryon has been formed; generally it has clamp connections,

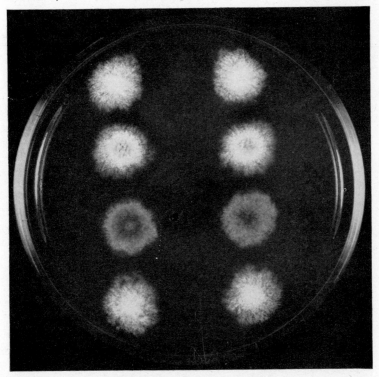

Figure 110. (*a*) *Aspergillus mutants:*
Petri dish containing minimal medium + adenine + methionine—all cultures are paired, all colonies are able to grow (cont.)

thicker hyphae, no asexual spores and more parallel branching. The heterokaryon may be left on the plate so that the fruit body may be formed but, unfortunately, not all of the Basidiomycetes will produce these structures on synthetic medium and the heterokaryon may have to be inoculated on to a more natural medium such as horse, cow or rabbit dung. It is important to note that light is essential for the formation of mature fruit bodies.

273

Some species of Aspergillus (regarded as members of the *Fungi imperfecti*) can be forced to produce crossed sexual spores by using strains that require an additional nutrient other than those supplied by the minimal medium (*Figure 110a, b and c*). For example, by means of the genetic mechanism known as complementation, a mutant requiring a substance X, and therefore only able to grow on minimal

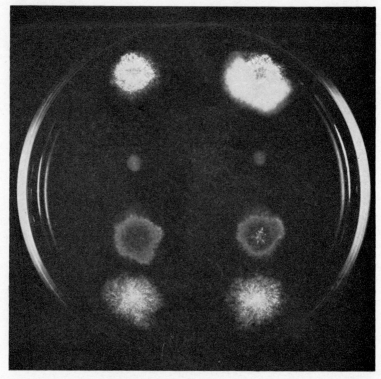

Figure 110.(b) Minimal medium+methionine, second culture unable to grow at normal rate owing to a deficiency of adenine in the medium (cont.)

medium supplemented with X, and a mutant requiring substance Y will, when mated, be able to grow on the minimal medium. Therefore, if conidia (asexual spores) of the two mutants are mixed and suspended in a liquid medium able to support the growth of both the mutants, and are incubated for 18–24 h to allow a slight amount of growth to occur, then plated on to minimal medium as wefts of mycelium, the culture is forced to grow as a heterokaryon, i.e. in a mated form. Perithecia are then formed after further incubation. An alternative method is to use mixed conidia and streak them along a line on a plate of minimal medium. Just prior to the streaking, a pipette containing liquid medium able to support the growth of the two mutants, is drawn along the line to allow a thin film of nutrients

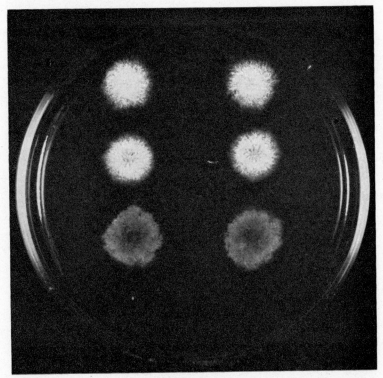

Figure 110.(c) Minimal medium+adenine, bottom culture requires methionine and is therefore unable to grow

to be absorbed by the minimal. The conidia will germinate owing to the extra nutrients but, for continued growth, a heterokaryon must be formed.

BULK CULTURING

Occasionally, large amounts of mycelium are required but before these can be obtained a number of problems have to be overcome.

Large vessels must be procured and sterilized, a method of aerating the culture must be devised and a method of preventing the organism from starving should be decided.

Aspirators of 10 or 15 litre capacity made of Pyrex glass make useful culture tanks as they are easily cleaned, sterilized and adapted for growing cultures. Roux bottles and penicillin flasks are useful for smaller amounts of liquid culture or for providing large surface areas for fungal growth on solid media.

Aeration of cultures can be achieved by bubbling air through the liquid medium. For small volumes the use of an aeration flask dispenses with the need for making bubblers, etc. For the large volumes, such as those likely to be found when using aspirators, bubblers of some form will have to be made.

It is very important to attach an inlet and an outlet filter to the flask in order to prevent any possible source of contamination. These filters can be made of non-absorbent cotton wool which is arranged in a piece of wide-bore glass tubing. Attachment to the flask is effected by using a piece of rubber tubing. A simple form of filter similar to that just described can be seen in *Figure 97*.

The very act of aeration is sufficient to keep the mycelium and medium from settling and forming dense growth. A higher yield will be experienced from an aerated culture than from a standing culture. If the culture vessel is not aerated, it is advisable to place the vessel on some form of shaker, as the shaking will permit of a slight aeration but its main importance is to keep the medium moving.

Sterilization and preparation of the medium might cause some problems. The amount of possible contaminants is reduced if, before preparing the medium, all the containers, watchglasses, weighing bottles, spatulas, etc., are sterilized and the medium prepared in sterile water under aseptic conditions. Where possible, the medium should be prepared hot and, when standardized for pH, poured into the sterile culture vessels. The medium should be autoclaved immepiately with the holding period at 12 lb./in.^{2} for 20–40 min depending on volume. At this fairly low pressure there should not be too much breakdown of media constituents. Unstable compounds must be sterilized separately and added to the flasks after sterilization of the latter. When the vessels have cooled, they are ready to be inoculated.

The inoculum can be of any suitable type: spore suspension, blended mycelium, or agar blocks containing actively growing cultures. The introduction of the inoculum must be performed with very strict aseptic technique, as a contaminant at this stage means the failure of the experiment and a big loss in time and material.

MUTATION

Mutations occur spontaneously in all living organisms but, as most of them are detrimental to the organism, they are not selected. Natural selection is the process by which advantageous mutations are developed for the benefit of the species. In the higher organisms where the natural nuclear state is diploid, i.e. the chromosomes in each nucleus are duplicated, the mutations are recessive to the normal state and are therefore masked and not noticed. In lower organisms where the chromosome number is haploid, i.e. the chromosomes are not duplicated in the nucleus, any mutation is more likely to be noticed. Occasionally, a worker wishes to cause an artificial mutation and for this a number of techniques have been developed. X-rays, u.v. light, and chemical mutagens are all used as means of inducing mutations.

Radiation

A most convenient method of inducing mutations is the use of a radioactive chemical, such as ^{32}P, which is incorporated into the nuclear structures.

Large and complicated pieces of apparatus are required in order to produce x-rays.

Ultra-violet light of a suitable wavelength (2537 Å) is more convenient than x-rays. The technique is as follows: the spores of the organism are exposed to the u.v. light for varying lengths of time so as to obtain a 90–99·9 per cent kill of viable spores. The kill can be determined by plating treated spores, and, as a control, untreated spores—and comparing the number of colonies that arise.

Chemical Mutagens

Chemicals such as β-propiolactone, ethyl methyl sulphonate, mustard gas, etc., can all be used to induce mutation. The chemical is incorporated in the medium at a concentration that will give a high percentage kill of viable spores. The concentration is generally quite low, in the region of 10^{-4} to 10^{-5}.

Testing of Treated Spores

The majority of mutations that will arise will be concerned with a bio-chemical deficiency involving nutrition. That is to say a chemical other than those supplied by the minimal medium is required to enable normal growth to occur.

After treatment the spores are plated on to a complete medium (one containing all the amino acids, vitamins, etc.) and incubated.

The cultures are numbered and inoculated on to minimal medium. After incubation, the inocula are checked for growth. Any abnormal colonies, or any colonies not growing on minimal medium, may be regarded as possible mutants, those colonies that exhibit normal growth being discarded. The next step is to test the cultures in order to determine the growth requirement needed to produce normal growth. Those cultures looking abnormal may only be mutants with regard to morphology and therefore may not require additional growth factors. Auxanography is a method whereby a mutant may be tested for its biochemical requirement.

Auxanography

The cultures are grown on separate plates of complete medium and incubated until abundant asexual spores are produced. The spores are collected and suspended in water and spread on to plates of minimal medium. Holes are cut in the medium by using a sterile cork borer (size 4) and the base of the hole sealed with a little liquefied minimal medium. Composite solutions are prepared so that each solution contains chemicals of the same group, i.e. solutions of amino acids, vitamins, nucleic acids, etc. A drop of each solution is placed in separate agar wells. Where growth occurs it will suggest the type of bio-chemical substance required. The next step is to identify positively the actual chemical required. For example, if growth occurs around the well containing amino acid solution, a further test is performed using solutions of separate amino acids. Alternatively, crystals of different amino acids can be spotted on to a plate seeded with spores, or small porcelain tubes may be inserted into the medium and the solutions placed in these. Some manufacturers produce sterile filter paper discs impregnated with different biochemical substances (e.g. the Multodisks manufactured by Oxoid Ltd.).

STOCK CULTURES

The preparation and upkeep of all cultures is essential in order to keep original cultures available. Cultures producing resistant spores are the easiest to keep healthy. The culture is grown on a slope of suitable medium and incubated until most of the surface area is covered by actively growing mycelium. The culture can then be stored in a refrigerator at 4°C. Cultures prepared in this way may be stored for many months before further sub-culturing is necessary.

For all other cultures it is essential to reduce the metabolic activity in order to prevent rapid exhaustion of the medium. By storing the cultures at low temperatures of from 2° to 4°C the growth rate is reduced. The rate of respiration can be reduced by the addition of sterile medicinal paraffin[4] (liquid paraffin). The culture is inoculated on to a slope of suitable medium and incubated. Once growth has been well established, the sterile liquid paraffin is added so that the entire slope is covered and the culture is then stored at a low temperature.

Some cultures, for example, *Penicillium spp.*, can be grown on damp natural media, such as maize, hemp seed, etc., and then dried in a desiccator using concentrated sulphuric acid or phosphorous pentoxide as a drying agent. The vegetative mycelium will be killed by this treatment but the spores, which have been formed during growth, will remain viable.

Freeze drying (lyophilization) is not commonly used as a means of storing fungal cultures, as not all species lend themselves to this treatment. The methods for freeze drying will be covered in the section on bacteria (see p. 282).

The choice of medium for stock cultures is very important and, as mentioned previously, natural mutations do occur. Mutants requiring additional growth factors can only grow until that growth factor in the medium is exhausted. In order that further growth should take place, the organism must undergo a further mutation. This second mutation generally allows the organism to grow, either by a back mutation to its original state or by a mutation to a gene that nullifies or suppresses the original requirement, i.e. a suppressor gene. Thus it is important to grow the stock cultures on a medium containing an excess of any additional growth factors.

BACTERIA

The preparation of a pure bacterial culture is generally a simple task. The techniques of dilution and streaking, in conjunction with selective media, are the methods most commonly used. Bacterial cultures are normally grown on a nutrient agar although some species require the addition of blood or serum. Before any attempt is made to produce a pure culture, it is essential to know whether the bacterium respires aerobically or anaerobically.

Streaking

Holding the plate in one hand, the culture is taken up in a loop or on the end of a straight wire and lightly smeared across the plate, with the wire held obliquely to the plate surface. The needle is then flamed along its entire length and allowed to cool. The coolness of the wire can be tested by lightly touching the agar; if the wire is too hot it will splutter and produce a furrow in the agar surface. Streaks are made across the original smear at an angle (approximately 120 degrees) and successive streaks are made in the same manner from this second streak. These streaks are made round the plate until the entire surface is covered. It is important that each successive streak does not cross a more densely populated smear (*see Figure 111*).

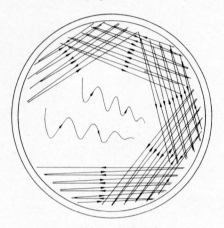

Figure 111. Plate streaking of bacteria

The technique of dilution is the same as that mentioned previously (see p. 259).

The use of selective media for pure culture work is only applicable when knowledge of the required organism is available.

INCUBATION

Bacteria are broadly classified into aerobic and anaerobic cultures depending upon their respiratory requirement.

Aerobic Incubation

Normal incubation, i.e. in the presence of free oxygen, is quite good enough for general aerobic incubation. Occasionally it is necessary to increase the carbon dioxide content to approximately 5 per cent. This can easily be carried out by placing the cultures in a suitable lidded container with a small beaker containing a few marble chips and a little dilute hydrochloric acid.

Anaerobic Incubation

The easiest way to establish anaerobic conditions is by growing the cultures in deep stab tubes. Test tubes are prepared containing 3 in. of solid medium, preferably a medium containing glucose, on the assumption that the culture will utilize glucose as a carbon source. The medium is inoculated by using a long straight wire so that the organism is stabbed down the centre of the agar and deposited at the bottom of the test tube. Alternatively, the agar can be melted, cooled to 45°C and inoculated with a loopful of suspension. Rotation will ensure even distribution of the bacteria throughout the medium. The cultures are then incubated in the normal way.

Glucose broth can be used if it is prepared in the following way. Long test tubes are half filled with the broth and then steamed for half an hour. Sterile, molten Vaseline is then gently poured into the tubes to cover the surface of the broth. Inoculation is effected by using a capillary pipette which is passed through the Vaseline while molten. Heating of the glucose broth drives the free oxygen out and the Vaseline seals the medium from the atmosphere. Gas-forming bacteria should not be inoculated into this medium as the gas produced will force the Vaseline plugs out of the tubes.

The oxidation of iron to rust can be utilized to produce anaerobic conditions. A liquid medium, with the addition of a sterile iron nail, tin-tack or piece of sheet iron, is inoculated and incubated in the normal way.

The use of specialized equipment, particularly the McIntosh and Fildes' jar, is quite common. The principle is as follows.

Hydrogen and oxygen are made to combine by the use of a catalyst, such as spongy palladium or spongy platinum, to produce water. The jar can be made of metal or glass and has a tight fitting lid from which the catalyst is suspended. The upper surface of the lid has two outlets with taps. Petri dishes or tubes are placed inside the jar with a methylene blue indicator and the lid of the jar is clamped into position. One outlet tap is opened and connected to a vacuum pump to evacuate the jar, which is sealed by closing the tap. The other outlet is connected to a low-pressure supply of hydrogen—a football bladder filled with hydrogen from a gas cylinder can be used as the low-pressure source—the tap is opened and hydrogen allowed to enter. The terminals to the catalyst are connected to the mains supply via a suitable resistance and the jar left to allow the remaining oxygen to combine with the hydrogen. After about 20 min the current is switched off and the supply of hydrogen disconnected after shutting the valve. Anaerobic conditions should be present within the jar.

The jar is incubated at the correct temperature for the required length of time and then removed and opened.

The indicator is used to give positive evidence that oxygen has been absent while the jar has been sealed. It consists of the following solutions:

(A) Take 6 ml. of 0·1N NaOH and make up to 100 ml with distilled water
(B) Take 3 ml. of 0·5 per cent aqueous methylene blue and make up to 100 ml with distilled water
(C) Take 100 ml. of 6 per cent w/v glucose in distilled water

Equal volumes of these three solutions plus a small crystal of thymol are placed in a test tube which is plugged with cotton wool. The contents are then boiled until they are colourless. The tube is placed in the jar while the contents are still colourless. Contact with oxygen turns the solution from colourless to blue.

STOCK CULTURES

The majority of bacteria reach their maximum growth in an ideal medium after 24 h at 37°C and, after this period, the cells gradually die. It is essential, therefore, to sub-culture regularly every three or four days at this temperature. Cultures which are stored at low temperatures in the dark may remain viable for several months depending upon the strain.

Certain bacteria produce resistant spores (e.g. *Bacillus subtilis, B. anthracis, Clostridium welchii*, etc.) which will remain viable for some months or years. These spores can be used for a stock culture.

Freeze drying is the method most commonly employed as a means of preserving cultures.

FREEZE DRYING

Cultures may be preserved for many years after freeze drying. Gradual drying of a solution results in the increased concentration of the salts, but if the solution is first frozen solid and water taken off there is no increase of concentration. The increase in concentration causes denaturation of proteins and results in the death of the bacteria. The basic way of freeze drying is first to freeze the bacteria suspension quickly and then to dry the frozen solution under vacuum, using a suitable desiccant. Small volumes of suspension do not need pre-freezing, as a high vacuum will reduce the temperature due to the latent heat of evaporation. A number of methods are available and the commonest ones are Greaves' and Prooms'.

Greaves' Method of Freeze Drying

Edwards High Vacuum, Ltd. manufacture a suitable piece of

apparatus for this purpose. It consists of a centrifuge covered by a glass bell jar which contains metal trays for the desiccant and a manifold for secondary freeze drying. The vacuum chamber (the bell jar) is evacuated by an oil-sealed high-vacuum pump, a Pirani type pressure gauge completes the apparatus.

The cultures are dried in hard glass ampoules having an internal diameter of 6 mm. These ampoules are known as Lambet tubes.

The ampoules are acid washed, rinsed with distilled water and dried. A strip of filter paper, giving the type of culture and the date, is placed in each ampoule. The ampoules are plugged with cotton wool and sterilized, 0·5 ml of culture is placed in each ampoule and a fresh, loose plug of sterile cotton wool is inserted and pushed right into the ampoule. The metal trays are charged with fresh phosphorous pentoxide (P_2O_5). For the primary drying, the ampoules are placed in the almost vertical holes of the centrifuge and the bell jar pressed firmly into position. The centrifuge, and then the rotary pump, are switched on and pressure on the bell jar helps to obtain a rapid vacuum. After a few minutes' operation, when a pressure of approximately 0·1 mm Hg is registered, the centrifuge is switched off to avoid over-heating. The culture should now be frozen in a thin layer on the inside surface of the ampoule. The vacuum pump is kept running for 6–8 h to ensure sufficient desiccation. During all operations the cultures should be kept in subdued light, preferably covered with a cloth. The cultures should now be ready for secondary drying. The vacuum is released and the ampoules removed from the drying chamber. Using a small gas flame or blow lamp, a thin capillary restriction is formed about 1·5 in. from the open end. The cotton wool plug should be between the restriction and the culture. The ampoules are pushed on to the rubber adaptors of the manifold and any adaptors not in use must be plugged with empty ampoules. The secondary drying is accomplished by recharging the desiccant trays with fresh P_2O_5, replacing the bell jar and evacuating for 6–18 h (the bell jar will not be evacuated and only acts as a shield in case any tubes shatter under the created vacuum). Remove the bell jar and, with the pump still running, the ampoules are sealed by applying a small flame to the constriction. The ampoules are tested for a high vacuum with a high frequency tester and those which do not show a blue-violet glow are discarded. The Pirani gauge should register a vacuum of at least 0·01 mm Hg during the final operation.

Proom's Method

This is also known as the chamber method of freeze drying. The essential difference between this and Greaves' method is that after the secondary drying, the vacuum in the ampoules is replaced by dry nitrogen. The drying is carried out in a vacuum desiccator in the bottom of which is P_2O_5. Over the P_2O_5 is a tray containing a mixture of glycerin and solid CO_2 (Cardice). Suspended over the first tray is a second tray containing more P_2O_5.

The ampoules containing the cultures are placed in the glycerin mixture to a depth of about 1 in. (the mixture has a temperature of approximately $-78°C$). The lid is replaced and the desiccator placed in a cork-lined box. The desiccator is evacuated to a high vacuum and left overnight. The following morning the desiccator is removed from the box and allowed to reach room temperature while still under vacuum. When at room temperature, the stopcock is connected to a source of dry nitrogen which is allowed to enter the desiccator. The lid is removed. This is the end of the primary drying. The desiccants are changed and the glycerin mixture removed from the desiccator and the tubes replaced. The desiccator is evacuated and left at room temperature for about a week. The vacuum in the desiccator is replaced with dry nitrogen as before, then the tubes removed and sealed in a blow-lamp flame.

A little dry silica gel can be placed in the top of each tube before sealing to act as an indicator to check for moisture. Silica gel is blue when dry but pink when moist.

A Simple Method of Freeze Drying

Small volumes may be freeze dried, without any expensive equipment, by using a laboratory desiccator with a three-way tap and a high vacuum pump: 0·5 ml of culture is placed in a sterile ampoule and stoppered with a loose cotton wool plug as before. The ampoule is placed in the desiccator in a sloping position with fresh P_2O_5 as a desiccant. The lid of the desiccator is pressed into position and connected to a high vacuum pump. Evacuation is gently carried out until the suspension starts to bubble slightly, and the pressure maintained until all gentle bubbling has ceased which takes about 30 min. If bubbling becomes too violent, air is admitted via the three-way tap. Once bubbling has ceased, the desiccator is evacuated to a high vacuum. Freezing of the suspension should take place within a few minutes though the pump is left running for about an hour. The desiccator is placed in the dark and left under vacuum for 24 h. Secondary drying is carried out in a very similar manner to Greaves' method. The ampoules are constricted and attached to the pressure tubing of the vacuum pump. The pump is switched on and the ampoules evacuated for 2 or 3 min; while still under vacuum the ampoules are sealed at the constriction.

OUCHTERLONY

A great deal of antigen-antibody reactions are performed in tubes with liquids at specific concentrations and the resulting reaction is seen as a precipitation or flocculation. Unfortunately if more than one reaction occurs, they are masked by the primary precipitation.

The use of clarified agar (page 251) as a base system for these reactions was introduced by Ouchterlony[5]. Recent modifications of his technique, using gel cutters in set patterns were introduced by Feinberg. These cutters are now marketed by Shandon Scientific Co. Ltd. who also produce a data sheet[6] giving references and the use of the cutters. The clear agar enables reactions to be observed as white precipitation bands. Any secondary or tertiary reaction occurring will also be noticed but as a separate band.

REFERENCES

[1]Feinberg, J. G. (1956). 'Clarification of Agar.' *Nature, Lond.* **178**, 1406

[2]Pringsheim, E. G. (1946). *Pure Cultures of the Algae*, 1st ed. Cambridge; University Press

[3]Hunter, E. O. Jr. and McViegh, I. (1961). 'The Affects of Selected Antibiotics on Pure Cultures of Algae.' *Amer. J. Bot.* **48**, 179–185

[4]Buell, C. B. and Weston, W. H. (1947). 'Application of the Mineral Oil Conservation to Maintaining Collections of Fungus Cultures.' *Amer. J. Bot.* **34**, 555

[5]Ouchterlony, O. (1949). 'Antigen - Antibody Reactions in Gels.' *Ark. Kemi. Min. Geol.* **26**, B1

[6]Data Sheet AG/559. 'Feinberg Agar Gel Cutters.' London; Shandon Scientific Company

BIBLIOGRAPHY

Alexopoulos, C. J. (1952). *Introductory Mycology*, 1st ed. London; Chapman and Hall

Beadle, G. W. and Tatum, E. L. (1945). 'Neurospora II. Methods of Producing and Detecting Mutations Concerned with Nutritional Requirements.' *Amer. J. Bot.* **32**, 678–686

Begg, C. M. M. (1959). *An Introduction to Genetics*, 1st ed. London; English Universities Press

Bernhardt, E. (1946). 'Time Saving in the Preparation of Corn-meal Agar and in the Identification of Yeast-like Fungi.' *Mycologia* **38**, 228

Bold, H. C. (1942). 'The Cultivation of Algae.' *Bot. Rev.* **8**, 69–139

Camp, W. G. (1936). 'A Method of Cultivating Myxomycete Plasmodia.' *Bull. Torrey Bot. Club* **63**, 205–210

Cannon, H. G. (1941). 'A Note on Fine Needles for Dissection.' *J. Roy. micr. Soc.* **61**, 58

Caston, J. G. B. (1947). 'An Apparatus for Continuous Yeast Culture.' *Science*, **106**, 43

Durbin, R. D. (1961). 'Techniques for the Observation and Isolation of Soil Micro-organisms.' *Bot. Rev.* **27**, 522

Fennel, D. I., Raper, K. B. and Flickinger, M. H. (1950). 'Further Investigations on the Preservation of Mould Cultures.' *Mycologia* **42**, 135

Hawker, L. E., Linton, A. H., Folkes, B. F. and Carlile, M. J. (1960). *An Introduction to the Biology of Micro-organisms*, 1st ed. London; Arnold

Holden, H. S. (1935). 'A New Type of Culture Vessel.' *Ann. Bot., Lond.* **49**, 401

Mackie and McCartney (1960). *Handbook of Bacteriology*, 10th ed. Ed. by R. Cruickshank, Edinburgh; Livingstone

Malakoff, M. T. (1936). 'A Technique for the Slide Culture of Fungi.' *Science* **84**, 490

Pappas, G. D. and Hoffman, H. (1952). 'The Use of Antibiotics for Obtaining Bacteria Free Cultures of Euglena.' *Ohio J. Sci.* **52**, 102–105

Provasoli, L., Pinter, I. J. and Packer, L. (1951). 'Use of Antibiotics in Obtaining Pure Cultures of Algae and Protozoa.' *Proc. Am. Soc. Protozool* **2**, 6

Raper, K. B. (1951). 'Isolation, Cultivation and Conservation of Simple Slime Moulds.' *Quart. Rev. Biol.* **26**, 169

— and Alexander, D. F. (1945). 'Preservation of Moulds by the Lyophil Process.' *Mycologia* **37**, 499

Srb, A. M. and Owen, R. D. (1952). *General Genetics*, San Francisco; Freeman

Tatum, L., Barratt, R. W., Fries, N. and Bonner, D. (1950). 'Biochemical Mutant Strains of Neurospora Produced by Physical and Chemical Treatment.' *Amer. J. Bot.* **37**, 38–45

CHAPTER 11

GROWTH

Growth in plants may be defined as a permanent increase in size. It is generally measured as increase in length or height, or increase in volume or weight. When increase in weight is measured, it is usually preferable to measure change in dry weight, that is the weight of the plant after the water has been removed, since the water content of plants can vary quite considerably. However, sometimes, as for instance during the germination of seeds before photosynthesis begins, the dry weight of a plant drops while the plant is obviously growing; in this case, increase of fresh weight would be a better measure of growth.

Two processes must be distinguished in the growth of plants (a) cell division and (b) cell expansion. New cells are formed by division in the meristematic regions at the tips of both stems and roots. Just behind the region of cell division is a region of cell expansion; it is here that the maximum elongation of the stem or root takes place.

*Experiment I.—To Show the Region of Elongation in a Root**

For this experiment it is necessary to use germinated seeds which have straight, clean roots. If a large class experiment is planned, the seeds, broad beans for example, can be germinated in damp vermiculite but, where only one or two seedlings are needed, the following method is a better one. The broad bean seeds are soaked overnight and then they are pinned to the underside of corks, which are placed in the top of jars partially filled with water. Each seed should be suspended just above the level of the water. As the root grows, the seed can be adjusted so that the root is not immersed in the water because this slows down growth. Blot the root dry before marking.

When the root is 1–1^1/$_2$ in. long, it can be marked with a pen and Indian ink at millimetre intervals.

* The experiments described in this and the succeeding chapters on the physiological aspects of plant life, are ones which are used frequently for the botany degree course in the Botany Department, University College, London. Some experiments have also been drawn from Loomis and Shull—*Methods in Plant Physiology* and Machlis and Torrey—*Plants in Action.*

The root can be left to grow suspended from the cork over water overnight or it can be planted in damp vermiculite. After this time it will be seen that in the region just behind the root cap, the markings are spaced wider apart showing the region of elongation (*Figure 112*).

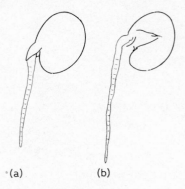

Figure 112. (a) Bean root marked at millimetre intervals; (b) same root after 24 hours, showing region of elongation

(a)　　　　　(b)

Experiment II.—To Show the Region of Elongation in a Shoot

A shoot of broad bean can be marked out in a similar manner to that of the root. It is advisable to use a shoot that has only one internode, as each internode has its own rate of growth.

In the case of the shoot, it will be seen that the main region of elongation is at the upper end of the internode (*Figure 113*).

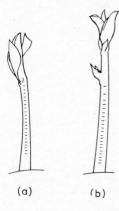

Figure 113. (a) Bean shoot marked at millimetre intervals; (b) showing region of elongation

(a)　　　　(b)

Experiment III.—Using a Smoked Drum Auxanometer (Farmer's Pattern)

The apparatus, as shown in *Figure 114*, consists of a drum covered with smoked paper, connected to a clock by means of a short arm.

The clock has four hands which can be set at fixed intervals from 15 min to 1 h. At the set time, the short arm from the drum engages one hand of the clock and this causes the drum to be rotated through a small arc of about 1 cm. When the clock hand is released, the drum is returned to its original position by means of a weight.

A long pointer of wood is necessary and this can be made for the experiment. It is supported by a clamp stand so that it will pivot freely. One end of the lever is attached to the tip of a growing plant and the other end has a bent, metal pin which marks the smoked drum when it is rotated. In this way an accurate daily record can be made of the growth of the plant.

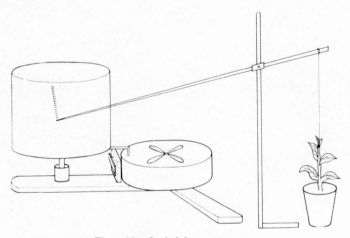

Figure 114. Smoked drum auxanometer

A smooth paper should be used to cover the drum and this is fixed securely with paste or Sellotape. The smoking of the drum is a messy operation and should be carried out in a fume cupboard. A piece of cotton wool is soaked in xylene or benzene and held with a pair of tongs. When this soaked cotton wool is lighted it produces clouds of black smoke. The paper covered drum should be turned carefully in the fumes so that it is covered evenly with a thin layer of soot. When the experiment is started, the time is scratched on the smoked paper.

If the pointer is pivoted so that there is a ratio of 10:1, then the distance between the horizontal scratches on the drum will be ten times the actual growth of the plant for the particular time set.

Experiment IV.—Using a Neilson–Jones Auxanometer

This apparatus consists of a gas jar fitted with a large cork. Through the cork are passed a 5 ml graduated pipette, half a knitting needle and a long hat pin.

Several precautions must be taken before setting up this experiment to ensure accurate results. The jar that is used must be acid washed and the base must be ground so that it is perfectly flat. It is also important that the cork is a very good fit.

A broad bean or pea seedling is impaled on the pin so that the tip of its root is approximately level with the tip of the knitting needle. About one third of the jar is filled with water and the knitting needle

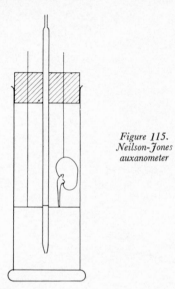

Figure 115.
Neilson-Jones
auxanometer

and the root tip are adjusted so that they both just touch the surface of the water (*Figure 115*). At intervals, water is sucked up into the pipette so that both the root tip and the end of the needle are above the water level. The water is allowed to run back slowly into the jar until the level just touches the root tip. At this point, a note is made of the volume of the water in the pipette. More water from the pipette is run into the jar until it is level with the tip of the knitting needle. Again the volume in the pipette is noted. The difference between the two volumes in the pipette is proportional to the distance between the root tip and the tip of the needle.

Experiment V.—Using a Cathetometer

This is essentially a low-powered microscope consisting of an objective, an eye-piece, a coarse-adjustment for the horizontal plane and another for the perpendicular.

There is a spirit level on top so that the horizontal position of the apparatus can be checked and this position can be adjusted by screws on the three feet (*Figure 116*).

If any difficulty is experienced obtaining a simple cathetometer (modern cathetometers have become extremely complex and expensive), a relatively inexpensive reading telescope will serve the purpose.

A germinated broad bean seedling can be pinned on to the underside of a cork in a flat sided vessel and set up in front of the cathetometer. Using a micrometer eye-piece, the growth of the root can be measured.

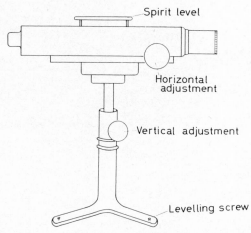

Figure 116. Cathetometer

Experiment VI.—Measurement of Leaf Growth

In this experiment an imprint of a leaf is obtained by placing it over a photographic document paper and exposing it to a light source. At intervals of a few days, other imprints are obtained of the same leaf to show the amount of growth produced. The area of the document paper which has been covered by the leaf is white, against a black background, and the outline can be traced with a planimeter to give the surface area of the leaf.

Any actively growing plant can be chosen for this experiment, such as Pelargonium, and the first stage must be carried out in a darkened room. A piece of document paper, cut so that it is slightly larger than the leaf, is placed under the leaf with the emulsion side in contact with the leaf surface. Care must be taken that the leaf does not become detached from the plant. Two pieces of glass are used to keep the leaf in contact with the photographic paper. One piece is placed over the paper behind the leaf and the other is placed over the surface of the leaf (*Figure 117*).

These are held in position while the leaf is exposed to a 500W light source for 1 sec. The document paper is developed in Contrast

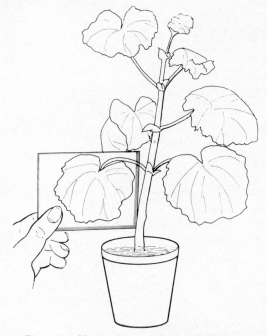

Figure 117. Photographic measurement of leaf growth

FF developer (diluted 1 part developer:5 parts water) for 45 sec, rinsed and fixed. After washing under running water for several hours, the paper is dried and the outline of the leaf can be traced. This is done with a planimeter. A set of instructions is issued with each instrument. The carriage is adjusted to the correct position on the tracer arm and the pole needle point is placed in a convenient position outside the leaf area so that the whole area can be covered by the tracer point. The tracer arm is moved in a clockwise direction and the number of revolutions of the measuring wheel can be converted to a measurement of area by a table supplied with the instrument. With the vernier scale, an accurate reading can be obtained.

Alternatively, the leaf can be covered with a piece of tracing paper which is marked out with a grid and the leaf area estimated by counting the number of squares.

Experiment VII.—Changes in Weight of Seedlings

A number of seedlings, peas for example, are germinated in damp vermiculite and, at set time intervals, a few are removed and weighed. A growth curve can be built up by plotting the time intervals against the weights of the seedlings.

At the beginning of the experiment, it is important to have a batch of seedlings which are uniform in growth, otherwise discrepancies will arise. It is also important to record the fresh weight and the dry weight of each batch of plant material since there is not necessarily an increase in both weights. This may be observed if fresh and dry weights are recorded of germinating seeds. The fresh weight will certainly increase but the dry weight will decrease owing to the using up of stored food material in the seed. When photosynthesis begins, a corresponding increase in the dry weight will be observed.

Each batch of seedlings should be washed in water to remove the vermiculite, laid on blotting paper to remove any excess water and then weighed in a tared beaker (fresh weight). To obtain the dry weight, the seedlings are then placed in a drying oven at 100°C overnight, cooled in a desiccator and weighed again. Several weighings should be made and drying should be continued until a constant weight is recorded.

TROPISMS IN PLANTS

A tropism is a response to a stimulus, such as gravity or light.

GEOTROPISM

In general, the roots of plants grow towards the gravitational stimulus while their stems grow away from it. Roots are thus said to be positively geotropic and stems negatively geotropic.

While the shoot and the root remain parallel to the line of the force of gravity, normal straight growth occurs, but when they occupy a position other than vertical, a curvature takes place. This curvature occurs in the actively elongating part of the organ concerned and it can be demonstrated by the following experiment.

Experiment VIII.—To Demonstrate Geotropism

Seedlings of peas or beans can be used for this experiment. The seeds are germinated and allowed to grow until the roots are 1–1^1/$_2$ in. long. A gas jar is lined with two layers of damp blotting paper and a little water is poured into the bottom of the jar to keep the paper moist. A piece of sheet cork is then cut to fit, so that it will stand firmly in the middle of the jar. The seedlings are pinned to the cork, one in a normal position with the root pointing downwards, another so that the root is horizontal and a third, with its root tip removed, is also placed horizontally.

After about 12 h it will be seen that the seedling with the root pointing downwards has continued to grow normally, while the first root which was placed horizontally has curved so that the tip is now

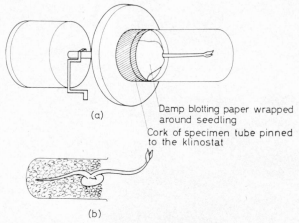

(a)

Damp blotting paper wrapped around seedling

Cork of specimen tube pinned to the klinostat

(b)

Figure 118. (a) Seedling rotated on klinostat; (b) seedling placed on the bench

pointing downwards. The third seedling, with the root tip removed, will have grown slightly but will not be curved, showing that the sensitive region was absent.

Sunflower seedlings can be used to demonstrate geotropism in the shoot. The seedlings are grown in damp vermiculite until the shoots are 4–5 in. long. Each seedling is then placed in a container of water and the shoot is tied in a horizontal position to a backboard of cork.

As the shoot grows, the upward curves can be marked on the cork sheet.

Klinostat—A klinostat can be used to rotate the plant in a horizontal position so that the influence of gravity affects all sides equally. The klinostat consists of a holder for the plant, which is connected to an electric motor or a clockwork mechanism. Two actively growing seedlings in specimen tubes are required for this experiment; broad beans are suitable. One plant is fixed on the klinostat and the other is placed in a horizontal position on the bench (*Figure 118*).

At the end of the experiment it will be seen that no curvature has taken place in the seedling attached to the klinostat, while the plant in the fixed horizontal position has a decided curve. This experiment should last for 24 h and should be carried out in the dark in order to avoid any complications due to phototropism.

Experiment IX.—To Demonstrate Phototropism

Grass seedlings are useful for demonstrating phototropism and seedlings of oats are excellent. The seeds should be germinated in the dark and allowed to grow until the coleoptiles are about $^1/_2$ in long.

A number of small caps of tin foil are prepared. This can be done by rolling each piece of foil round a small piece of a matchstick and screwing each one at the top. These caps are placed over the tips of half the number of growing seedlings. All the seedlings are exposed to a one sided light source. This can be done by fixing a tungsten filament lamp inside a cardboard box with a slit in one side. The seedlings are placed in front of the box and left for 24 h.

As the tip of the shoot is the region of perception, it will be seen that the capped seedlings remain in an upright position while the others will be curved towards the source of light.

NUTRIENT SOLUTIONS

Experiment X.—Water Cultures

Many seedlings can be grown successfully in nutrient solutions, e.g. buckwheat, sunflower. An experiment can be carried out to demonstrate the growth of seedlings using a series of nutrient solutions where certain mineral salts have been omitted.

Complete solution (Sachs)

Calcium sulphate	0·25 g
Calcium phosphate	0·25 g
Magnesium sulphate	0·25 g
Sodium chloride	0·08 g
Potassium nitrate	0·70 g
Ferric chloride	0·005 g
Water	1 l.

Solution minus calcium—For calcium sulphate use potassium sulphate 0·20 g; for calcium phosphate use sodium phosphate 0·71 g.

Solution minus iron—Omit Ferric chloride.

Solution minus nitrogen—For potassium nitrate use potassium chloride 0·52 g.

Solution minus phosphorus—For calcium phosphate use calcium nitrate 0·16 g.

Solution minus sulphur—For calcium sulphate use calcium chloride 0·16 g; for magnesium sulphate use magnesium chloride 0·21 g.

Solution minus magnesium—For magnesium sulphate use potassium sulphate 0·17 g.

Solution minus potassium—For potassium nitrate use sodium nitrate 0·59 g.

Large glass jars are covered with black paper, to prevent algal growth, and are fitted with corks. Two holes are drilled through each cork, one large enough to take the seedling, allowing for its growth and the other to take a narrow piece of bent glass tubing to the bottom of the jar.

The seeds can be germinated on damp blotting paper or in damp vermiculite. As soon as the seedlings are large enough to handle, they are supported in the cork by a small plug of non-absorbent cotton wool. Air is blown through the glass tube by means of a bicycle pump; this should be carried out each day to prevent stagnation of the solution. The experiment should be allowed to continue for at least one month and records should be made of the different rates of growth and the appearance of the seedlings.

It is sometimes easier to pin the seedling through a piece of sheet cork which is cut to fit the jar and which will float on top of the solution.

An experiment which uses a small quantity of nutrient solution can be set up, using 3 in. × 1 in. specimen tubes instead of large jars; for this demonstration cress seedlings are useful.

GROWTH SUBSTANCES

Past research work has shown that there are active substances in the roots and shoots of plants, which regulate growth. The natural distribution of varying concentrations of these substances can inhibit or stimulate growth. The tropisms demonstrated in previous experiments (p. 293) are the result of this activity. Apart from the naturally occurring growth substances, numerous synthetic compounds have been found to have a similar effect on plant growth.

Plants can be treated experimentally with these substances, which are known to be effective in very low concentrations. The roots are even more sensitive than the shoots in this respect. (Higher concentrations can be toxic.)

One of the important natural growth substances is indole acetic acid (I.A.A.). This can be applied to root systems in dilute solution but is more conveniently used in paste form on shoots. The preparation of both solutions and pastes is given below.

Preparation of Growth Substance Solutions

Dissolve 0·1 g of indole acetic acid in 1 ml of ethanol and make up to 100 ml with warm distilled water. This will give a 1:1,000 solution; using this as a stock solution, make the following dilutions.

        40   ml stock diluted to 100 ml 1: 2,500 solution
        10   ml stock diluted to 100 ml 1:10,000 solution
         4   ml stock diluted to 100 ml 1:25,000 solution
     1·25 ml stock diluted to 100 ml 1:80,000 solution

The remainder of the stock solution should be kept in the refrigerator.

Preparation of Pastes

Each batch of paste will require 10 ml of dilute solution (A) and 10 g of lanolin (B).

Method—A and B are heated separately to 60°C, then B is added to A while being stirred continuously. The stirring should continue until an homogenous cream is obtained. This cream will thicken upon cooling, when it is ready for use. Note should be made that the resultant paste will contain half the concentration of indole acetic acid present in the initial dilute solution, for example a paste made with a 1:2,500 solution will result in a 1:5,000 paste.

The effects of growth substances such as naphthalene acetic acid (N.A.A.) and the gibberillins can be studied similarly as can 2,4-dichlorophenoxyacetic acid (2,4-D) which causes extremely abnormal growth usually resulting in death.

As with indole acetic acid, these compounds are effective in very low concentrations. They are best used as solutions.

BIBLIOGRAPHY

Audus, L. J. (1959). *Plant Growth Substances*, 1st ed. London; Leonard Hill
4th International Congress on Plant Growth Regulation (1961). *Plant Growth Regulation*, U.S.A.; Iowa State University Press
Leopold, A. C. (1964). *Plant Growth and Development*, 1st ed. New York; McGraw Hill
Skoog, F. (Ed.) (1951). *Plant Growth Substances*, 1st ed. Milwaukee; University of Wisconsin Press

Brimble, L. J. F. (1957). *Intermediate Botany*, 4th ed. London; Macmillan

Hentschel, C. C. and Ivimey Cook, W. R. (1947). *Biology for Medical Students*, 4th ed. London; Longmans, Green

James, W. O. (1950). *An Introduction to Plant Physiology*, 4th ed. London; Oxford University Press

Miller, E. C. (1938). *Plant Physiology*, 2nd ed. London and New York; McGraw-Hill

Vines, A. E. and Rees, N. (1964). *Plant and Animal Biology*, Vol. II, 2nd ed. London; Pitman

CHAPTER 12

PHOTOSYNTHESIS AND RESPIRATION

PHOTOSYNTHESIS

Photosynthesis, or carbon assimilation, is the process by which green plants, with the aid of light energy, synthesize organic substances from atmospheric carbon dioxide and water. During this process oxygen is liberated; an overall equation can be written:

$$6\ CO_2 + 6H_2O \xrightarrow[\text{chlorophyll}]{\text{light}} C_6\ H_{12}\ O_6 + 6O_2$$

carbon dioxide + water   carbohydrate + oxygen

The green chlorophyll pigments, which are essential for the absorption of light energy by the plant, are located in small green bodies, called chloroplasts, in the plant cells.

All green parts of plants can photosynthesize but most photosynthesis takes place in the leaves, carbon dioxide from the air diffusing into the leaves through the stomata. The organic products of photosynthesis are varied but in many plants the products are stored temporarily in the leaves as sugars or starch before being translocated to other parts of the plant. Since starch can be readily detected visually by the blue-black colour it gives with iodine, this test for the presence of starch is a convenient method of demonstrating the occurrence of photosynthesis.

The chloroplasts of flowering plants contain two green chlorophyll pigments, chlorophyll *a* and chlorophyll *b*, together with two yellow-orange pigments, carotene and xanthophyll. All these pigments are probably essential for photosynthesis, the green ones for the absorption of light energy while the yellow pigments appear to protect the green ones from the bleaching effect of light. All the pigments can be extracted by alcohol or acetone and the mixture separated into its component parts.

Other photosynthetic plants include the algae and some of the bacteria. Photosynthesis in algae is similar to that in higher plants but some of the pigments differ. The pigments of photosynthetic bacteria are different again but the characteristic feature of bacterial photosynthesis is that oxygen is never produced.

Experiment I.—To Demonstrate that Carbon Dioxide is Necessary for Photosynthesis

Two healthy plants, such as Pelargonium should be taken which have been kept in the dark for 12 h. One leaf from each plant should be tested to check that there is no starch present. This is done by immersing the leaves in boiling water, decolourizing them in 95 per cent alcohol in a beaker on a hot plate, rinsing with water and then testing with iodine solution (p. 184). There should be no reaction with the iodine at the beginning of the experiment.

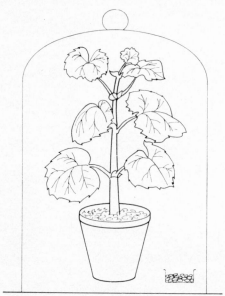

Figure 119. To demonstrate that carbon dioxide is necessary for photosynthesis

One plant is placed in a polythene bag or under a bell jar (*Figure 119*), with a small dish containing sodium hydroxide (flakes or pellets) to take up the carbon dioxide which is present in the air. The other plant is left untreated. Both plants are placed in strong sunlight for several hours. In the absence of sunlight the plants should be illuminated artificially. A ring of tungsten filament lamps or a fluorescent tube is suitable.

After several hours illumination, a leaf from each plant is detached. They are immersed in boiling water and decolourized in

95 per cent alcohol on a hot-plate. The leaves are rinsed with water and tested with iodine solution.

The leaf taken from the plant under the bell jar, which has been deprived of carbon dioxide, will not react at all. The leaf from the untreated plant, however, will show a blue-black colour.

The former treatment, giving a negative result, shows an absence of starch and therefore that photosynthesis is not taking place. The latter treatment, giving a positive result, shows that starch is present and that there is normal photosynthetic activity.

Experiment Ia—This experiment, and the following one, are useful if plant material is in short supply.

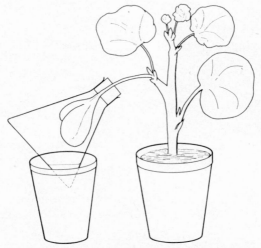

Figure 120. To demonstrate that carbon dioxide is necessary for photosynthesis

One healthy pot plant of Pelargonium is used which has been left in the dark for 12 h. A 500 ml conical flask with a rubber bung to fit it is taken; a hole is bored in the bung and it is slit vertically through to the hole. The slit is pulled open and slipped round the petiole of one leaf on the specimen plant, with the tapered end towards the leaf. 10 ml of 40 per cent sodium hydroxide solution is poured into the bottom of the flask. The petiole of the leaf is carefully bent and the leaf slid into the flask. The bung is pushed well into the neck of the flask, which can be supported in another flower pot (*Figure 120*). As in the previous experiment, after several hours of illumination the treated leaf is detached from the plant and tested for starch.

Since this leaf has been deprived of carbon dioxide the reaction with iodine will be negative, whereas the reaction in the leaves which have been exposed to the atmosphere will be positive, showing that starch is present and proving that there has been normal photosynthesis taking place.

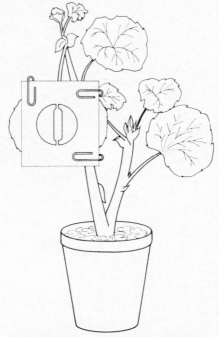

Figure 121. To demonstrate that light is necessary for photosynthesis showing stencils in position

Experiment Ib—Leaf discs can be used for this experiment. These discs are cut from a leaf using a No. 4 cork borer. Half the number of discs (8 or 9) are placed on damp filter paper, in an open Petri dish the other half are placed in an open Petri dish, which is in turn placed inside a desiccator containing a small beaker of 40 per cent sodium hydroxide. The two dishes are illuminated and tested as in Experiment I.

Experiment II.—To Demonstrate that Light is Necessary for Photosynthesis

A potted plant of Pelargonium which has been kept in the dark for 12 h is used. Two stencils are taken, one is placed on top of the leaf and the other directly underneath. These are held in position with paper clips (*Figure 121*). After illuminating for several hours, the stencils are removed, the leaf is decolourized and tested for starch. It will be found that the portion shielded from the light with the stencils has no starch present, whereas the rest of the leaf shows the presence of starch.

The reason for the preliminary treatment of the plant in all these experiments is now apparent. If the plant is left in the dark for a prolonged period, the process of photosynthesis cannot continue and, during the period of darkness, the sugar required by the plant must come from the starch which is stored during periods of light. This starch is reconverted to sugar, which is translocated to the various parts of the plant which require sugar. So, at the end of a prolonged period of darkness, the leaves will be starch free, and can be treated in a way necessary to show the limitations of photosynthesis.

Leaf discs can also be used for this experiment. The discs are placed on damp filter paper in open Petri dishes. One dish is placed in the dark and the other is illuminated. Starch is tested for as in the previous experiment.

Experiment III.—To Show that Chlorophyll must be Present for Photosynthesis to take Place

A potted plant of variegated Pelargonium which has been kept in the dark until starch-free, is chosen. The plant is left exposed to

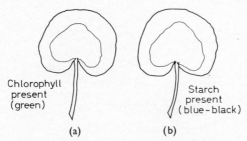

Chlorophyll present (green)

Starch present (blue-black)

(a)   (b)

Figure 122. (a) Variegated leaf untreated—the central portion is green showing that chlorophyll is present; (b) the same leaf after treatment showing the presence of starch

illumination without further treatment. After several hours a leaf is detached and a drawing made to show the area and position of the green portion of the leaf. The leaf is then decolourized and tested for starch. The intense blue-black staining, due to the presence of

303

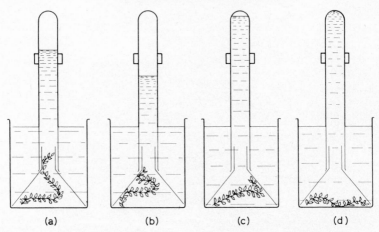

Figure 123. To demonstrate oxygen evolution (a) tap water; (b) tap water with a little potassium bicarbonate added; (c) boiled water; (d) kept in the dark

starch, will be seen only in the area of the leaf which was green before decolourizing (*Figure 122*), proving that chlorophyll must be present if the plant is to photosynthesize. The cream coloured parts will give a negative reaction.

Experiment IV.—To Show that Oxygen is Given off During Photosynthesis

For this experiment it is convenient to use an aquatic green plant, since any gas given off during photosynthesis may be collected by downward displacement of water.

A healthy plant of Elodea is chosen and placed in a 600 ml beaker. A funnel, slightly smaller than the diameter of the beaker, is taken and placed over the plant so as to cover it completely. It is important to use a funnel with a short stem or one that has been cut down. The beaker is filled with water until the surface is $1/2$ in. above the stem of the funnel. A test tube is filled with water, and a finger placed over the mouth of the tube which is then inverted. The inverted tube is placed in the beaker and, when the mouth is below the surface, the finger can be removed. The tube is slid over the end of the funnel stem. The beaker is placed in sunlight, if possible, or illuminated as in previous experiments. Bubbles of gas should soon rise in the funnel stem and so up into the tube. When sufficient gas has been collected by the downward displacement of the water, remove the tube from the water and insert a glowing splint into the mouth. If enough gas has been collected the splint will relight, showing the gas to be oxygen.

The carbon dioxide, used during photosynthesis in this case, was atmospheric carbon dioxide dissolved in the water. If the carbon dioxide concentration is raised by adding a little potassium bicarbonate, the rate of photosynthesis, and therefore the oxygen evolution, will be speeded up. Alternatively, no oxygen will be evolved if the experimental water is boiled to drive off carbon dioxide and then cooled before use.

The need for light can also be demonstrated by placing the beaker in the dark, when once again no oxygen will be evolved.

Four beakers can be set up, as shown in *Figure 123*, to show these effects.

The last experiment demonstrated qualitatively the production of oxygen by a water plant during photosynthesis. The oxygen production can be estimated quantitatively if the experiment is carried out in such a manner that all the oxygen produced remains dissolved in solution and none is evolved as gas.

Experiment V.—The Winkler Method for the Estimation of Dissolved Oxygen

During this experiment a series of chemical reactions is brought about by analysing a known volume of the solution. The last reaction liberates a product which can be titrated with a standard solution of sodium thiosulphate.

If it is known that:

1 ml 0·01N thiosulphate ≡ 0·0558 ml oxygen ≡ 0·08 mg oxygen,

then, from the result of the titration, the amount of oxygen present may be calculated.

Reagents required:

A 40 per cent manganous chloride: 40 g manganous chloride made up to 100 ml with distilled water.

B 10 g potassium iodide plus 70 g potassium hydroxide dissolved in 100 ml distilled water.

C Standard 0·01N sodium thiosulphate solution; 1,000 ml is a suitable quantity to prepare.

D Concentrated hydrochloric acid.

E 1 per cent starch solution: 1 g of soluble starch mixed to a paste with a little water and made up to 100 ml with boiling water. Care must be taken to stir well while the boiling water is being added.

In addition to these reagents, a number of acid-clean 60 ml bottles with well fitting stoppers will be required and also a quantity of water. The water should be allowed to stand for 24 h at about 25°C.

The reason for this preliminary warming is that, at low temperatures, water will be more saturated with oxygen than at higher temperatures. Upon warming, oxygen will separate out from the water in the form of bubbles. This separation must be avoided in the experimental bottles, by prewarming the water for 24 h. After this time the separation of excess oxygen will be complete and the water will be ready for use.

The photosynthetic organism used during this estimation is the green alga *Chlorella*.

Method—Solutions A, B and D are placed into burettes. The jets of the burettes are extended by joining a piece of glass tubing, drawn out into a jet, with a piece of rubber tubing. This extension should enable the tip of the jet to reach the bottom of the 60 ml bottles. Six bottles are used. Into each bottle is pipetted 5 ml of *Chlorella* suspension (1·0 mg dry weight per ml in dilute magnesium sulphate) and 5 ml of M/7·5 potassium bicarbonate to act as a source of carbon dioxide. The effect of various external factors may be observed, using this method, such as the effect of light intensity, darkness, CO_2 concentration etc. The experimental bottles exposed to these varying factors should be left for 1 h. Two control bottles should be analysed immediately in the following way: each stopper should be removed in turn and 0·5 ml of solution A run into the bottom of the bottles. Next 1 ml of solution B is added and the bottles stoppered quickly and carefully. The contents of the bottles are mixed by rotating them between the hands. The precipitate is allowed to settle before adding 2 ml of solution D to the bottom of the bottles. These are restoppered, and on mixing again the precipitate will redissolve. The addition of these reagents will kill the *Chlorella* cells and stop further evolution of oxygen. The contents of these two bottles may be titrated immediately to give the initial oxygen concentration, or left until the experimental bottles are ready for analysis. The titration is carried out in the following manner.

The contents of the control bottles are transferred to two 250 ml flasks and each titrated with 0·01N sodium thiosulphate solution (soln. C), adding a few drops of starch solution (soln. E) as an indicator when the end-point is approached. The total oxygen dissolved in the solution in each bottle is calculated. The average of the two estimations will be the initial oxygen concentration.

After 1 h the Winkler reagents are added to the experimental bottles and analysed as for the initial oxygen concentration. As the amount of *Chlorella* used is known, the percentage of oxygen evolved may be calculated, after subtracting the initial oxygen concentration.

EXTRACTION OF CHLOROPHYLL

Before chlorophyll can be examined it must be extracted from plant material. For this, it is convenient to use dried nettle leaf powder.

This powder can be prepared in the following way. The leaves are allowed to dry naturally on trays or a bench top and are turned daily. When they are completely dry they are passed through a mill. The resultant powder may be kept indefinitely.

Mix 3 g of the powder in a beaker with 40 ml 80 per cent acetone. When the solution is well coloured with pigments, it should be filtered through a Buchner funnel, the extract placed in a separating funnel and 40 ml of petroleum ether added. It is mixed by rotating between the hands then, holding the stopper in place, the funnel is inverted and the pressure released by opening the tap. 70 ml of distilled water is run down the inside of the funnel which is again rotated gently to mix. The pigments will pass into the ethereal layer. The bottom layer from the funnel is run off and the upper layer washed twice with water. The upper layer is then run off and divided into two portions. To one portion 20 ml of 92 per cent methyl alcohol is added. Two layers will separate out, the ethereal layer containing the blue-green pigment chlorophyll *a* and the alcoholic layer containing the pure green chlorophyll *b*.

To the other half of the original ethereal extract, 8 ml of 30 per cent potassium hydroxide in methyl alcohol is added and mixed well. After the green colouration has disappeared, 40 ml water is added and the mixture allowed to separate. The upper ethereal layer will contain the pigments carotene and xanthophyll.

The pigments extracted in the above manner may be separated from the petroleum ether extract by means of simple chromatography in the following manner.

Experiment VI.—Chromatographic Separation of Pigments

A small evaporating basin is taken and a circle of Whatman No. 4 filter paper placed on it. 1 ml of petroleum ether extract is spotted on to the centre of the filter paper which can be dried, by using a hair drier, as each drop is added to the paper. When the 1 ml concentrated spot has been thoroughly dried, the evaporating basin and filter paper are removed to a fume cupboard. The chromatogram is developed by dropping carbon disulphide on the spot of mixed pigments. As the carbon disulphide spreads outwards, so the pigments should separate into distinct bands of chlorophyll *a*, chlorophyll *b* and xanthophyll. Carotene is very seldom seen by this method, which is not always successful.

Experiment VII.—Separation of Pigments by Column Chromatography

A piece of soda glass tubing, approximately $5/8$ in. diameter and 6 in. long is taken. One end of the tube should be rotated in a bunsen flame until the opening is practically closed. It is allowed to cool, and then the base of the tube is plugged with a little glass wool (glass wool should not be handled with the fingers; forceps should be used). The tube is filled with magnesium oxide (heavy) powder. As the powder is added little by little, it is packed down by ramming with a glass rod. It is essential that this packing down is done thoroughly and uniformly. Another plug of glass wool is placed on top of the column, which is then placed into a rubber bung in a Buchner flask, and the flask attached to a filter pump. 40 ml of the petroleum ether extract (prepared as on p. 307) is poured on to the column and suction applied until all but a small amount has run through, then the suction is immediately stopped.

The column is developed by sucking through 50 ml of petroleum ether containing 5 per cent acetone and 0·5 per cent ethanol (ethyl alcohol). The pigments will separate by moving down the column in bands. The yellow pigments will separate first and will move ahead of the blue-green chlorophyll *a*. The last pigment to appear will be the slowest moving chlorophyll *b*.

RESPIRATION

During the plant's entire life, food stores are built up and broken down. This breaking down process is respiration. During this process, molecular oxygen is taken in and the stored carbohydrates are broken down, with the evolution of carbon dioxide and energy in the form of heat. Since molecular oxygen is used, this process can be called aerobic respiration as opposed to anaerobic respiration during which molecular oxygen is not available. Most plants respire aerobically but some, however, produce carbon dioxide and energy in the absence of oxygen; this is the process known as anaerobic respiration or fermentation In this case, carbohydrate is broken down to form chiefly ethyl alcohol, carbon dioxide and energy. The overall equations for the two types of respiration are as follows:

(1) Aerobic respiration:
$$C_6H_{12}O_6 + 6O_2 \rightarrow 6CO_2 + 6H_2O + \text{energy}$$

(2) Anaerobic respiration:
$$C_6H_{12}O_6 \rightarrow 2CO_2 + 2C_2H_5OH + \text{energy}$$

In plants which naturally require molecular oxygen, aerobic respiration continues throughout the plant life until natural death occurs. The anaerobic respiration of the same plants will last only for a limited time, whilst some lower plants, such as yeast, can respire for an extended period before the accumulation of alcohol causes death.

The true anaerobes are organisms which cannot respire in the presence of free oxygen.

The following experiment can be carried out to examine the various aspects of respiration.

Experiment VIII.—Demonstration of CO_2 Evolution by Flow System

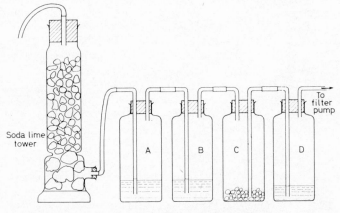

Figure 124. Carbon dioxide evolution demonstrated by a flow system. A and B contain arbitrary quantities of barium hydroxide solution; C contains germinating peas; D contains 50 ml of barium hydroxide solution

The object of this experiment is to allow plant material to respire in a carbon dioxide free atmosphere, and to examine quantitatively the gas respired. This is carried out by means of a flow system where a stream of CO_2 free air is passed over the plant material. The flow system is set up in the following manner.

Connect a soda lime tower to a series of gas jars or bottles A, B, C and D as in *Figure 124*.

The jars or bottles should be fairly tall and narrow and joined to each other by means of delivery tubes. The entry tube must extend to the bottom of each bottle and the exit tube should begin just below the cork, except in jar C where this procedure is reversed.

The corks plus delivery tubes should be removed from the four jars A, B, C and D. An arbitrary quantity of 0·01N barium hydroxide solution (3·15 g/l. made up in CO_2 free water, i.e. distilled water boiled in a conical flask and cooled with a bung carrying a soda lime tube in place) is placed in jars A and B. A weighed sample of plant material, such as peas soaked overnight in water, is placed in jar C and black polythene wrapped round the jar. Exactly 50 ml of 0·01N barium hydroxide solution should be pipetted into jar D and a few drops of phenolphthalein solution added. The corks and delivery tubes are replaced, but jar D is not connected. A filter pump is attached to jar C and air is carefully drawn through the system so flushing out any CO_2 which may be present. The filter pump is disconnected and jar D connected to the flow system. By means of the filter pump, air is drawn through the entire system for a set period of time, say 1–2 h. At the end of this time, jar D is disconnected and the partially neutralized barium hydroxide solution is titrated with 0·01N hydrochloric acid. A fresh 50 ml of 0·01N barium hydroxide is placed in a conical flask, with a few drops of phenolphthalein added, and titrated with 0·01N hydrochloric acid. The result of the first titration is subtracted from that of the last. This will give an indirect measurement of the amount of barium carbonate which has been precipitated and therefore the amount of carbon dioxide evolved during respiration.

Should an algal suspension be used as the experimental plant material, then the position of the delivery tubes in jar C should be reversed, i.e. the entry tube should extend to the bottom of the jar and the exit tube should extend just below the cork. Should a potted plant be used, a bell jar should replace jar C. Any photosynthetic plant material should be excluded from the light by wrapping the container, i.e. bell jar or gas jar, with black polythene. In the case of a potted plant, the pot should be placed in a polythene bag to prevent the gases from the soil being carried through the system.

ANAEROBIC RESPIRATION

During the preceding experiment the plant material respired aerobically, i.e. in the presence of oxygen. Most plants, however, continue to produce carbon dioxide in the absence of oxygen. This is called anaerobic respiration or fermentation. During this process, carbohydrate is broken down to give chiefly ethyl alcohol and carbon dioxide. The anaerobic respiration of a green plant lasts only for a limited time whilst some lower plants, such as yeast, can respire for an extended period before the accumulation of ethyl alcohol causes death. The true anaerobes are mostly bacteria of the type which cause gangrene and food poisoning.

Experiment IX.—To Demonstrate Anaerobic Respiration of Seeds of Green Plant Material

Four or five pea seeds should be soaked overnight. A boiling tube 1 in. × 6 in. and the base of a pin dish or an evaporating basin approximately 3 in. diameter should be used. The boiling tube is completely filled with mercury and about $^3/_4$–1 in. of mercury is poured into the dish. Holding a square of polythene tightly over the mouth of the tube, the tube is inverted in the dish of mercury and the polythene is then pulled away. The soaked peas are slipped under the mouth of the tube with forceps. The peas will rise to the top of the tube. The boiling tube is supported with a clamp and the peas left to respire for 24 h (*Figure 125*). At the end of this time the

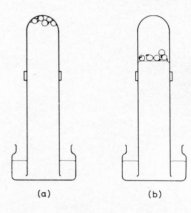

(a)   (b)

Figure 125. Demonstration of anaerobic respiration: (a) germinating peas in an inverted test tube filled with mercury; (b) after 24 h, showing gas evolved during respiration

mercury will have become depressed and the peas will be surrounded by a pocket of gas. Two or three pellets of potassium or sodium hydroxide can now be inserted into the tube so that they travel to the surface of the mercury. After a while the level of the mercury will rise again as the gas is absorbed by the caustic pellets. This absorption shows that the gas is carbon dioxide.

Experiment X.—To Demonstrate Anaerobic Respiration of Yeast

A suspension of yeast is made by stirring 15 ml of water into 4 g of bakers' yeast. This suspension is placed in a boiling tube together with a small inverted test tube which is evacuated in the following manner. A good quality cork or rubber bung, of a size to fit the boiling tube, is taken and two holes are bored through it to take two pieces of glass tubing. One of these tubes is connected to a filter pump. The bung is placed into the mouth of the boiling tube and the pump turned on, a finger being placed over the other outlet tube; this will cause the tube to become evacuated. As soon as the yeast suspension bubbles slightly, the vacuum should be released by pulling the finger away from the outlet tube. As the air enters the boiling tube the yeast suspension will fill the inverted test tube. At this time, the amount of air, if any, still trapped in the inverted tube is noted. The rubber bung is removed and the neck of the tube plugged loosely with cotton wool. The boiling tube is placed in a 40°C incubator or water bath for 10 min. At the end of this time any change in the amount of gas in the inverted tube is observed. A knife point of glucose is now added to the yeast suspension and this re-incubated (*Figure 126*).

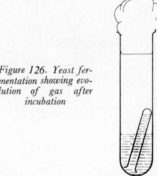

Figure 126. Yeast fermentation showing evolution of gas after incubation

Once again the amount of gas in the inverted tube is noted. There will be a marked increase in volume, showing the evolution of a gas after the addition of glucose. A pellet of sodium or potassium hydroxide is dropped into the yeast suspension and agitated carefully to assist the dispersal of the caustic substance. Again the volume of gas is observed. It will be seen that the volume will decrease as the gas is absorbed by the caustic solution, showing it to be carbon dioxide.

Experiment XI.—Anaerobic Respiration Demonstrated by the Flow System

The flow system in Experiment VIII may be used to demonstrate anaerobic respiration, by detaching the soda lime tower and the filter pump and attaching an oxygen free nitrogen cylinder to jar A.

The apparatus is set up and the analysis carried out as for Experiment VIII using germinating peas. An algal suspension is not suitable material.

As respiration is taking place under anaerobic conditions, ethyl alcohol will build up in the plant cells causing collapse and death, so the evolution of carbon dioxide will stop.

Apart from the evolution of carbon dioxide during aerobic respiration, and to a lesser extent anaerobic respiration, a large amount of energy is released. This energy causes a rise in temperature which can be measured in the following experiment.

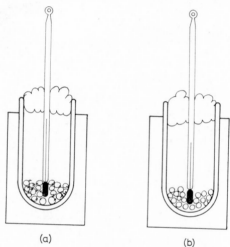

(a)   (b)

Figure 127. Demonstration of heat evolved during respiration: (a) with germinating peas; (b) with boiled peas

Experiment XII.—*To Demonstrate that Heat is Evolved During Respiration*

Two samples of pea seeds, say 30 seeds in each sample, are taken. One set of seeds is soaked overnight, then placed on damp muslin stretched loosely over a dish containing a little water. When the peas have begun to germinate (2 days) the other set of seeds should be boiled to kill them and left until they are cold. A sample from each group of seeds is placed in a vacuum flask, the live seeds in one flask (a), the boiled seeds in another (b) (*see Figure 127*). Some cotton wool is wrapped round a 0–110°C thermometer and made into a tight plug to fit the mouth of each flask. The plugs are placed in the mouths of the vacuum flasks and the temperature noted.

Occasionally bacterial growth may occur in control flask (b) and it is advisable to use a second control in which the pea seeds have been boiled with mercuric chloride or sulphate. The pea seeds are allowed to respire overnight and the gradual rise in temperature in the jar containing the live peas is observed. The peas which have been killed, on the other hand, will show no rise in temperature as no respiration has taken place.

Respiration may be measured very accurately by manometric methods. Owing to the rather complicated apparatus and mode of practice required for these methods, they will be described in detail in Chapter 14.

BIBLIOGRAPHY

Cassels Steele, C. (1934). *An Introduction to Plant Biochemistry*, 1st ed. London Bell

James, W. O. (1953). *Plant Respiration*, 1st ed. Oxford; Clarendon Press

Rabinowitch, E. I. (1945). *Photosynthesis, Vol. I.*, 1st ed. New York; Interscience

— (1951). *Photosynthesis, Vol. II.* (Part I) 1st ed. New York; Interscience

— (1956). *Photosynthesis, Vol. II.* (Part II) 1st ed. New York; Interscience

Spoehr, H. A. (1926). *Photosynthesis*, 1st ed. U.S.A.; Chemical Catalogue Co

Terrier, J., Touffant, G. and Carles, J. (1957). *Photosynthesis*, 1st ed. London; Hutchinson

CHAPTER 13

WATER RELATIONS

When considering the passage of water through a plant there is, as well as the internal movement, the entry and exit of water. The entry is absorption through the roots and root hairs, and the exit is transpiration which is simply the evaporation of water from the leaves.

ABSORPTION AND TRANSPIRATION

The main organs for absorption of water and minerals are the roots, via the root hairs of the plant. Absorption is, in simple terms, the drawing of water into the plant from its surroundings. What causes absorption to take place is still uncertain[1], but it is closely related to transpiration and several of the experiments normally carried out in the practical class demonstrate both these activities.

Experiment I.—To Show Absorption by the Roots

A 50 ml measuring cylinder is taken and in it is placed a young seedling whose root system will extend down into the cylinder so that the entire root is well below the 50 ml graduation mark. A square or circle of polythene sheet is cut large enough to form a cap over the cylinder. A slit is made in the polythene to its centre. The measuring cylinder is filled with water so that the level is just under the 50 ml mark. The polythene is slipped around the mouth of the measuring cylinder and the seedling lowered until its root system is below water. At this point the level of the water is noted. If it is above the graduated scale, a small amount should be tipped out. With the aid of a rubber band or Sellotape, the polythene is secured to the sides of the cylinder (*see Figure 128*).

The apparatus is put aside for 12 h, after which time the fall in water level is noted, showing that water has been absorbed by the root system.

If measuring cylinders are not obtainable in sufficient numbers for large class experiments, the following method may be used.

A hole is drilled in a cork, large enough to take a young wheat seedling without damaging the root or root hairs. The cork is fitted into the corresponding size specimen tube containing some water. The seedling is lowered through the hole in the cork until the roots

315

are well immersed. The level of the water in the tube is marked with a diamond or wax pencil. It is then placed in a moderate temperature, approximately 20°C, and the drop in the level of the water is observed from time to time.

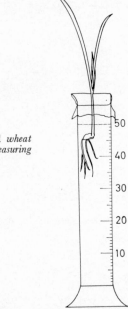

Figure 128. A wheat seedling in a measuring cylinder

Any piece of apparatus which measures absorption of water is called a potometer and is convenient to use when observing external factors affecting absorption, such as temperature or illumination. According to which factor is required, the potometer jar may be immersed in a warm water bath or ice bath and in these cases the potometer must have reached equilibrium before the experiment commences. It may be left in daylight or fluorescent light, in a darkened room or cupboard, and the subsequent rise or fall in the absorption rate noted.

A potometer measures both absorption and transpiration. It can be assumed that, generally speaking, the two activities occur simultaneously and at the same speed as each other. Although the actual measurements taken during experiments with potometers are direct readings of water absorption, it can be assumed that they are also indirect measurements of transpiration.

Apart from the simple types of potometers used so far, there are other types of more complex design. These potometers have an integral reservoir for additional water, a small vessel for the seedling or shoot and a very fine capillary tube, calibrated accurately to afford visible means of observing and measuring absorption.

THE THODAY AND GANONG POTOMETERS

These potometers are basically the same in principle. The measurement of absorption and transpiration in each case is taken from the movement of a bubble of air, or the meniscus of the water in a

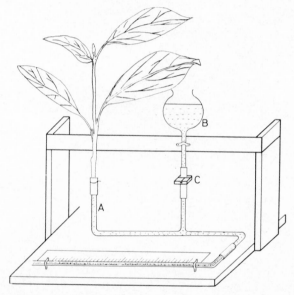

Figure 129. Thoday potometer set up with a shoot of laurel

capillary tube. The Thoday potometer (*Figure 129*) is the simpler of the two and can easily be constructed in the laboratory, while the Ganong potometer (*Figure 130*) is slightly more complicated and would need to be bought, or made by a glassblower.

Experiment II.—Using a Thoday Potometer

The Thoday potometer (*Figure 129*) consists of a branch or shoot tube (A) which is connected to a reservoir (B) for extra water. This

317

reservoir is a thistle funnel attached by means of rubber tubing to the shoot tube, and is controlled by a screw clip (C). From the reservoir, a piece of glass tubing is connected to a capillary tube, behind which is a linear scale.

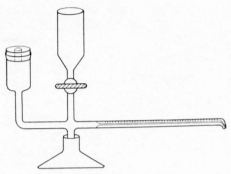

Figure 130. Ganong potometer

Some hours before commencing the experiment, the cut branches of the experimental plant (cherry laurel or rhododendron) should be trimmed. This should be carried out under water to prevent the entry of air into the vessels of the stem. The branches are left in water until required. The reason for preparing these branches several hours before the time of the experiment is that if the cherry laurel has been without water for a day or so during transit from the supply unit, after trimming and placing in water, the rate of absorption rises rapidly because of a water deficit in the shoot. This acceleration is only temporary and, by the time the branches are required for use, the rate will have steadied.

The potometer is completely filled with water and the screw clip closed below the thistle funnel. The experimental branch is slipped into the rubber tubing attached to the shoot tube, so that the end of the stem is in the water. Care should be taken not to trap any air bubbles under the branch. In order to ensure an air-tight joint, the rubber tubing should be lightly wired round the branch, using copper wire. If the seal around the shoot is air tight, the water in the capillary tube will move towards the calibrated scale. As soon as the meniscus reaches the beginning of the scale, the time should be noted.

The meniscus will travel along the capillary tube fairly rapidly, according to the plant material used and the effect of any external factors. The time should be noted as the meniscus reaches the end of the calibrated scale. The screw clip is opened to allow the meniscus to return beyond the zero mark. The screw clip is shut once again and, when the meniscus is level with the zero mark, timing can begin again. The actual volume of water absorbed can be calculated if the bore of the capillary tube is known.

The external factors known to affect the rate of absorption and transpiration can be simulated in the laboratory, by placing the potometer near an electric fire or fan for a higher temperature or a movement of air respectively. A humid atmosphere can be produced by covering the branch with a bell jar, lined at the bottom with moist blotting paper.

The Ganong potometer—This varies only slightly from the Thoday. As has been stated previously, the basic principles are the same but the apparatus itself is a little more complicated. The spare reservoir of water, complete with tap, becomes an integral part of the apparatus instead of the thistle funnel connected with rubber tubing and controlled by a screw clip. The capillary tube is already graduated and is standing free, instead of being supported against a backboard scale.

These are the main differences and it may be noted that although the Ganong potometer is an elegant piece of apparatus, the Thoday potometer is less inclined to be broken and also, should damage occur, can be easily repaired. If, instead of the thistle funnel of the Thoday potometer being permanently attached to the frame, it is held in place with a rubber band, this also prevents breakages when handling and storing, as the apparatus is not rigid.

If it is necessary to use an entire plant, including roots, a potometer must be used which has a much larger plant tube[2].

A small amount of red ink, added to the water used in a potometer, will demonstrate the transpiration stream, i.e. the passage that the water takes through the plant. After the measurement of absorption or transpiration, the experimental shoot should be cut across the stem. The staining will show that the passage of water is through the xylem tissue only.

As transpiration takes place, the loss of water may be measured by a simple weighing procedure, as described in the following experiment.

Experiment III.—Loss of Weight Due to Transpiration

A healthy potted plant of Pelargonium is chosen, the pot is placed in a polythene bag and the bag tied securely to the base of the stem with string. This will prevent any loss of water through the porous clay of the pot and from the surface of the soil. The weight of the plant is recorded. It is left to transpire freely in the laboratory away from draughts or extraneous heat until the following day when it is re-weighed and the loss in weight noted.

Some of the external factors affecting the transpiration rate may be simulated in the laboratory, as described in the following simple treatments.

Before the plant is subjected to any treatment, an initial weighing must be carried out, and the period of time the plant is left to transpire must be constant. If it is not possible to use the same plant for each treatment, then plants of similar age and size should be used. The loss in weight, after transpiration in natural conditions, should be noted as a comparison with the loss after treatment.

External factors influencing transpiration, such as temperature, wind, light and dark, may be simulated by such methods as placing the potted plant in front of an electric fire or an electric fan. A dark cupboard can be used to keep the plant without light and a fluorescent tube or ring of tungsten filament lamps will illuminate the plant in the absence of sufficient natural light.

The loss of weight due to transpiration is quite considerable. Any change due to photosynthesis and respiration is very small and may be considered negligible by comparison. It is therefore disregarded when recording loss in weight during these experiments.

SHOOTS IN TUBES

The loss of weight due to transpiration may also be measured using shoots or branches of privet or cherry laurel cut from healthy plants.

A 3 in. × 1 in. specimen tube is filled with water. The shoot is placed through a drilled, split cork and pushed into the top of the tube. The apparatus is weighed and the shoot left to transpire for several hours. It is then re-weighed and the loss in weight recorded at intervals during the transpiration period.

External factors affecting transpiration can be simulated as for the potted plant.

This experiment may be carried out with quite small shoots, placed in rimmed test tubes instead of specimen tubes. In this case a piece of cotton is tied round the rim of the test tube which is suspended from the beam of the balance to weigh. The tubes are placed in a rack during the periods of transpiration.

Experiment IV.—To Show the Importance of the Leaf in Transpiration

Five branches of cherry laurel, with about six leaves to each branch are taken. Using lanolin or Vaseline, the upper surface of the leaves and the stem on one branch, the under surface of the leaves and the stem on the second branch and both surfaces of the leaves and the stem on the third are greased. The stem only on the fourth branch is greased and the fifth branch is left ungreased. Grease is applied to the cut end of the stems of all the branches.

Each branch is weighed separately and the results recorded. The branches are suspended so that the air can circulate freely around them and they are left for one week.

At the end of this time, the branches are re-weighed and the results are recorded. It will be found that the untreated branch will have lost considerable weight. The branch which only had the stem greased will have lost the same proportion in weight, as will the one with the upper side of the leaves, and the stem greased. The two branches remaining, i.e. the one with the upper and underside of the leaves and the stem greased, will show very little difference in weight when compared with the initial weighing.

From these results it can be clearly seen that not only are the leaves the organs of transpiration, but in the case of the cherry laurel it is the underside of the leaf from which most water is lost.

The above experiment may be carried out using single leaves of *Ficus elastica*. Indeed, for a single experiment for demonstration the use of Ficus leaves is the classic method and is to be preferred. Naturally, for large class experiments, Ficus would be impracticable and the cherry laurel more suitable.

STOMATA

It is known that stomata exist on the surface of a leaf (they also exist all over the plant except the root system but in such small numbers compared with those on the leaves that their existence is not important here), and that they are able to open and close, so it becomes necessary to investigate the causes of this movement in more detail.

Experiment V.—Microscopic Examination of Guard Cells

An epidermal strip is taken (see Chapter 5) fixed in alcohol and mounted in Heath's reagent (2·5 per cent iodine in 100 per cent phenol with 1 or 2 ml of water added to dissolve the latter). The phenol will prevent any alteration of the turgidity of the cell.

When this preparation is examined under a microscope, dark

particles, which are starch grains, can be seen in the guard cells. It should be observed to what extent the stomatal pore is open.

Next two healthy shoots or plants of Pelargonium are taken one being placed in the dark and the other in the light for 12 h. An epidermal strip from each plant is quickly removed and fixed. If possible the strip from the plant in the dark is removed first. On examination, it will be seen that the stomatal aperture of the leaf kept in the dark will be closed, while that of the leaf which has been illuminated will be open.

Experiment VI.—Using Cobalt Chloride Paper

The amount of water evaporated from the surface of a leaf may be measured using a hygrometric paper, such as cobalt chloride paper, which changes in colour according to the water vapour present. The amount of water evaporated depends upon the size of the stomatal aperture. This method may be used for the detection of the stomatal aperture and also the position and number of stomata.

The following experiment shows the preliminary making of the hygrometric paper, the standard colours normally used with it and the actual method of use.

Preparation of Cobalt Chloride Paper

Two or three discs of Whatman No. 1 filter paper (the size is immaterial but a 12 cm disc will make a considerable number of strips) are placed in water for 1 min. The excess water is removed by squeezing gently between blotting paper and then the discs are placed in a 15 per cent aqueous solution of cobalt chloride for 1 min. The discs are removed and blotted as before and placed in a warm oven at 80°C to dry.

Preparation of Standard Colours

Two aqueous solutions of methylene blue, one containing 0·125 g/litre methylene blue and the other one quarter of this strength, i.e. 0·0312 g/litre methylene blue are prepared.

Using fresh discs of filter paper, the initial treatment is carried out in water, then half the discs are immersed in the strong solution of methylene blue and the other half in the weak solution. They should be immersed for 1 min, blotted, and dried in an oven at 80°C.

Strong standard—The stronger coloured set of methylene blue discs are soaked for 3 min in a 1:40,000 eosin solution, i.e. 0·025 g/litre. They are then removed, squeezed gently between blotting paper and dried.

Weak standard—The weaker coloured set of methylene blue discs are soaked for 30 sec in a 1:10,000 eosin solution, i.e. 0·1 g/litre. They are then removed, blotted and dried.

Preparation of the Tricoloured Test Strips

There should now be three sets of prepared discs, (a) the cobalt chloride discs, (b) the strong standard discs and (c) the weak standard discs.

Cut all these discs into narrow strips about 3 mm wide. Take a white sheet of paper and place a thin streak of Secotine along the top edge. Attach the ends of the narrow strips in the following order: strong standard, cobalt chloride, weak standard, and so on. (Sellotape can be used instead of Secotine.) Next, stick pieces of black masking tape about 2 mm wide at intervals across the coloured strips, as shown in *Figure 131b*.

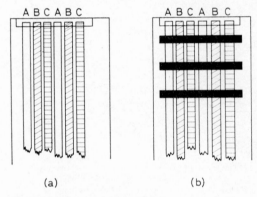

(a)   (b)

Figure 131. Preparation of tricoloured strips: (a) ends of strips attached to a sheet of white paper; (b) masking tape stuck across the strips

Detach the coloured strips from the white paper by cutting just below the line of Secotine. Turn the strips over and stick masking tape on the back to correspond with the masking tape on the front.

The sets of test papers are produced by cutting along the middle of each strip of masking tape, and between each weak and strong standard. Each test strip consists of a strong standard, a cobalt chloride paper and a weak standard, held together by the masking tape (*see Figure 132*).

These small sets of indicator papers should be placed over a desiccant in miniature desiccators. Specimen tubes (3 in. × 1 in.), containing a few lumps of granular calcium chloride, can be used as long as the desiccant is covered by a disc of copper mesh. Several sets of papers may be placed in each small desiccator, which should be closed with a tightly fitting rubber bung.

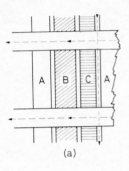

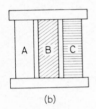

Figure 132. (a) The cut is made along the middle of the masking tape; (b) the completed tricoloured strip

Method of Use

Hold a tricoloured strip near the surface of an electric light bulb to intensify the colour of the cobalt chloride and then attach it to the surface of the leaf which is to be measured. Comparison of the distribution of the stomata can be made by attaching strips to the upper as well as to the lower surfaces. Care must be taken not to touch the cobalt chloride paper with the fingers; tweezers or forceps are useful at this stage.

Cover the strip on the leaf quickly with a piece of polythene and fold it over the edge of the leaf. Hold the strip and the polythene in place with two paper clips (see *Figure 133*).

Comparison of the time taken for the colour of the cobalt chloride paper to change from the colour of the strong standard to that of the weak standard can be made between one plant and another under similar external conditions, or between measurements on the same plant under differing conditions.

The tricoloured strip may be re-used after drying on an electric light bulb.

Another method in common use for measuring stomata involves an apparatus called a porometer. This is employed in order to observe the reaction of the stomata to changing conditions.

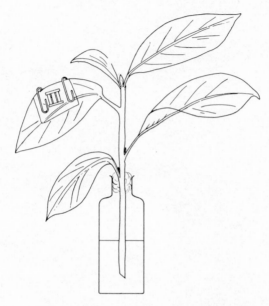

Figure 133. Tricoloured strip attached to leaf

Experiment VII.—Using a Porometer

This apparatus is basically a T-piece of glass tubing. Attached to one arm of the horizontal is a small cup, with a thickened rim ground flat. To the other arm is attached a piece of rubber tubing with a screw clip and a mouthpiece. The vertical arm is backed by a calibrated scale and the open end of the tube is inserted into a beaker of water which is tinted with eosin.

Gelatin washers are needed for this experiment and may be prepared as follows:

Make a 30 per cent aqueous solution of gelatin and, while still warm, pour into Petri dishes to a depth of 2 mm. Leave to set. Cut out the washers from the solidified gelatin, using two sizes of cork borers. The inside and outside diameters of the washers should be slightly smaller and larger respectively than the corresponding diameters of the cup. From a branch of cherry laurel standing in water bend a leaf down and arrange it on the porometer slide with the surface to be examined uppermost (*Figure 134*).

Place a gelatin washer on the leaf surface, bring the porometer cup down on to the washer and hold firmly in position by means of the small Terry clip. Large veins should be avoided when attaching the cup.

Open the screw clip in front of the mouthpiece and suck up the liquid in the vertical tube, noting the level. Close the screw clip and time the fall of the liquid.

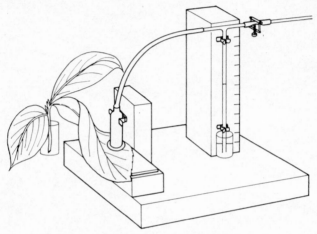

Figure 134. A porometer with the cup attached to the under surface of a leaf

What is happening is this; as the liquid falls, it draws air through the leaf tissue covered by the funnel. Because this air must be replaced, air also enters through the stomata on the other side of the leaf outside the funnel. The resistance set up against the flow of air depends on the number of stomata present on the surface of the leaf and the extent of stomatal opening.

Care must be taken when repeating a measurement or carrying out a series of measurements to make sure that the level of the liquid in the vertical tube is at the same position on the calibrated scale.

OSMOSIS

The root tissue of a plant consists of living cells which can absorb moisture from their surroundings; the process by which they do this is believed to be osmosis.

In each vacuolated cell there is a solution of many substances, including salts and sugars. This arrangement, when in contact with water under certain conditions, starts a process known as osmosis, which is the diffusion of water from one solution to another through a semi-permeable membrane.

The conditions under which this process will take place are these: There must be two solutions present, separated by a membrane which allows water to pass through but not the dissolved salts, i.e. a semi-permeable membrane. If one solution contains a higher concentration of dissolved salts than the other, water will pass through the membrane from the side of the weaker concentration of salts to the higher concentration of salts.

When a vacuolated plant cell is placed in water or a dilute solution of salts, water passes, by osmosis, from the external solution into the vacuole of the cell. This continues until the cell becomes fully turgid, when a state of equilibrium is reached.

Presumably, the root cells rarely attain equilibrium with the soil solution, as water is continually moving from the root into the stem and passing to the leaves in the transpiration stream.

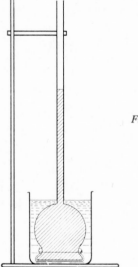

Figure 135. To demonstrate osmosis

Experiment VIII.—To Demonstrate Osmosis or Osmotic Pressure

A thistle funnel with a long stem is used, or one that has been lengthened by attaching a piece of glass tubing. A ring of plasticine is placed round the neck of the funnel, the mouth is covered with a cellophane jam jar cover and secured with an elastic band. The cellophane will act as the semi-permeable membrane. The funnel is inverted in a beaker and the bulb filled with a 20 per cent sugar solution until the level rises 2 in. up the stem. The beaker is filled with water and the funnel supported with a retort stand and clamp, so that the lip of the bulb just clears the bottom of the beaker (*Figure 135*).

The level of the sugar solution is marked on the stem of the funnel with a diamond or wax pencil. After a short while the level in the stem will be seen to rise.

ROOT PRESSURE

As water is absorbed by the root hairs, quite a considerable pressure is set up in the root. This is known simply as root pressure and it can be demonstrated in either of the following ways.

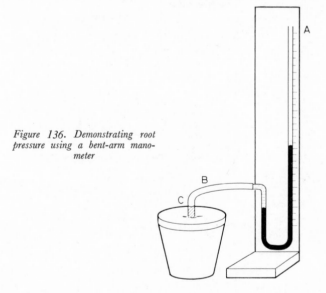

Figure 136. Demonstrating root pressure using a bent-arm manometer

Experiment IXa.—To Demonstrate Root Pressure

A strong potted plant of *Bryophyllum* is taken and decapitated so as to leave about 1 in.–2 in. of stem. A piece of rubber tubing 2 in. long is attached to the cut stump. A bent-arm manometer is half filled with water. Mercury is introduced into the manometer at A until the water is pushed round the short arm to B. A finger is placed over the end of the manometer, the water allowed to fall to C and the manometer quickly slipped into the rubber tube attached to the plant stump (*Figure 136*).

There should be no need to remove the manometer from its calibrated back board in order to set up this experiment. Root pressure may be measured by recording the rise of mercury in the manometer.

Experiment IXb.—To Demonstrate Root Pressure

If a bent arm manometer with a calibrated back board is not available, an extremely simple apparatus can be set up in the following way.

Figure 137. To demonstrate root pressure. The capillary tubing is attached to the plant stump by a piece of rubber tubing

Prepare the plant as in the previous experiment, and attach to the stump a length of capillary tubing 2 ft–3 ft long, using a piece of rubber tubing 2 in. long. The glass tube should be supported by a retort stand and clamp, and half filled with water. The surface of the water in the tube is covered with a little oil to prevent evaporation. Mark the level of the water on the glass tube with a diamond or wax pencil and place the whole apparatus in a warm place in the laboratory. Root pressure will force the water upwards in the tube (*Figure 137*).

This experiment does not demonstrate the considerable force exerted by the root pressure as clearly as the previous experiment, where the substance being displaced is the very heavy metal mercury but, as a demonstration of a more elementary nature, it is quite adequate.

TURGOR AND PLASMOLYSIS

When a plant cell has reached the stage where there is no flow of water between the external surroundings and the vacuole it becomes swollen, and presses against neighbouring cells which are also distended. These rigid cells are said to be in a state of turgor or are turgid.

The reverse of turgor is plasmolysis. In this condition, the cells are no longer rigid and when examined under the microscope will appear distorted (*Figure 138b*).

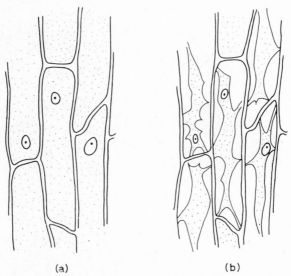

(a)   (b)

Figure 138. Cells of an onion scale (a) normal (b) plasmolysed

Plasmolysis is brought about by the loss of water from the vacuole, causing the protoplasm to shrink away from the cell walls. It is the result of the external surrounding liquid being of a higher osmotic value than that inside the cell. This condition reverses the direction of the flow of water which is drawn out of the cell.

Plasmolysis may be easily demonstrated in the laboratory by using an onion scale or spirogyra. In both cases the material must be fresh and healthy.

Experiment X.—To Demonstrate Plasmolysis

A fresh onion is taken and the outside skin removed. With a knife a series of cuts are made into the onion and another set at right angles to the first. Using a needle or forceps, the resultant small square sections of tissue are stripped off. A section of tissue is mounted in a strong sucrose or glycerin solution on a slide, and examined under a microscope. The cells will be plasmolysed. These cells are compared with the normal turgid cells in a section mounted in water.

DIALYSIS

Dialysis is the means of separating a crystalloid and a colloidal substance. A membrane is used which will retain the colloid but allow the crystalloid to diffuse through. Since many of the substances contained in plant tissue are of a colloidal nature, dialysis is a useful means of partially purifying extracts of plant proteins, etc.

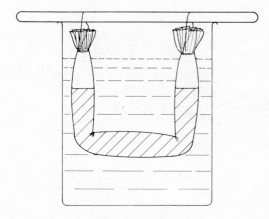

Figure 139. Dialysis

Experiment XI.—To Demonstrate Dialysis

The membrane used for this experiment is tubing bought especial-ly for the purpose. Visking tubing is similar to sausage skin and can be bought in various widths according to the amount of material to be dialysed.

A little starch (0·25 g) is mixed in a few ml of water. 50 ml of water is boiled and poured on to the suspension of starch. This is boiled for a few more minutes and then allowed to cool, when 0·5 g sodium chloride is added. The resulting mixture is a colloidal suspension adulterated by a crystalloid solution.

A piece of dialysis tubing $1^{1}/_{2}$ in. wide is taken, one end is tied with a piece of cotton and the prepared mixture poured into the tube. The other end of the tube is tied with cotton as before. The tube is suspended from a glass rod and placed in a litre beaker full of water (*Figure 139*).

After one hour, the water is tested with silver nitrate. A white precipitate will show the presence of sodium chloride but the test with iodine for starch will be negative. If the water is changed frequently and tested before each change, the final washing will be found to be free of sodium chloride. At this stage the material in the dialysis tube is entirely free from the crystalloid solution.

REFERENCES

[1]Curtis, O. F. and Clark, D. G. (1950). *An Introduction to Plant Physiology*, 1st ed. New York; McGraw-Hill

[2]Meyer, B. S., Anderson, D. B. and Swanson, C. A. (1962). *Laboratory Plant Physiology*, 3rd ed. New York; Van Nostrand

BIBLIOGRAPHY

Crafts, A. S., Currier, H. B. and Stocking, C. R. (1949). *Water in the Physiology of Plants*, 1st ed. U.S.A.; Chronica Botanica Co.

Curtis, O. F. (1935). *The Translocation of Solutes in Plants*, 1st ed. New York; McGraw-Hill

Newcomb, E. H., Gerlaff, G. C. and Whittingham, W. F. (1964). *Plants in Perspective—a Laboratory Manual of Modern Biology*, 1st ed. London; Freeman

CHAPTER 14

MANOMETRY

The physiological reactions of plant life, which involve gaseous exchange, can often be measured by manometric methods. The measurement of the oxygen evolved during photosynthesis, the oxygen uptake and the carbon dioxide output during respiration, have been dealt with in the relevant chapters. If, however, the plant tissue concerned is placed in a closed system of known volume, a positive or negative pressure will ensue during any gas reaction. If a manometer containing a coloured fluid is placed in line with this system, the pressure change may be accurately measured. This is the principle upon which all manometric methods depend. Several types of manometric apparatus are in use, the most common being the Warburg constant volume manometer.

THE WARBURG CONSTANT VOLUME MANOMETER

The manometer consists of a U-tube with a capillary bore of approximately 0·8 mm (*Figure 140a*). The arms of the manometer are about 350 mm long. One arm is open to the air and the other carries a three-way stopcock and a sidearm fitted with a ground glass joint. A rubber reservoir holding a coloured fluid is attached to the bottom of the manometer. The fluid level may be adjusted in the capillary tube by means of an external screw. The whole manometer is mounted on a back board to which is attached a metric scale.

A small flask is attached to the manometer by means of the ground glass joint. The flask, shown in *Figure 140b*, normally consists of a main chamber (A), a centre well (B), a sidearm (C) and a sidearm stopper (D). Other types of flasks in use are shown in *Figure 141*.

The manometer is attached to a constant temperature tank so that the flask is immersed in the water. All glassware must be scrupulously clean.

Cleaning

Method 1—Any paper from the centre well should be removed and the flasks and sidearm stoppers placed under hot, running water to remove the excess grease. Alternatively, the necks of the flasks and

333

the stoppers can be wiped with a piece of cotton wool soaked in ether.

All the sidearm stoppers should be placed in a 100 ml beaker, together with one or two pieces of soap. A small piece of soap is placed in each flask and both the flasks and the stoppers are placed in a saucepan and covered with distilled water.

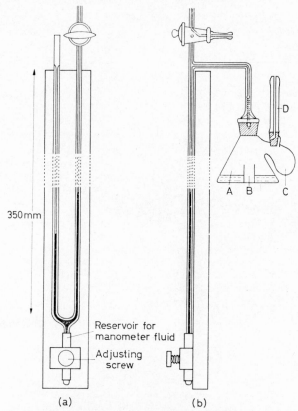

350 mm

Reservoir for manometer fluid

Adjusting screw

A B C

D

(a)   (b)

Figure 140. A Warburg constant volume respirometer and flask:
(a) manometer, (b) manometer and flask

The water is brought to the boil, then the heat lowered until the soap has completely dissolved, i.e. 15–20 min. This will remove the dirt and the last traces of grease from the glassware.

The flasks and stoppers are removed from the hot soap solution, rinsed 12 times with tap water and twice with distilled water. They are then drained and placed to dry, upside down if possible, in an oven at a temperature of 80°C for 45–60 min. Alternatively, both flasks and sidearm stoppers can be cleaned with one of the laboratory cleansers (p. 57).

N.B. Care should be taken when rinsing and draining the flasks that the water in the centre well is emptied out between each rinse and after draining.

The final operation is to clean the cones of the manometers and this may be done with cotton wool soaked in ether.

When the flasks and sidearm stoppers are dry, they should be cooled and stored away, the stoppers being in place but not ground in. A cork is placed in the neck of each flask to keep out dust.

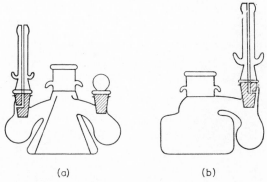

Figure 141. (a) *Dickens and Simer flask for measuring CO_2 liberation and absorption;* (b) *general flask for photosynthetic reactions*

Method 2—The centre well paper and sidearm stopper are removed and the flask degreased by running under hot water. The flask is emptied, removed from the vicinity of any naked flame and, while still hot, filled with ether. If the flask is sufficiently hot, the ether will boil. When the boiling has ceased, the ether is emptied into a beaker for further use in other flasks, and the flask rinsed four times with tap water, filled with freshly prepared chromic acid cleaning fluid (Chapter 1) and left for 20–30 min. The sidearm stoppers are treated in a similar way.

The acid is emptied from the flasks and stoppers and they are then rinsed twelve times with tap water and twice with distilled water. The flasks and stoppers are dried as in the first method.

The manometer cones are cleaned as before.

Prompt attention to cleaning and storing, before grease stiffens unduly and the organic contents become foul, will not only prove time saving but will reduce the risk of breakages to a minimum. After breakages and subsequent repairs, the equipment must be recalibrated. Calibration is not a difficult procedure but it is time consuming and tedious. It is worth while, therefore, to treat the Warburg apparatus with care.

Manometer Fluid

Several types of fluid can be used since, in theory, it is the density only which is important.

The following fluid (after Krebs) has been used over a long period in the Botany Department of University College, London, and has been found satisfactory for all general purposes.

Sodium Bromide	44	g
Stergene, Lissapol or Teepol	1	ml
Evan's Blue	0·3	g
Distilled water	to 1	litre

The density of the fluid (sp. gr. 1·033) is checked. Should the density be too low more sodium bromide can be added and if too high, more water.

Constant Temperature Tanks

Until recent years, the tanks used were rectangular in shape, with positions for seven manometers on each of the long sides. Recently, circular tanks have been introduced and have been found to possess several advantages over the rectangular types which, however, are still widely used. Whichever type of tank is installed, it must be possible to regulate the water accurately, at any given temperature above 20°C. A thermoregulator (see Chapter 1) is incorporated into the heating circuit to ensure the fine degree of control required. There must be a means of keeping the water circulated and a shaking mechanism to keep the contents of the flask mixed during the experiment.

Rectangular tanks—Rectangular tanks are normally heated by electric elements and the degree of heat is adjusted by a control switch, with various positions. The elements should be switched to 'high' to bring the temperature of the water from cold up to the required heat. It should only be necessary to use the low or medium setting in conjunction with a thermoregulator in order to maintain the required temperature.

The water in the tank is circulated by a centrally placed shaft which carries two or three propeller-type blades. The shaft is connected to a small gearbox beneath the tank, which in turn is connected to an electric motor.

During warm weather a cooling coil may be immersed in the tanks through which cold water may be passed. Alternatively the coil may be connected to a refrigeration plant.

The shaking mechanism in these tanks may be one of two kinds. In the first case the manometer and flask are shaken from side to side in the same plane; in the second case the flask moves through a small arc in the water as the manometer back board is pivoted.

A rectangular Warburg tank is shown in *Figure 142*.

Figure 142. Rectangular Warburg tank

Circular tanks—Circular tanks may be fitted either with electric elements or with electrodes to heat the water. The elements operate

337

as in the rectangular tank, but the electrode type of heating requires the addition of 1·5 per cent sodium chloride to the water to produce an electrolytic solution. The electrode type of heater is normally fitted with a booster heater for the initial heating of the water.

In circular tanks the water is circulated by a centrifugal pump placed beneath the tank and stirred from above with a small laboratory stirrer.

The pivotal type of shaking mechanism is used on modern circular tanks. A circular Warburg tank is shown in *Figure 143*.

Figure 143. Circular Warburg tank

On both types of tanks the shaking should be stopped to facilitate the reading of the manometer. Each side of the rectangular tank may be read separately. Normally the mechanism in the circular tank is so arranged that the entire ring of manometers may be rotated, which enables the operator to remain seated and brings each manometer in front of him in turn.

338

When used for photosynthetic work, the tanks may be fitted with fluorescent tubes.

When an experiment must be carried out in total darkness, metal struts may be attached to the top of the tank to provide support for some means of blackout, either plastic or material sheeting.

USE OF FLASK AND MANOMETER

A synopsis of the procedure to measure oxygen uptake in respiration is given below:

(1) Place 0·15 ml or 0·2 ml of potassium hydroxide solution (10 or 20 per cent) in the centre well of the flask.

(2) Any substance to be added during the experiment should be placed in the sidearm in solution. (The sidearm will hold up to 0·5 ml easily.) Take care during these operations not to wet the ground surface of the neck of the flask or sidearm. Should this happen, dry immediately with a piece of filter paper.

(3) Grease the sidearm stopper with anhydrous wool fat (lanolin), i.e. rotate a glass rod in the grease, hold the rod against the ground glass portion of the stopper and rotate. This should leave a thin streak of grease on the stopper. Two streaks are sufficient for the stopper but care must be taken to avoid the outlet hole. Place the stopper in the sidearm and grind in carefully so as to exclude air bubbles and make a good seal. If no specific gas mixtures are to be passed before the experiment commences, close the sidearm(s) vent(s) by turning the stopper until its outlet is opposite the vent in the sidearm. If gases are to be passed, leave the vents open.

(4) Place the experimental material in the main compartment.

(5) If KOH is being used, insert a piece of Whatman No. 40 filter paper 2 cm square and rolled into a tube, into the centre well in order to increase the surface area for carbon dioxide absorption.

(6) Grease the cone of the manometer as for the sidearm stopper, but this time use three streaks of grease. Attach the flask, grind on slightly and attach springs.

(7) Place in the constant temperature tank.

When the manometers and the experimental flasks have been set up and the latter immersed in a constant temperature water bath, there is one more control which must be included in the procedure. This is the inclusion of a thermobarometer which will measure the pressure changes caused by atmospheric pressure.

Thermobarometer

This apparatus is simply a manometer to which is attached a flask containing about 2 ml of water and a knife point of mercuric sulphate. In actual fact a thermobarometer is a duplication of an experimental flask and manometer but water is substituted for experimental material. The mercuric sulphate is added to prevent the growth of any organism present in the water, thus preventing any pressure change due to the respiration of such organisms.

It is usual to use one thermobarometer on each side of a rectangular tank, irrespective of the number of manometers which are used.

Once the experimental manometers have been placed on the tank with their taps open and the thermobarometer placed in position (usually in a central position between the other manometers), the shaking mechanism on the tank may be started. The rate of shaking must be checked and adjusted at the beginning of the experiment. When measuring the uptake of oxygen in the experimental flasks, the shaking of the flasks aids gaseous exchange. Experiments have been carried out comparing the rate of oxygen uptake with the rate of shaking and it has been found that 100–120 complete strokes/min is a satisfactory speed, provided that the rate of oxygen uptake is not more than 300–400 mm³/h. If, however, the sidearm(s) of the experimental flask contains a reactant to be added at a set time, care must be taken not to slop this solution into the main compartment prematurely. The speed of shaking can be reduced prior to the addition of a reactant and increased immediately afterwards.

Shaking should continue for a few minutes to allow the grease on the flask joints to soften. The flasks are ground in, in the following manner.

(1) With one hand support the bottom of each flask and sidearm individually while still in the tank and with the other hand rotate the sidearm stopper, grinding it into the sidearm socket. If specific gases are to be passed through the flasks, leave the sidearm vent open, otherwise close it.

(2) With one hand support the sidearm of the manometer and with the other hand under the flask, grind the flask on to the manometer cone. Allow the flasks to equilibrate for 10 min before setting the manometer as follows.

(3) Provided that no specific gases are to be passed, and oxygen uptake is to be measured, run the manometer fluid to the bottom of the manometer by unscrewing the adjusting screw. Close the stopcock and run the manometer fluid up again until it reaches the zero or 150 mm mark on the right hand arm of the manometer. The object is to start the experiment with the fluid in the left hand arm of the manometer as close to the top of the calibrated scale as possible (between 250–280 mm). Once the preliminary adjustment has been made, a final adjustment may be made using a rubber teat. Place the teat on the outlet above the stopcock and open the tap. There should be no change in the level of the manometer fluid. Now depress the fluid below the tap 5–10 mm by squeezing the teat. Shut the tap, while still applying pressure, and once again adjust to zero. Should the fluid in the left hand arm run beyond the calibration scale when

the zero point has been adjusted in the other arm, a little pressure may be released by placing a finger tightly over the outlet above the tap. Open the tap and carefully release the pressure fractionally, raising the fluid below the tap by about 5 mm. Again adjust to zero.

Measurement of Gas Output

With the tap open, the manometer fluid is raised to the top of both arms of the manometer. The tap is closed and the fluid adjusted to zero or 150 mm in the right hand arm. The fluid in the left arm should be as low as possible (approximately 5 mm). Additional adjustment may be made by placing a depressed rubber teat on the outlet above the stopcock. The teat should be kept fully depressed with the fingers of one hand while the tap is opened with the other. When the tap is fully open, the pressure on the teat is released very slightly, thereby sucking up the fluid in the right hand arm by a few units on the scale. The tap is now shut and adjusted to zero again.

During this adjustment the sidearm vent must be closed. If the gaseous atmosphere in the flask must be altered, the passing of the specific gases must be carried out before setting the manometer.

When the manometer has been set, readings may begin and may be taken at 5, 10, 15 or 20 min intervals according to the speed of the reaction. The shaking mechanism should be stopped during readings. The fluid in the right hand arm should be adjusted to zero and the level of fluid in the left hand arm should be noted, reading to the bottom of the meniscus. The position of the meniscus can be read to the nearest 0·5 mm. The thermobarometer should be set by raising the fluid to just below the zero point, shutting the tap and adjusting the right arm to zero It should be read with each set of readings and the changes in pressure should be added to or subtracted from the pressure changes in the experimental flask (see Table 9).

TABLE 9

Time (min)	Experimental flask			Thermobarometer	
	Reading	Change	Corrected change	Reading	Change
0	271·5			171·0	
10	255·0	—16·5	—17·0	171·5	+0·5
20	236·0	—19·0	—19·5	172·0	+0·5
30	215·5	—20·5	—19·5	171·0	—1·0

The changes recorded by the thermobarometer should not vary to any considerable degree. If this happens, a leaking joint should be suspected or a fault in the thermostatic control of the tank.

The thermobarometer is very sensitive and a seemingly steady set of readings may change erratically if storms are prevalent; even a strong draught may cause fluctuations so it is wise to close all windows in line with the Warburg tank.

If the manometer fluid reaches the end of the scale before the end of the experiment, a reading should be recorded, the manometer reset as before and the new reading entered immediately on the data sheet in brackets beside the previous reading.

Tipping

If any substance(s) is to be added during the experiment, it should be tipped into the main compartment directly after a reading has been taken, in the following way. The manometer is removed from the tank and the index finger placed over the open end to prevent fluid sucking over. A little of the fluid is tipped from the main compartment into the sidearm bulb and the contents of the sidearm bulb are tipped into the main compartment. The bulb is rinsed again, and the manometer replaced in the tank before removing the finger. It is then shaken immediately.

USE OF SPECIFIC GAS ATMOSPHERES

Using Standard Gas Cylinders

The gas stream should pass through a wash bottle before being passed into the flask. Single flasks may be gassed by being attached to the gas source. A number of flasks, up to a complete tank full, in fact, may be gassed simultaneously by using a manifold, i.e. a glass or metal tube running the length of the tank and having six outlets on each side. A rubber tube fitted with a screw clip is attached to each outlet. One end of the manifold is attached to the gas supply and the other end is fitted with a rubber tube and screw clip and acts as a safety outlet. The gassing procedure is as follows.

(1) Open the stockcock taps and check that the sidearm vent(s) is open. Attach the gas supply either directly to one manometer or indirectly via the manifold by attaching as many outlets as required to the manometers. If the entire manifold is not required, shut off all extra outlets by means of the screw clips except the end safety outlet. Open all other screw clips.

(2) (a) Turn on the gas supply cautiously and check that the force of gas is not causing undue bubbling of reactants in the single flask.
(b) When using a manifold this difficulty should not be encountered during the first stage of gassing.

(3) (a) Leave the single flask gassing for 10 min at the end of which time turn down the gas supply, then close the stopcock and immediately after close the sidearm vent. Shut off the gas supply at source and set the manometer for reading.

(b) When using a manifold, close the safety valve cautiously. Adjust the screw clips and check that gas is coming through by a pressure difference registered on the manometer.

(The gas pressure may also be checked by placing a finger over the sidearm stopper opening, when an increased pressure will depress the manometer fluid. Alternatively, a piece of bent glass tubing can be attached to the sidearm stopper. The drawn out end of this tube should reach just below the surface of the water in the tank. A stream of bubbles will indicate the flow of gas.)

Allow the gas to pass for 10 min. Close all sidearm vents, stopcock taps and screw clips as for the single flasks but take great care, after each manometer has been closed, to observe the effect of increased pressure on the other flasks and manometers. It is wise to reduce the flow of gas at the source when half the manometers have been shut off. At the end of the operation, when all the outlet tubes have been disconnected, open the safety valve and shut off the gas supply. Set the manometer for reading, taking care not to allow any gas leakage through the manometer tap.

The entire gassing operation may be carried out while the manometers are still on their stands, but it is preferable to have them attached to the tank with the flasks immersed and shaken throughout procedure.

Gassing with Limited Amounts of Specific Gases

There are times when a gas mixture is required which is not available in cylinders. These mixtures can be prepared in the laboratory in amounts to suit the requirements of the experiment. With a small volume of gas with no pressure behind it, it becomes impossible to pass gas for 10 min. In this case a volume of gas 40 times the volume of the flask is passed. When the number of flasks to be gassed is known the total volume of the gas required may be calculated before preparing the mixture.

Preparation of gas mixtures—One of the easiest ways of preparing gas mixtures without using any complicated apparatus is the displacement method. For this method the gas mixtures are usually contained in a large bottle or flask (a Winchester quart bottle is suitable). This bottle should be fitted as for a wash bottle, i.e. fitted with a rubber bung and two delivery tubes; one reaching to the bottom of the bottle and one finishing just below the bung. The bung can be waxed to ensure an air-tight seal. A piece of rubber tubing about 18 in. long should be attached to each of the delivery tubes, and a screw

clip fitted as close to the mouth of the delivery tube as possible. The
container is now ready for use in the following manner.

(1) Completely fill the container with water by opening the screw clips
and running in water through the longer delivery tube, taking care
not to trap any bubbles. When full, close the screw clips tightly.

(2) The various gases are passed through the short delivery tube in the
quantities required: e.g. if 2,000 ml of gas mixture are required, consisting of 5 per cent carbon dioxide, 20 per cent oxygen and 75 per
cent hydrogen, a standard cylinder of each gas can be used in turn.
Connect the cylinder to the short delivery tube, open the screw clips
and displace 100 ml of water with carbon dioxide, 400 ml of water
with oxygen and 1,500 ml with hydrogen. The displaced water
should be collected and measured in a measuring cylinder. As far as
possible, hold the cylinder so that the level of water in the cylinder is
level with that in the container, throughout the displacement. The
screw clips should be closed between each addition of gas.

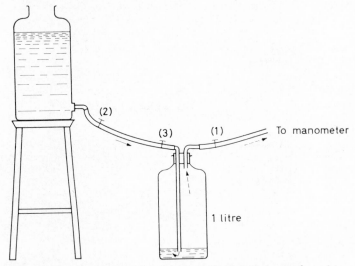

Figure 144. Assembly of apparatus required for passing limited amounts of gas mixtures

(3) When the gas mixture is ready for use it may be passed through the
flasks by displacing the gas with water in the following way. Fill a
large aspirator with water and attach a length of rubber tubing fitted
with a screw clip. Place the aspirator on a small stool on a bench and
attach the rubber tubing to the bottle containing the gas mixture
(*Figure 144*). Attach the gas bottle to the manometer and pass 1 litre
of gas through the manometer. This takes 3 or 4 minutes.

N.B. Always open and shut the screw clip (1) between the gas bottle and manometer first.

Cleaning of Mercury Prior to Calibration

Mercury can be used to calibrate the flasks and manometers and it is important that the apparatus and the mercury are perfectly clean. The Warburg flask and manometer should be cleaned with chromic acid cleaning fluid (Chapter 1). The mercury, assuming it is in a reasonable state, can be adequately cleaned by one of the following methods:

(1) It can be squeezed through a clean chamois leather, rubber gloves being worn for this operation.

(2) A filter paper can be placed in a filter funnel, pierced several times and damped slightly with distilled water. When the mercury is poured into the funnel the dirt will adhere to the damp filter paper and the clean mercury will fall through the pierced holes.

(3) The mercury to be cleaned can be placed in a mortar together with an equal volume of granulated sugar and ground together for several minutes. The mortar is then placed under cold running water to wash away the sugar and the adherent dirt. As much water as possible should be poured off and the last traces can be removed by blotting the surface of the mercury with filter paper, or by heating to 110°C in a fume cupboard.

Calibration Method A

Apparatus required—

(1) A retort stand complete with boss head and clamp.

(2) A large enamelled or polythene tray approximately 18 in. × 24 in.

(3) A 50 ml tared beaker.

(4) A piece of rubber tubing 5 in. long of a diameter which will fit either the gas inlet tube of the manometer or the outlet extension of the stopcock. One end of the tube is closed with a screw clip to form a reservoir for the mercury.

(5) Two or three screw clips, a rubber teat, a Warburg flask, two springs and some clean mercury.

(6) The manometer which is to be calibrated is placed against a calibrated back board with the sidearm lightly resting against the top of the board. The connecting vertical arm is marked with a diamond pencil at the 150 mm or 0 mark.

Method—

(1) Place everything to be used during the calibration in the tray. Place the long side of the tray at the edge of the bench.

(2) Fill the flask with clean mercury and deal with any air bubbles by drawing them to the surface with a piece of nichrome wire. Grind the sidearm stoppers into position.

(3) Place the rubber teat on the small tube at the base of the manometer

and attach the manometer to the flask. This is easily done if the flask is placed at the edge of the tray and the manometer is held in a vertical position at the side of the bench with the sidearm and cone positioned directly above the flask. Lower the manometer into the neck of the flask. The mercury will run along the sidearm of the manometer; any excess will drop down the vertical arm and collect in the rubber teat. The object of this part of the operation is to fill the sidearm with mercury. Should insufficient mercury be carried over from the flask, remove the manometer, refill the flask and insert the manometer again. Repeat this procedure until the sidearm is completely filled. Place the springs in position. Remove the rubber teat.

(4) Clamp the manometer in a horizontal position, 12 in. above the tray, with the sidearm pointing downwards.

(5) Completely fill the 5 in. long rubber tube with mercury and attach either to the stopcock extension or to the gas outlet tube of the manometer.

(6) Adjust the three-way stopcock so as to provide a through passage between the mercury reservoir and the horizontal manometer arm which is supported by the clamp. Force the mercury along the arm by placing screw clips on the rubber tube, one by one, starting at the bottom. As each screw clip is fully closed, continue with the one above until the mercury has reached the calibration mark on the side of the arm.

(7) Close the stopcock and check that the position of the mercury is unaltered. Remove the mercury reservoir and any mercury trapped in the tap. Tilt the manometer slightly, open the stopcock and run the mercury from the horizontal arm into the tared beaker.

(8) Remove the manometer from the clamp and, with great care, remove the flask from the manometer, allowing the mercury in the sidearm to run back into the flask. Tip the contents of the flask into the tared beaker. Measure the temperature of the mercury. If any mercury is lost at this point the whole procedure must be carried out again.

(9) Weigh the beaker plus the mercury and calculate the weight of the mercury.

(10) Duplicate weights should be obtained for each manometer and flask with not more than 0·5 g difference.

(11) The weight of mercury obtained should now be converted to millilitres of mercury. The volume which results will be a true measurement only for the flask and manometer which were calibrated together.

$$\text{i.e. volume} = \frac{\text{wt of Hg}}{\text{sp.gr. of Hg}}$$

The specific gravity of mercury varies according to temperature, and Table 10 covers a workable range, but a textbook of physical constants would give further data. To ensure that they are always used together, all removable parts of the flask and manometer should be permanently numbered.

TABLE 10

Temperature (°C)	Mass in g/cm³ (sp.gr.)	Temperature (°C)	Mass in g/cm³ (sp.gr.)
15	13·5585	28	13·5266
16	13·5561	29	13·5242
17	13·5536	30	13·5217
18	13·5512	31	13·5193
19	13·5487	32	13·5168
20	13·5462	33	13·5144
21	13·5438	34	13·5119
22	13·5413	35	13·5095
23	13·5389	36	13·5070
24	13·5364	37	13·5046
25	13·5340	38	13·5021
26	13·5315	39	13·4997
27	13·5291	40	13·4973

(Each ascending degree in temperature lowers the mass by 0·0024 g approx.)

Calibration Method B

A method of calibration was introduced by Dickens (1951) whereby flasks and manometers may be calibrated individually so that any

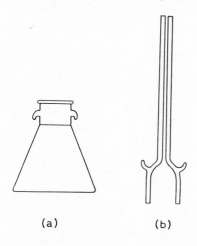

Figure 145. (a) Calibration flask; (b) calibration stopper

(a)   (b)

flask can be used with any manometer. Before this method can be carried out, a calibration flask and stopper must be made[1] (see Figure 145). The calibration flask is used when calibrating the manometer, and the calibration stopper when calibrating the flask. All work should be carried out in a tray as before.

Calibration of flask using calibration stopper—

(1) Weigh the empty flask, complete with sidearm stopper(s) and calibration stopper.

(2) Place the flask in the tray and remove all stoppers. Fill completely with mercury. Draw any air bubbles to the surface with the aid of a nichrome wire.

(3) Replace the sidearm stoppers, grinding them in slightly and then replace the calibration stopper. As this last stopper is placed in position the mercury will rise in the capillary tube and the excess will spill over. When successfully filled, the stoppers should remain in position and the mercury should fill the capillary tube of the calibration stopper to the top. Brush off any mercury clinging to the sides of the flask with a small brush.

(4) Weigh the flask complete with mercury.

(5) Remove the flask to the tray, take out the calibration stopper, insert a thermometer and record the temperature.

(6) Empty out the mercury and repeat the procedure again from (2). There should not be more than 0·2 g difference in weight between any two weighings. See the calibration calculations for the final stage.

N.B. This whole operation should be carried out as quickly as possible and with the minimum amount of handling. Mercury expands rapidly with only a small rise in temperature. The heat of a hand will cause this expansion and so produce an erroneous result when weighing.

It is wise to wear rubber gloves when handling mercury since the vapour is poisonous and can be absorbed through the skin.

The metal itself amalgamates with many other metals.

Calibration of manometer using calibration flask—The manometer is calibrated as in Method A but the calibration flask is substituted for the Warburg flask used previously. Before doing this, the calibration flask itself should be calibrated as for the experimental flask above.

Calibration Calculations

When the experimental flask, the manometer and the calibration flask have been measured as previously described, the result should be three weighings of mercury, plus the temperature of each sample of mercury at the time of weighing. These weights should be converted into ml of mercury, using Table 10 or a textbook of physical constants to obtain the specific gravity of mercury at various temperatures:

$$\text{i.e. Volume} = \frac{\text{wt of Hg}}{\text{sp. gr. of Hg}}$$

Now let v=Volume of experimental flask closed by calibration stopper.

    m=Volume of manometer capillary to calibration mark and the calibration flask.

    c=Volume of calibration flask closed by calibration stopper.

$\therefore m-c$=Volume of manometer capillary − volume of calibration flask closed by calibration stopper.

Therefore the final equation will be

$$V=v+(m-c)$$

where V will equal the final combined volume of any flask with any manometer.

When the volume of the flask has been found, a series of constants must be calculated. An overall constant K can be given as an equation, the derivation of which may be found in *Manometric Techniques*[2].

$$K=\frac{V_G\dfrac{273}{T}+V_F\alpha}{10}$$

where V_G=Volume of gas phase in flask and manometer tube down to zero mark (in ml).

    T=Temperature of tank in degrees absolute (273+temp. in °C).

    V_F=Volume of fluid in flask (in ml).

    α=Solubility of gas in liquid in the flask.

Since $V_G=(V_T-V_F)$ where V_T equals total volume calculated by calibration, it is convenient to rearrange this equation as follows:

$$K=V_T\times\frac{273}{T\times10}-V_F\times\frac{\left(\dfrac{273}{T}\right)-\alpha}{10}$$

i.e. $K=V_T\times C_1-V_F\times C_2$

The value of the constant C_1 depends only on the temperature and values are listed in Table II for commonly used temperatures.

The value of C_2 depends both on temperature and on the solubility coefficient (α) of the gas being measured. Table 11 shows the values of α for oxygen and carbon dioxide at different temperatures. Values for intermediate temperatures can be found by interpolation.

349

TABLE 11

C_1	$C°$	αO_2	αCO_2	C_2	
				O_2	CO_2
0·0932	20	0·0310	0·878	0·090	0·005
0·0916	25	0·0283	0·759	0·089	0·016
0·0901	30	0·0261	0·665	0·088	0·023
0·0881	37	0·0239	0·567	0·086	0·031

Calibration Method C

Flasks and manometers may be calibrated to within 5 per cent accuracy by adding excess acid to a known quantity of freshly prepared sodium carbonate solution. The actual pressure, caused by the carbon dioxide liberated, may be read on the manometer scale and then compared with the theoretical output of carbon dioxide.

Method—Place 2·0 ml M/200 sodium carbonate in the main compartment of the flask to be calibrated. Place 0·3 ml 0·05N H_2SO_4 in the sidearm. Grease the sidearm stopper and place in position. Grease the cone of the manometer and attach the flask, using springs. Place the flask and manometer in position in the constant temperature tank, along with a thermobarometer. Commence shaking and after grinding in the sidearm stopper and flask and setting the manometer, start reading. Take two or three readings at 10 min intervals until the readings are fairly steady, then tip the acid into the main compartment and take further readings until the pressure becomes constant. From the readings calculate the total pressure change (h) corrected for the thermobarometer. The theoretically calculated carbon dioxide production is 224 mm^3. Therefore the K_{CO_2} of the manometer and flask used is 224/h. The flask volume can be calculated from the initial equations, hence K for other gases may be determined.

BARCROFT MANOMETER

The other type of respirometer which may be encountered is the Barcroft differential manometer. The main difference between this and the Warburg constant volume manometer is that the former uses two flasks, one attached to each arm of the manometer. In this case one flask is the reaction vessel and the other a compensation vessel.

Thus the need for a separate thermobarometer is eliminated, since the compensation vessel, as the name suggests, compensates for any fluctuating atmospheric pressures.

BIBLIOGRAPHY

The use and calibration of this type of respirometer may be found in *Manometric Techniques*[2].

REFERENCES

[1]Long, C. (Ed.) (1961). *Biochemists Handbook*, 1st ed. London; Spon
[2]Umbreit, W. W., Burris, R. H. and Stauffer, J. F. (1957). *Manometric Techniques and Tissue Culture*, 3rd ed. Minneapolis; Burgess

BIBLIOGRAPHY

Dixon, M. (1951). *Manometric Methods*, 3rd ed. Cambridge; University Press
Linday, E. M. (1962). *Practical Introduction to Microbiology*, 1st ed. London; Spon

CHAPTER 15

CHROMATOGRAPHY

The three main types of chromatography depend on methods using adsorption, partition and ion-exchange.

In adsorption chromatography, the different components of the solute are separated by adsorption. This type of chromatography is usually carried out in columns. These are packed with the adsorbent and, with the addition of the solvent or solvents, the different substances are separated as they are adsorbed in varying zones in the columns according to their affinity to the adsorbent and to the solvent.

Partition chromatography relies on the separation of a substance between two phases. This is similar to the separation of a solute between an aqueous and an organic phase in a separating funnel. A large part of partition chromatography is carried out on paper.

Ion-exchange chromatography depends on the exchange of either cations or anions. This type of chromatography is generally carried out in columns which are packed with an ion-exchange resin. Ions are removed from the solute and replaced by ions from the resin.

As this chapter can cover only a small part of these processes, it has been divided into three parts; the first, techniques using paper chromatography, the second, techniques using column chromatography and the third, thin layer chromatography.

PAPER CHROMATOGRAPHY

The paper which is used in chromatography contains a high percentage of cellulose and this has a great capacity to hold water. The paper acts as a carrier for the aqueous phase of the two-phase solvent system, which is the stationary phase and the developing solvent (the organic phase) which is the mobile phase.

The solute is separated into its different components which move at varying rates along the paper dependent upon their differing partition coefficients.

352

The RF factor—This factor expresses the relative rate of movement of the solute and the solvent and can be expressed by the following equation:

$$RF \text{ (ratio of flow)} = \frac{\text{Distance solute runs}}{\text{Distance solvent runs}}$$

Marker Solutions

If the same set of conditions are maintained, a mixture of substances will separate out in the same way consistently to give reproducible results. A known substance, therefore, can be used as a marker to identify an unknown substance.

Preparation of the Tank

Tanks that are made of wood, or wood and glass, must be made air-tight by sealing them with paraffin wax of a high melting point. If wooden tanks are used, each tank must be kept for one solvent only.

The trough can be made of any material which does not react with the solvent used. Stainless steel troughs are suitable for most solvents and glass troughs can also be used.

For the best separation of certain groups of compounds it is necessary to equilibrate the tank before running a chromatogram. This is done by saturating the atmosphere inside the tank by placing a beaker containing the aqueous phase of the solvent system on the bottom of the tank, or by pouring this phase directly into the bottom of the tank. The latter method is generally applied to small tanks.

Temperature plays a very important part in running a chromatogram as it affects the rate of flow and sometimes the separation. The temperature should be as constant as possible and for sensitive work a temperature-controlled room should be used.

Solvents

The choice of solvent is a wide one and depends on the material to be separated.

For amino acids the following solvents are commonly used: water-saturated phenol, water-saturated collidine or a butanol-acetic acid-water mixture. For sugars, two common solvents are water-saturated phenol or a butanol-acetic acid-water mixture. For carboxylic acid, n-butanol-ammonia mixtures can be used.

There are many other solvents for particular purposes but it is impossible to list them here.

M*   353

Types and Grades of Paper

As previously stated, the paper which is used for chromatography must be of a high quality and contain a high percentage of pure cellulose. Whatman's produce a wide range of papers for chromatographic purposes and each paper varies in its rate, uniformity of flow, strength and carrying capacity.

The direction of flow is marked on the packet.

Spotting

A constriction pipette or a Kahn pipette can be used for this work. Spots can be applied over one another provided that the first is allowed to dry before the addition of the next. The drying can be done by using a hair drier.

Small amounts of material can be applied to the paper in a small streak instead of a spot, as this will provide greater resolution when the chromatogram has been developed.

A larger quantity of material can be applied in a streak right across the sheet of paper.

PREPARATION OF A ONE-DIMENSIONAL CHROMATOGRAM

A distance from the top of the paper is measured to allow room for fixing in the tank and, at this point, a line is drawn right across the sheet. At equal distances along the line, it should be planned where the spots will be placed. A margin of $1^1/_2$ in. is generally left at each edge and the spots placed approximately 1 in. apart, with the marker in the middle (*see Figure 146*).

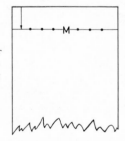

Figure 146. A sheet of chromatography paper marked out prior to running the chromatogram

One marker is sufficient for small chromatograms but several should be used for a large one, as the solvent front does not run exactly straight.

When the spots or streaks have been dried, the paper is folded so that it can hang freely over one glass rod and be held in position by a second rod. (Clamps can also be used.) Only the end of the paper nearest the spotted material is placed in the solvent trough (*Figure 147*).

Sufficient quantity of the solvent should be added to the trough so that the chromatogram will run for a predetermined time. If it is known that the solvent will run off the end of the paper, then the latter should be cut with pinking shears.

The solvent is drawn from the trough and through the paper by capillary action, the substances present in the sample moving at varying rates behind the liquid front.

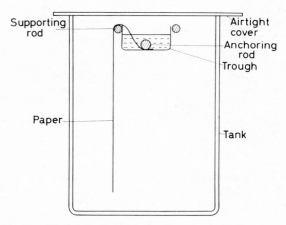

Figure 147. End view of a chromatography tank

After running the chromatogram, the papers are removed and hung in a hot air oven to dry. If the solvent is highly flammable, however, the papers should be hung in a fume cupboard.

The only results that are visible are separation of coloured materials, such as some plant pigments, so the paper is usually sprayed with a reagent giving specific colours to the separated substances. There is such a wide range of these reagents that it is impossible to list them in detail.

Ultra-violet light may also be used to locate certain classes of substance; some normally show up as fluorescent spots, while others may absorb u.v. light and appear as darker areas on a slightly fluorescent background.

TWO-DIMENSIONAL CHROMATOGRAMS

Where a complex mixture of related components is under investigation, a complete separation of the different substances is not possible when only one solvent is used. However, two solvents can be used to effect complementary types of separation and so resolve all the substances in the sample.

The spot is applied near one corner of the paper approximately 4 in. in from the two edges to allow room for hanging in the trough. A marker is not usually applied.

The paper is hung in the tank so that the longest side is run first. After drying the paper is turned round and run for a second time at right angles to the first.

The chromatograms so far described have been descending ones but ascending chromatograms can also be run.

ASCENDING CHROMATOGRAMS

These are usually carried out for quickness or for small scale work and are not generally as efficient as descending chromatograms.

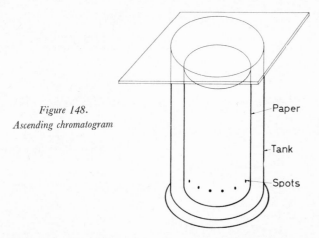

Figure 148.
Ascending chromatogram

Paper

Tank

Spots

There is one big advantage, however, as the apparatus needed is quite simple and inexpensive.

The spot should be placed as near the bottom of the paper as possible, allowing for the fact that the spots must not be in the solvent. The paper is rolled into a cylinder and stapled so that the two edges do not quite meet. It is then placed in the solvent in the tank. In this case the tank also is usually cylindrical (*Figure 148*).

COLUMN CHROMATOGRAPHY

Columns were first used in the botanical field by the Polish botanist Tswett in his work to separate plant pigments. He did this by using a column packed with an adsorbent. The solution of pigments was added to the column and developed by the addition of a solvent. He found that some pigments were adsorbed more strongly than others and in this way it was possible to separate the various pigments into different zones in the column. The strongly adsorbed pigments (chlorophyll *b*) remained at the top of the column while the weakly adsorbed pigments moved further down the column (see Experiment VII, Chapter 12).

At first, column chromatography was limited to the separation of coloured substances which could be visually identified but, as advances were made, it became possible to detect the separation of colourless substances by adsorption methods and also by partition and ion-exchange columns. After the introduction of paper chromatography, partition columns lost a great deal of their importance and nowadays perhaps the most important of the three are the ion-exchange columns. These can be adapted for exact analytical work for the separation and assay of ionized substances.

Columns have an additional advantage over paper because they can be used for the separation of much larger quantities of material.

ADSORPTION COLUMNS

These columns can be used for the separation and partial identification of substances and also for quantitative analysis.

Coloured plant pigments and dyes can be separated into visual zones in the column but many other colourless substances, such as lipoids and terpenes, can be separated by adopting special procedures, either for the identification of the zones in the column or by eluting and collecting the eluate in fractions. Adsorption columns are used extensively for the separation of sugars.

It is most important that the adsorbent and the eluting solvent have the greatest possible specificity for the substances it is desired to separate[1].

Among the adsorbents commonly used are alumina, magnesium oxide, calcium carbonate, talc and charcoal. The latter is frequently used in a column for the separation of organic phosphates.

A fine powder provides a large surface area for adsorption but the rate of flow may be very slow indeed. If it is necessary to use a fine powder, this process can be hastened by exerting pressure at the top of the column.

The size of the column can vary considerably, according to the amount of the substance which is being handled. The packing of the column is important and this can be carried out either by a wet or a dry method.

First the bottom of the column must be plugged with a suitable material, such as glass wool, to prevent the powder from being washed away. For a large column, a perforated plate is useful as a base for the material which is used for plugging. The column is then packed with the adsorbent. This can be done either by making a thick suspension of the adsorbent in the solvent which is to be used for the experiment, or by filling the column with the solvent and adding small quantities of powder until the required height has been built up. These methods are successful with heavy adsorbents but fine powders settle very slowly, especially when a dense solvent is used. In the latter case it is often better to pack the column in a dry state but care must be taken to build up the zones of powder as evenly as possible so that there are no large air cavities. A simple plunger can be made by attaching a rubber bung to a piece of glass rod. The diameter of the bung should be just under the diameter of the column. Alternatively, small amounts of powder can be added and allowed to settle by tapping the bottom of the column gently on the bench. The solvent is run through the column and once the packing material has been wetted it must not be allowed to run dry. A reservoir can be placed above the column and filled with excess liquid to prevent this occurring (*Figure 149*).

When the separation of the solute has been completed, each zone must be separated from the next. This can be carried out by eluting with a suitable solvent or solvents and collecting the eluate in fractions using a fraction collector. This instrument can be set to measure fractions of uniform volume or containing a predetermined number of drops, or it can be set to collect each fraction for a predetermined time. It consists of a horizontal wheel, carrying test tubes, which rotates so that a test tube is placed in position under the column until the predetermined amount of the eluate has been collected, when another test tube is moved into position.

When coloured substances have been separated and the zones are visible in the column, the column, provided that it has parallel sides, can be drained and the adsorbent extruded so that each zone can be cut free from the others. Each zone is placed in a short column and eluted with a suitable solvent.

COLUMN CHROMATOGRAPHY

PARTITION COLUMNS

Partition columns have not been extensively used since the introduction of paper chromatography. One older type of column was packed with silica gel which will tenaciously hold the water phase. This principle has been described under paper chromatography. Cellulose powder is commonly used and the columns are packed in the same manner as for adsorption columns. These columns can be used for the separation of amino acids and for sugars.

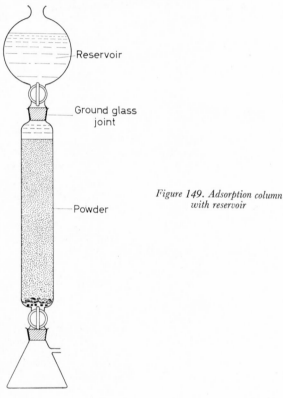

Reservoir

Ground glass joint

Powder

Figure 149. Adsorption column with reservoir

ION-EXCHANGE COLUMNS

These columns are becoming increasingly important but they can only be used to separate charged substances, such as amino acids, organic acids, etc.; they cannot be used for untreated sugars.

The columns are packed with a resin that will either exchange positively charged ions (cations) or negatively charged ions (anions).

If the substance which is to be separated is positively charged, then a cation exchange resin must be used and, similarly, if the substance is negatively charged, an anion exchange resin is used.

Resins which contain acidic or phenolic groups in their structure will exchange cations and those which contain amino groups will exchange anions.

When the column has been packed with a cationic resin, it must be activated by passing an acidic solution through the column when H^+ ions from the solution fill all the exchangeable sites on the resin. When a solution containing positively charged solutes is added, these cations are retained by the resin and displace H^+ ions. After non-cationic substances have been washed thoroughly from the column, the adsorbed cationic substances are themselves eluted (displaced) from the resin by the passage of a solution containing an excess of cations which are adsorbed more strongly by the resin. Substances adsorbed only weakly by the resin are eluted first, and so on until the separation is complete.

A column containing an anion exchange resin is activated by a solution containing anions, like OH^-, and is used to separate negatively charged substances.

The size of the column is dependent on the quantity and type of the substance to be separated and generally a small preparatory experiment is carried out so that the size of the column can be assessed.

For a small column, a thistle funnel with a constriction at the end of the stem can be utilized. The bottom of the column is plugged in the same way as for an adsorption column.

Ion-exchange columns are never packed dry. One method is to set up a thistle funnel and to fill it with water up to the neck. A thick suspension is made of the resin in water and this is poured carefully into the top of the column. The excess water is allowed to run through into a suitable container by opening a screw clip at the bottom of the column.

The resin must not be allowed to run dry, however, so the level of the liquid must be above the level of the resin. If any air bubbles are trapped in the column, the screw clip is tightened and the rubber tubing is squeezed gently. At the same time the resin in the column should be agitated with a glass rod.

Large columns require more packing than smaller ones, although they are plugged as for adsorption columns. One method is to fill the column partially with water and then to add the resin in bands. The water level should always be above the level of the resin and the column can be connected to a reservoir by setting up an apparatus as shown in *Figure 150*. The tubing from the column to the reservoir should reach, without kinking, from the top of the column down to floor level or at least below the bottom of the column and up to a reservoir situated above the column. It is very important that all the joints are completely air-tight.

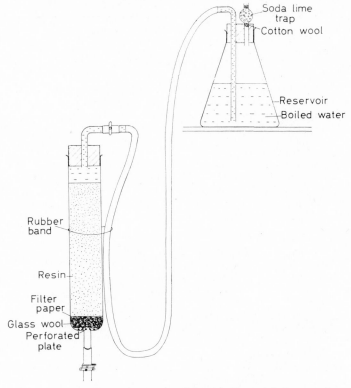

Figure 150. Ion-exchange column set up with a soda lime trap in the reservoir to prevent carbon dioxide entering the apparatus

After the column is set up in this way, it can be activated and then washed with distilled water before the introduction of the solute.

Resins

As has been previously mentioned resins are either cation exchangers or anion exchangers. They can be divided further into strong or weak cation exchangers and strong or weak anion exchangers.

The common types of resin can be purchased in a range of particle sizes applicable to the job in hand.

Some of the most commonly used resins in biological work have been listed below.

TABLE 12

Strong cation exchangers	Weak cation exchangers	Strong anion exchangers	Weak anion exchangers
Zeo-Karb 215 Zeo-Karb 225 Dowex 50	Zeo-Karb 226	De-Acidite FF Dowex 1	De-Acidite E Dowex 2

USE OF RADIOISOTOPES

Mixtures containing *labelled* substances can be separated as usual and the resultant radioactive spots measured directly for activity using an end-window Geiger–Müller tube, or after elution using the liquid scintillation technique.

The exact area of radioactivity can be ascertained by exposing a sheet of photographic film to the chromatogram for an extended period of time. The chromatogram should be fastened securely to the emulsion side of the photographic film with the aid of a paper clip, wrapped in a sheet of metallic paper and returned to the protective envelope. A note should be made on the envelope of the chromatogram of the serial number, the date and time of the start of the exposure. This whole operation should be carried out in a dark room.

After sufficient exposure, the photographic film should be developed and the resultant negative or radioautograph will show the areas of radioactivity as dark patches. If the film is superimposed upon the chromatogram, the actual areas of radioactivity can be marked upon it.

THIN LAYER CHROMATOGRAPHY

The basic technique of thin layer chromatography is the coating of a glass plate with a film of adsorbent which is completely dried before applying spots of the mixture to be analysed. After drying, the plate is developed in a suitable solvent.

The main advantage which this technique has over the other methods of chromatographic analysis is the speed with which the whole procedure can be carried out. This, coupled with the fact that smaller quantities of material are required, should render the method suitable for schools. Another advantage is that there is a vast range of adsorbents and ion-exchangers that can be used to form the thin layer.

The three types of chromatography mentioned previously, namely: adsorption, partition and ion-exchange, can all be carried out using the thin-layer method. The type of method which is used will depend upon the material which is to be analysed.

Adsorbents and Ion-exchangers

Varying grades of silica gel and aluminium oxide are most frequently used for adsorption chromatography. Powdered cellulose can be used for partition chromatography. It can be impregnated with paraffin or silicones for the same purpose, as can some grades of silica gel or kieselguhr. Chromatography carried out on impregnated plates is commonly known as "reversed phase".

Thin layer ion exchange chromatography uses cellulose ion exchangers of a different mesh to those used for column chromatography (e.g. DE, Sephadex etc.).

Solvents

Solvents must be chosen with care as with all chromatography. A spot check can be carried out to determine the best solvent to use. It is preferable to change the solvent rather than the adsorbent.

Some of the solvents which can be used are:

Acetone	Di-ethyl ether
Alcohol	n-Butanol
Benzene	n-Propanol
Carbon Tetrachloride	Acetic acid
Chloroform	Water
Cyclohexane	Mixture of acids, alcohol and water

Detection Reagents

A wide range of detecting reagents can be used, even such chemicals as concentrated sulphuric acid, which if used with paper chromatography would have disastrous results.

Some typical reagents are:

Sulphuric acid	Diphenyl carbazide
Potassium dichromate	Iodine solution
Ninhydrin	Iodine vapour

In addition to these reagents, u.v. light can be used also for detection purposes.

PREPARATION OF CHROMATOGRAPHIC PLATES

A great deal of the apparatus required is similar to that used for paper chromatograms but on a smaller scale. Basic sets of equipment can be obtained from laboratory suppliers, but the cost of small operations can be cut by improvisation, e.g. window glass cut to sizes 5×20 cm, 10×20 cm and 20 cm square for plates. Various containers such as battery or Kilner jars can be used for tanks (a means of providing an air-tight lid may be required). If window glass is used, care must be taken to grind the sharp edges with a wet emery stone. Before use, the plates must be thoroughly cleaned using a liquid detergent (p. 57) and a mild domestic abrasive. After cleaning, the plates are rinsed thoroughly with tap water and then with distilled water. They are placed in a rack, care being taken to handle the plates by their edges only, and completely dried in an oven.

The selected adsorbent is made into a slurry for the coating procedure and shaken in a stoppered flask with the appropriate liquid for the required time. Several adsorbents contain a percentage of plaster of Paris so the actual addition of liquid to the adsorbent should be left until everything is ready for the spreading process.

With the alignment tray on a bench, the dried and cooled glass plates are placed closely side by side on top of the tray with a small 5×20 cm plate at each end. The trough is filled with the slurry of adsorbent and placed in position at the left hand end of the tray above the plates, having first adjusted the thickness of the layer by whatever means are provided on the trough. The ejection slit is opened and the trough is drawn smoothly from the left to the right hand end of the tray. The empty trough is removed and rinsed, taking care not to damage the metal plate along the ejection slit.

When the coated plates have lost their shiny look, they are removed from the tray and either left to dry overnight or placed upon the drying rack and activated ready for use.

Activation is carried out by heating the coated plates. Generally speaking, longer heating at higher temperatures results in greater adsorption activity. A stock of activated plates can be prepared prior to use, provided that they are stored in a convenient sized desiccator over an efficient desiccant.

It should be noted that when preparing cellulose plates, the final dry layer of adsorbent will be approximately half that of the original slurry plated.

There are slight differences in pattern of the equipment. Several modifications are used to prevent movement of the glass plates during coating. Some troughs can be adjusted to provide a wide range of layer depth, others have only one or two adjustments or none at all. Most patterns provide a movable trough, but a few models have a stationery trough so that the plates are moved.

Instant thin layer plates can be obtained for adsorption and partition chromatography. They are bought as solid sheets of adsorbent material without a backing of glass. The material to be analysed is applied directly to the sheet which is rigid enough to stand in a tank for development as usual.

One-Dimensional Chromatography

The mixture to be analysed should be applied as a solution using a solvent which has a low elutive action with regard to the mixture. Varying amounts of mixture can be applied according to the type of chromatography required. Spots of mixture should be applied with a micro-pipette at a starting line 1·5–2·0 cm from the lower edge of the plate. This line may be marked lightly with a needle or sharp pencil and the resultant dust blown away. A mark should be made in a similar way at one side of the plate, at right angles to the direction of flow, and at a distance of 10 cm from the starting line. This mark will give an indication of the distance travelled by the solvent front during development. Some basic kits provide a template for use when spotting the chromatogram. Since the solvent used for the mixture is usually very volatile, the spots will dry rapidly at room temperature. However, a hot-air drier can be used, as with paper chromatography, for solvents of low volatility.

Each chromatogram should be labelled clearly on the upper third of the plate.

Development of the chromatogram—Several patterns of developing tank are available for ascending chromatography, which is the method most commonly used. The simplest pattern is the rectangular or circular tank (battery or preserving jars). More complicated tanks have refinements ensuring a fully saturated atmosphere and require smaller amounts of developing solvents, but naturally they are more expensive.

Special tanks can be obtained for other more specialized methods, i.e. descending chromatography, horizontal continuous-flow chromatography and gradient techniques.

Using a rectangular or circular tank for ascending chromatography, the developing solvent is placed in the bottom to a depth of 0·5–1·0 cm. The air-tight lid is placed in position and the tank is left at room temperature for a short while to allow the solvent to volatilize and saturate the atmosphere inside. The tank is now ready for the development of *one* or *two* chromatograms for preliminary work, or where reproducibility of results is not of prime importance. When *several* plates for preliminary work are to be developed, or reproducible results are essential, precautions must be taken to ensure a completely saturated atmosphere throughout the development. In this case the tank must be lined with filter paper or blotting paper which is then saturated with the selected solvent, in addition to the $0·5$–$1·0$ cm in the bottom of the tank. The lid is replaced until the plates are ready. Since the development time is relatively short, the room temperature is irrelevant. It is an advantage to use a fume cupboard at this stage as a safety precaution as some solvents are highly volatile, flammable and many are extremely toxic.

The plate is placed in the tank with the starting line at the bottom, using the plate holder provided. The lid is replaced and the solvent is allowed to run for the shortest distance necessary for distinct separation (usually not more than 100 mm). The solvent front is marked immediately the plate is removed, after which it is dried either at room temperature or in a drying oven (80°C). If several chromatography plates are developed simultaneously they must all be removed together, since immediately the tank is opened the saturation of the atmosphere alters rapidly, making further processing of half-developed plates extremely unwise. R_F values can be drastically altered by a change in atmospheric saturation during development, which results in erroneous conclusions.

Stepwise development may be necessary for better separation of components. In this case, the plates are partially developed with the requisite solvent. They are then completely dried and returned to the tank for further development. The operation is continued until the plate is fully developed.

Two-Dimensional Chromatography

If insufficient separation of substances has occurred with the one-dimensional method, the two-dimensional technique may be used. The spotting of the thin layer is carried out in exactly the same way as for paper chromatography. The spot is applied to the layer on a diagonal line from one corner of the plate to the other and is 2 cm from the corner. The chromatogram is developed with one solvent, removed from the tank, dried and returned to the tank to be developed with the second solvent. This solvent should be run at right angles to the direction of flow of the first solvent. After this second development, the thin layer is dried in a drying oven.

CHOICE OF SOLVENTS

On theoretical grounds the choice of solvent may be narrowed down to two or three but the final decision must often be made after several experiments. Instead of running full scale chromatograms the following alternative procedure may be used.

Several small *equal* volumes of the mixture being analysed are "spotted" on to a thin layer plate and completely dried. A known volume of a selected solvent is applied to the exact centre of one spot of the mixture, with the aid of a micro-pipette. The same volume of another solvent is applied to another "spot" and so on. When the solvents have volatilized their usefulness can be decided upon by the extent of the separation of the mixture components. The distinct zones of separation can be observed with the use of techniques described below.

DETECTION OF SEPARATED COMPOUNDS

As mentioned previously many compounds are visible on the dried plates, e.g. dyes and pigments. Other compounds are visible by absorption of fluorescence when viewed under u.v. light. The substance which absorbs u.v. light is more easily visible if viewed against a fluorescent background. For this reason the adsorbent used for coating the plate may contain a low concentration of a fluorescent substance.

A wide range of reagents are available which, when applied render visible substances which cannot be detected in the ways already suggested. It is usual to apply these reagents with a fine atomizer connected to a supply of compressed air. Alternatively a laboratory aerosol can be used very satisfactorily. After spraying with the appropriate reagent, the separated substance may be immediately visible or may require further heating.

USE OF RADIOISOTOPES

Thin-layer chromatography can be used for the separation of labelled substances. The procedure is the same as before, but the operator will of course observe the precautions which are necessary when dealing with radio-active substances (pp. 78, 79).

Radioautographs can be prepared from the developed thin-layer chromatograms in the same way as from paper chromatograms.

The radioactivity present in the spots can be measured directly on the plate using an end window Geiger counter. Alternatively, assays can be made after elution from the plate using an end window counter or the scintillation counting technique.

PREPARATIVE THIN LAYER CHROMATOGRAPHY

Comparatively large amounts of components can be isolated by thin layer chromatography. In this case the coating layers of adsorbents are much thicker than those used for small scale analytical work. Layers of between 1–5 mm can be used which means that the slurry should have a thicker consistency. If a thin slurry is used, the layer would spread and collapse before setting. Layers of more than 1–1·5 mm should have a shallow trough scored upon the starting line to hold the mixture which is to be purified. After applying the mixture, drying can be facilitated by the use of a hot-air drier, an infra-red lamp, or the glass can be heated from underneath. After development, the required substance can be eluted as described later.

Once again the main advantage of this method of preparative chromatography is the speed with which the entire operation can be carried out. Two days work using paper chromatographic methods can be completed in the same number of hours using the thin layer technique.

THE R_F VALUE

The R_F value can be calculated using the equation on p. 353. Factors affecting the reproducibility of R_F values are enumerated below.

(1) Slight differences in quality of dry adsorbents, in preparation of the slurry and activation procedure.

To overcome these problems the same batch of dry adsorbent should be used for a complete series of experiments. The slurry should contain exactly the same amount of dry powder and liquid when several batches of plates are prepared. The slurry should be shaken for exactly the same amount of time and the coated plates activated for the same time and temperature from batch to batch.

(2) Uneven thickness in the direction of solvent flow will have a marked effect. Slight variation in thickness of the layers from different batches, however, does not seem to cause much deviation from the expected result.

(3) The solvents which are used must be of consistently high quality or spurious results will ensue.

(4) The degree of saturation of the surrounding atmosphere is important. The precautions already suggested should be carried out, together with a check to ensure that no vapour is leaking through the lid of the tank.

(5) As with other methods a change of R_F value will be observed when changing from ascending to horizontal or descending chromato-

graphy. There should be no radical change in R_F value within each method.

ELUTION

It is sometimes necessary to recover a substance from a thin layer chromatogram after separation, e.g. for accurate quantitative measurement. The exact position of the substance is decided upon either by visible detection, u.v. light, or by a method using an appropriate colour reagent without adulterating the main quantity of the substance. This can be done by running a small quantity of the same mixture along both sides of the main sample. After the development and drying of the chromatogram, the main portion of the plate is masked with a suitable piece of glass, leaving the small "marker" samples exposed. The reagent is then applied. The exact position of the required substance can be fixed by marking off the area on the untreated portion of the chromatogram corresponding to the relevant spots on the sprayed portion.

The position of the substance to be recovered should be marked using a sharp pencil, extending the area well beyond the suspected limit of the substance edge. The adsorbent can be scraped carefully from the glass plate with a small spatula. The resultant powder or in the case of cellulose plates, the mat, can be transferred to a beaker and the required substance eluted with suitable solvents.

GAS CHROMATOGRAPHY

This type of chromatography is becoming increasingly important and successful. Instead of a liquid solvent, a gas is used for the separation and there are many varied and complicated techniques which are outside the scope of this book.

ELECTROPHORESIS

Electrophoresis forms another technique for separating substances but the underlying principle of the method is totally different from partition chromatography.

Separation depends upon the fact that many molecules carry electric charges so that if they are subjected to a potential difference they tend to move towards the electrode of opposite charge. The rate of movement and hence the separation is dependent primarily upon the magnitude of the charge carried by the molecule but the overall size and shape of the molecule also affects the electrophoretic mobility.

THIN LAYER ELECTROPHORESIS

Thin layer electrophoresis is carried out in the same way as for paper electrophoresis but the filter paper strip, which carries the mixture being separated, is replaced by a glass plate coated with a thin layer of silica gel.

REFERENCE

[1]Tiselius, A. (1952). 'Some Recent Advances in Chromatography.' *Endeavour* **11**, 5

BIBLIOGRAPHY

Aronoff, S. (1956). *Techniques of Radiobiochemistry*, 1st ed. Des Moines; Iowa State College Press

Block, R. J., Durrum, E. L. and Zweig, G. (1955). *Paper Chromatography and Paper Electrophoresis*, 1st ed. New York; Academic Press

Laboratory Practice (1965). *Thin Layer Chromatography*, 1st ed. London; United Trade Press

Lederer, E. and Lederer, M. (1957). *Chromatography*, 2nd ed. Amsterdam, London and New York; Elsevier Pub. Co.

Randerath, K. (1963). *Thin Layer Chromatography*, 1st ed. London; Academic Press

Smith, I. (1960). *Chromatographic and Electrophoretic Techniques*, Vol. II, 1st ed. Bath; Pitman

Stahl, E. (1965). *Thin Layer Chromatography; a Laboratory Handbook*, 1st ed. London; Academic Press

Truter, E. V. (1963). *Thin Film Chromatography*, 1st ed. London; Cleaver-Hume

Williams, T. I. (1954). *The Elements of Chromatography*, 1st ed. London; Blackie

CHAPTER 16

DISTILLATION TECHNIQUES

In the purification or separation of substances in the laboratory, distillation techniques play an important part. The allied processes of extraction and refluxing will also be discussed in this chapter.

Apart from the apparatus for actual experimental work, a mention must be made of two of the main types of still used in a laboratory to distil water in quantity. It is good practice to have a supply of water distilled from a metal still of the type shown in *Figure 151*. This type of still may be heated either by gas or by electricity and will produce varying amounts of distilled water per hour according to the size of the model. The quality of this water makes it useful for all general purposes. If, however, distilled water is required which is free from trace elements and any fluorescent material, then a still must be used which is constructed of glass throughout. Here again the still may be heated either by gas or electricity. An efficient glass still is shown in *Figure 152a*. The still flask in this case is of 1 litre capacity and is suitable for heating either with a Meker burner or an electric mantle*. A larger capacity flask may be used, i.e. of a 5 litre capacity in which case electric heating is more efficient and an integral heating element can be employed (*Figure 152b*). The output of distilled water from this type of still varies. The smaller capacity flask distils approximately 1 litre/h, while the larger flask will give a higher yield. The water produced in this way is suitable for making media, where the concentration of specific trace elements must be strictly controlled, and for fluorimetry where all the distilled water used both for solutions and for rinsing glassware must be absolutely pure and dust free.

All permanent water stills must be registered with H.M. Customs and Excise Department.

DE-IONIZING EQUIPMENT

Water of sufficient purity for general use may be obtained without distillation by passing the water through a de-ionizing apparatus.

---

*The mantle can be made to order by Electro-thermal Engineering Co., 270 Neville Road, E.1.

Two ion exchange resins (one an anion exchanger and the other a cation exchanger) can either be mixed to form a bed or two columns of the separate resins may be joined to form a continuous column. Several patterns of apparatus for using these resins may be obtained

Figure 151. A Manesty water still
(By courtesy of Manesty Machines Ltd.)

from Messrs. Gallenkamp & Co. Ltd. Before use, the apparatus must be charged by following the instructions issued with it. A cleaning and recharging process is also required after de-ionizing a stated amount of water. The output of purified water per hour varies according to the model.

The apparatus used for distillation on an experimental basis is principally the same as for the larger scale stills described above. There must be a vessel to hold the liquid to be distilled, a condenser, and a receiver for the distillate. In addition there is sometimes a subsidiary condenser or fractionating column.

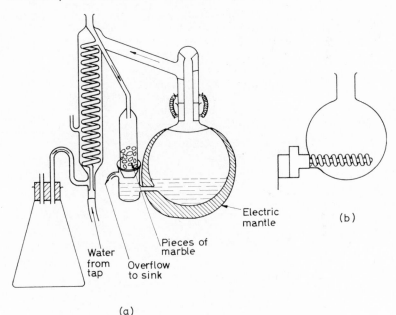

Water from tap Overflow to sink Pieces of marble Electric mantle (b)

(a)

Figure 152. (a) Glass still; (b) a still flask with an integral heating element

All these components vary in size, shape and volume according to their specific use.

Still Flasks

Still flasks fall roughly into two categories. Round or pear-shaped flasks (*Figure 153*) which must have a cork inserted into the neck of each flask to carry a thermometer and a delivery tube. In addition to the single-necked boiling flasks there are multi-necked varieties which are convenient when mechanical agitation is required during

373

distillation, or when a separatory funnel is required to facilitate the addition of more liquid, as might happen during prolonged refluxing. These multi-necked flasks have reinforced necks and are known as bolt-head flasks (*Figure 153c*). If a multi-necked flask is unobtainable, a three-way adaptor may be inserted in a single-necked bolt-head flask.

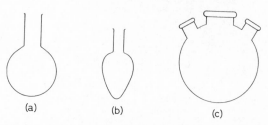

(a) (b) (c)

Figure 153. (a) Round-bottomed flask; (b) pear-shaped flask; (c) bolt-head flask (multi-necked)

In the second type of flask, as shown in *Figure 154a*, there is no necessity for an external delivery tube as this is an integral part of the flask. The modified Claisen flask (*Figure 154b*) has the same integral delivery tube but has also an additional vertical sidearm. This sidearm may be elongated (*Figure 154c*) so that it can be used as a fractionating column if required.

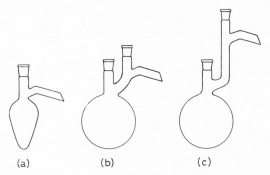

(a) (b) (c)

Figure 154. (a) Ordinary Claisen flask; (b) and (c) modified Claisen flasks

As with the first group of flasks, the shape and volume of the bulb of the flask varies according to the nature of the work to be carried out, for example, when working with volumes of 20 ml or less it would be wise to use a pear-shaped rather than a round-bottomed flask. The integral delivery tube may be elongated to form the inner tube of a condenser, needing only the addition of a condenser jacket to present a compact set-up with virtually no joints.

It must be realized that an ideal set-up of any apparatus to contain liquids and vapours should have as few joints as possible. Therefore this second type of flask is eminently more efficient than the first which requires fractionating columns and condensers fitted externally. Nowadays apparatus with interchangeable ground glass joints simplifies the assembly of a distillation set-up and reduces the risk of leakage at the joints. Most of the glassware described in this chapter may be obtained with interchangeable ground glass joints.

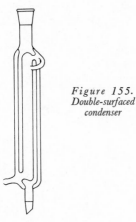

Figure 155.
Double-surfaced
condenser

Condensers

The most commonly used condenser is the Liebig pattern (*see Figure 27*, Chapter 2). This consists of a central tube carrying the distillate and surrounded by a jacket through which water is flowing continuously. The entire condenser is made of glass.

The water jacket alone may be used with a Claisen flask as described previously. The jacket should be fitted to the sidearm with two pieces of heavy rubber tubing. A double-surfaced condenser (*Figure 155*) is sometimes used. Condensers may be obtained in various sizes and it should be noted that a double-surfaced condenser is more efficient than a Liebig condenser of the same length.

Fractionating Columns

Fractionating columns are added to the distillation set-up when

375

the liquid to be distilled has a boiling point close to that of the other constituent(s) in the total volume of liquid. These columns are of various patterns but all serve the same purpose, i.e. when the still flask is heated, the various constituents will vaporize as soon as their boiling point is reached. When separating two or more liquids with large intervals between their boiling points, each constituent will vaporize, pass immediately through a condenser and will be received relatively free from any of the other constituents. The temperature will remain fairly static at the boiling point of the fraction which is distilling. When the whole of this fraction has been collected, the temperature will rise sharply to that of the boiling point of the next fraction and so on until only one fraction is left as a residue in the flask. If, however, the components of the mixture have boiling points which are close together then as the temperature of the component with the lowest boiling point is reached, the vapour which passes over will carry an appreciable percentage of vapour from the next fraction also. In this situation, a fractionating column must be placed in the distillation set-up between the still flask and the condenser. The column consists of a long tube containing an arrangement of glass rings, coils, etc. This arrangement will allow the through passage of a vapour but will present a large number of glass surfaces with which the vapour will come into intimate contact. The effect of this process is to lower the temperature of the vapour very slightly, resulting in a partial condensation. The condensate thus formed will contain a large percentage of the less volatile fraction, i.e. the fraction with the higher boiling point, and a small percentage of the more volatile fraction, i.e. the fraction distilling first with the lower boiling point. The condensate will pass down the fractionating column and so mix intimately with the ascending vapour. During this mixing, the small percentage of the more volatile fraction will again be vaporized and will pass over into the condenser, while the less volatile fraction will eventually drop back into the still flask. Thus the fractionating column causes a continuous series of partial condensations, resulting in a relatively pure fraction passing over to be finally condensed, any adulterating fraction being returned to the still flask. Once again distillation will stop when each fraction has been collected and will start again when the temperature has reached that of the next fraction.

Fractionating columns may be obtained as separate pieces of apparatus, which may be attached to the distillation set-up when required. Alternatively the elongated sidearm of a Claisen flask may be used as an integral column. In either case the column may have a permanent arrangement of glass surfaces inside made by indenting the glass so that spurs of glass extend inwards and downwards. Each pair of spurs is arranged to form a spiral from the top to the bottom of the column. This type of permanent column is of the Vigreux pattern (*Figure 156a*). Another slightly more efficient column may be made by winding a spiral of glass rod round a central glass rod. The spiral plus the central rod should be placed inside the column, making sure that the spiral fits tightly against the sides of the tube. This is the Dufton column (*Figure 156b*). The most efficient type of

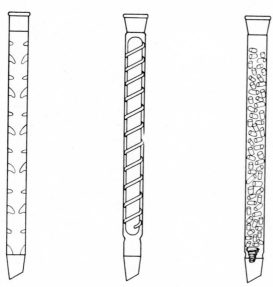

Figure 156. (a) Vigreux column; (b) Dufton column; (c) Hempel column packed with glass cylinders

column is one which is packed with small pieces of glass or wire, like glass cylinders, glass or wire helices or gauze rings. These columns are of the Hempel pattern (*Figure 156c*).

Fractionating columns must not be allowed to cool excessively and to prevent this, they may be lagged with asbestos cord or an electrically heated jacket may be used.

Receivers

Conical flasks are the most convenient vessels to use for general purposes. Other types of receiving vessels may be used for specific purposes and will be shown in the illustrations for standard distillation set-ups.

When assembling the following apparatus it should be ascertained that all corks fit tightly and all glass joints are ground in thoroughly. Whenever possible double purpose apparatus, i.e. flasks with integral delivery tubes and columns, should be used. The condenser must always be clamped as well as the still flask and the claws of the clamp should be lined with cork.

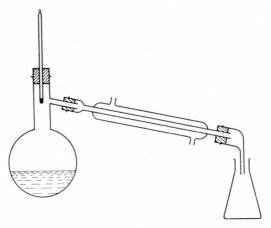

Figure 157. Standard distillation assembly

The set-up shown in *Figure 157* is the simplest and shows the basic requirements for distillation. The flask may be heated by a bunsen burner under a wire gauze or by an oil or water bath in the case of flammable liquids. (These heat supplies apply to all distillation set-ups described in this chapter except those used for steam distillation.) Variations and refinements of this simple set-up are shown in the following illustrations.

Vacuum Distillation

Figure 158 shows a set-up of Quickfit apparatus used for vacuum distillation as used to distil substances which decompose at their normal boiling point. The receiver flask may be cooled in a cold water or an ice bath.

(A similar apparatus should be used when distilling flammable liquids. In this case the safety valve leading into the still flask is unnecessary and a simple adaptor (*Figure 159*) may be used. The outlet tube in the adaptor leading to the receiver should have a

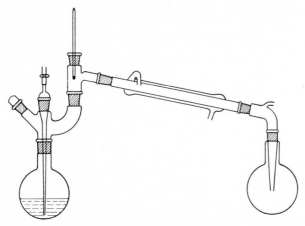

Figure 158. Vacuum distillation assembly

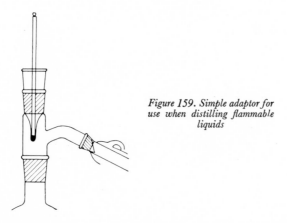

Figure 159. Simple adaptor for use when distilling flammable liquids

rubber tube attached to it and this should be led into a sink over-flow.)

When working with small volumes, a small pear-shaped Claisen flask should be used. However, whatever the scale of the apparatus the basic set-up is the same, i.e. an enclosed system for vacuum distillation plus a safety valve, and a safety outlet leading from the vessel receiving a flammable distillate.

Distillation Using a Fractionating Column

When introducing a fractionating column into the set-up, whether as an integral column (*Figure 160*) or as a separate component (*Figure 161*), the thermometer should always be inserted in the neck of the column with the bulb on the level with the delivery tube. The use of a bolt-head flask in *Figure 161* ensures extra strength in the neck of the flask. Heat may be supplied by a bunsen burner, sand bath, water bath, electric mantle or a hot plate, but it must be applied slowly and regulated so as to provide a slow distillation.

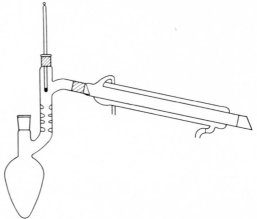

Figure 160. Fractional distillation assembly using Claisen flask with an integral column

REFLUXING AND EXTRACTION

Refluxing

If it is desired to digest a substance in a hot solvent over a period of time, a condenser should be fitted to the still flask in a vertical position (*see Figure 27*), so as to give a reflux action. If extra solvent has to be added during refluxing, a double-necked flask should be used, the second neck carrying a separatory funnel.

Extraction

Fats and waxes, etc., may be separated from a sample of material by extraction in the following manner. The sample is placed in a porous container and a solvent is dropped on to it continuously. The dissolved fat phase passes through the porous container and is collected below, while the insoluble matter remains behind. Since the process must be continuous over a reasonable period of time, a specially designed extraction apparatus must be used in conjunction with a Liebig condenser. The apparatus most commonly used is a Soxhlet extractor (*Figure 162*) in conjunction with porous cellulose

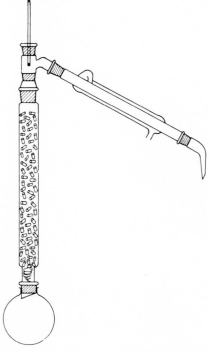

*Figure 161. Fractional distillation assembly
using a column as a separate component*

thimbles of various sizes. The sample to be analysed should be placed in a tared thimble and weighed. The top of the thimble may be plugged with a little glass wool to prevent the sample floating out during extraction. The solvent to be used should be placed in a tared bolt-head flask (half-full), the extractor plus the thimble placed in position, and a Liebig condenser attached to the extractor in a vertical position (*Figure 163*). This assembly should be heated over a water bath. As the solvent vaporizes, it will pass up through the apparatus until it reaches the condenser. The condensate will

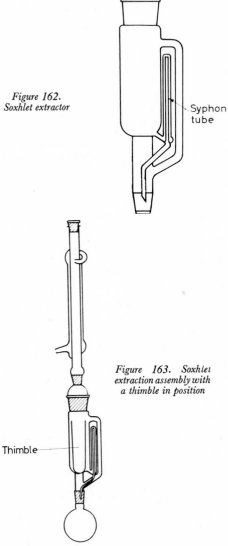

Figure 162.
Soxhlet extractor

Syphon
tube

Figure 163. Soxhlet extraction assembly with a thimble in position

Thimble

drop back into the thimble and the extraction will begin. The extractor is made so that, for a period of time, the thimble is partially immersed in solvent. This aids the process of extraction considerably. A small siphon is attached to the side of the extractor and, when the level of solvent reaches the peak of the siphon tube, the extract surrounding the thimble is siphoned back into the flask. At the end of several hours (or overnight) the extraction should be complete. The extract may be taken down to dryness *in situ* and the amount of fat phase calculated after weighing. The thimble will contain all the insoluble phase and may also be calculated as a percentage of the whole.

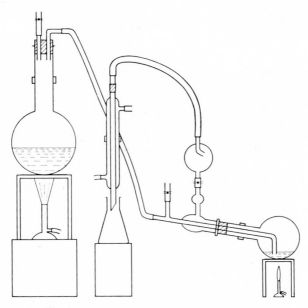

Figure 164. Semi-micro steam distillation assembly

By judicious choice of solvents any specific fraction of fat or wax may be extracted fractionately using the appropriate solvent for each fraction in turn.

STEAM DISTILLATION

Steam distillation is a means of distilling a volatile substance at a lower temperature than would be reached by the previous methods. As can be seen by the name of the technique, the liquid being distilled is heated by passing steam through it. This may be either a macro or micro-technique. In the former case a conventional distillation set-up is used with the addition of a steam generator (a steam generator is shown in *Figure 164*). The generator should be heated to boiling point with the screw clip open. When steam is being generated, close the screw clip carefully, shielding the hand with a glove or cloth, so that the force of steam passed into the still flask does not shoot any of the liquid over into the condenser. A small amount of heat should be applied to the still flask to maintain a constant level of liquid being collected. Distillation should continue until water distils over, when it may be terminated by shutting off all extraneous heat, both to the still flask and to the steam generator, and opening the screw clip.

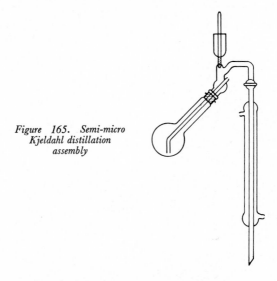

Figure 165. Semi-micro Kjeldahl distillation assembly

Micro-steam distillation may be carried out either with microflasks, condensers, etc., or with a specially made compact apparatus as is used when estimating ammonia or volatile acids. In the former case micro apparatus can be employed in the biological laboratory where steam distillation is used chiefly as a means of estimating ammonia or volatile acids, such as acetic acid formed during bacterial fermentation. This estimation is usually carried out on the micro scale.

When estimating ammonia or volatile acids, the samples should be in an alkaline or acidic solution respectively; sodium hydroxide being used for the alkaline solution and a non-volatile acid, such as sulphuric acid, for the acidic solution. Distillation should continue until a distillate of ten times the volume of the original sample is obtained, when a reasonably complete recovery of either ammonia or volatile acid will have been made. Here care must be taken not to allow the steam generator to cool without shutting it off from the still and opening the safety valve. Failure to do this will cause a sucking over of the contents of the flask.

A blank determination should be carried out in conjunction with both the above estimations.

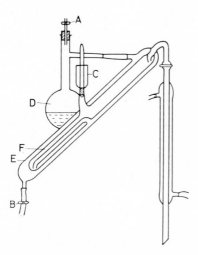

Figure 166. Markham still for micro-steam distillation

In the latter case the specially designed compact apparatus comprises a vessel for holding the liquid to be distilled, a condenser, a steam jacket and a reservoir through which reagents may be added during distillation. In both cases a steam generator is still required.

The two preceding figures show a micro Kjeldahl apparatus (*Figure 165*), in which the still flask is used previously for digestion, and a Markham still (*Figure 166*) which is also used for total nitrogen estimation. In this case the initial digestion is carried out in another vessel and a measured aliquot of the resulting solution is introduced into the inner compartment of the Markham still prior to steam distillation (see p. 398).

BIBLIOGRAPHY

Coulson, E. A. and Herington, E. F. G. (1958). *Laboratory Distillation Practice*, 1st ed. London; Newnes

Vogel, A. I. (1957). *Elementary Practical Organic Chemistry*, Part I, 1st ed. London; Longmans, Green

Wiberg, K. B. (1960). *Laboratory Techniques in Organic Chemistry*, 1st ed. New York; McGraw-Hill

CHAPTER 17

ANALYSIS OF SOILS, WATERS AND PLANT MATERIAL

In nature, plants grow in a wide range of soils, fresh water and salt water. The relationship between the plant species and the substrate can be analysed in terms of chemical, physical and biological characteristics.

Information about the sizes of soil particles and the proportions of each present, the organic matter content, pH, moisture content and mineral nutrient content indicate the suitability of a soil as a medium for the growth of plants.

However, no simple form of chemical analysis can simulate the conditions existing in the soil during the period of active plant growth and so give a reliable measure of the amounts of nutrients available for uptake by the plants. For this reason, the amounts of the different elements present in plants are often used as an indication of their relative availability in the soil.

Plant analyses are also carried out to determine the amounts of certain nutrients cycling between plants and the medium in which they grow.

SOILS AND WATERS[1, 2]

COLLECTION OF SAMPLES FOR ANALYSIS IN THE LABORATORY

The purpose for which the sample is required will determine the method of sampling. The size of the sample, the depth to which it is taken and the number of samples required, depend upon statistical considerations[3, 4] which will not be discussed here.

Water samples are conveniently collected and transported in screw-top polythene bottles of a suitable capacity.

Samples of soil are taken with a trowel, spade, screw auger or cylindrical borer. The screw auger, which resembles an outsize woodwork bit, is screwed into the ground to the required depth, then pulled out with the sample of soil held in the screw thread. Cylindrical borers remove a soil core of known volume.

Samples of soil can be carried to the laboratory in aluminium screw-cap cans, polythene bags, or waxed, stoppered specimen tubes, to minimize moisture loss.

It is essential that tools and containers are clean before samples come into contact with them.

Every sample must be clearly labelled so that it can be identified with certainty at a later date.

PREPARATION AND STORAGE OF SAMPLES

In the laboratory, water samples may be stored until they can be analysed. They may be stored for long periods without deterioration in a refrigerator (if a crystal of thymol or a drop of toluene is added), or in deep freeze. A quantity of fresh soil from the larger samples or complete small samples should be set aside for the determination of moisture content, nitrate, nitrite and ammonia determinations, hydrogen ion concentration (pH) and, possibly for availability estimates of certain mineral elements (see below).

The remainder of the soil sample should be broken up and spread out to become air-dry. When air-dry, the material can be crushed in a pestle and mortar without actually grinding the soil particles. The soil should be passed through a sieve with holes 2 mm in diameter, coarse material being returned to the mortar for further crushing. This process is repeated until all particles except stones and organic matter pass through the sieve.

The stones and gravel are weighed and the weight recorded as a proportion of the original sample.

The "fine earth" or material passing the 2 mm sieve is weighed, mixed thoroughly, and stored in a labelled screw-top bottle or soil can.

Where small quantities of soil are used in a determination, it is necessary to use material which has been passed through a 0·5 mm sieve, to reduce sampling errors.

MECHANICAL ANALYSIS OF SOIL PASSING A 2 mm SIEVE

Mechanical analysis consists essentially of two distinct operations:

Separation of the Soil into its Component Particles

To effect a complete separation of soil particles it is necessary to disperse the material in water. Before this can be done effectively, organic matter must be removed completely from the sample, by igniting in a muffle furnace at 350°C, and calcium carbonate must be dissolved out with dilute hydrochloric acid. Various dispersing agents are recommended, such as sodium oxalate or sodium sesquicarbonate. Dispersion is aided by mechanical agitation of the soil, suspension in an end-over-end shaker, or by a motor dispersion unit.

Determination of the Proportion of Particles in Different Size Ranges

The property of the larger particles in the dispersion that is selected to specify their size is the ability to pass, or be retained by, standard sieves. Smaller particles are separated by their velocity of sedimentation in a vertical column of water at 20°C.

Table 13 shows the particle size groups and the limiting velocities in water at 20°C, for each group separated in the International System of mechanical analysis.

TABLE 13

Description of particles	Maximum diameter of particle in mm	Method of defining upper size limit	Settling velocity at 20°C in cm/sec.
Coarse sand	2·0	2 mm round hole sieve	347
Fine sand	0·2	70 mesh sieve	3·47
Silt	0·02	Sedimentation: 10 cm/4 min 48 sec	0·0347
Clay	0·002	Sedimentation: 10 cm/8 hr	0·000347

After C. S. Piper (1942)[1]

The silt and clay fractions are determined by allowing the dispersion to sediment in a large gas cylinder (40 cm high and approximately 6·5 cm internal diameter is a convenient size) having a capacity of about 1,250 ml. Samples are removed from the cylinder by means of a 20 ml pipette with a specially lengthened lower stem. The tip of the pipette is lowered to a depth 10 cm below the surface and a sample of the suspension is sucked up gently after the specified settling period has elapsed (4 min 48 sec for silt, 8 h for clay).

Further details are to be found in standard textbooks[1].

The results of analysis should be tabulated as the oven-dry percentage of each fraction in the original oven-dry soil, as follows:

> Coarse sand
> Fine sand
> Silt
> Clay
> Loss on acid treatment (or solution)
> Total.

SOIL MOISTURE CONTENT

To determine the moisture content of a fresh or an air-dry soil, about 10 g should be transferred to a weighed silica or porcelain dish. The dish should be placed in an oven at 105°C and the contents dried for 12–24 h before cooling in a desiccator and weighing. The soil should be reheated and reweighed until a constant weight is achieved. The result is expressed as follows:

$$\frac{\text{weight of original sample} - \text{weight of dried sample}}{\text{weight of original sample}} \times 100$$

= percentage moisture content.

Field Capacity Determination

Field capacity is the amount of water held in the soil after it has been thoroughly wetted by rainfall or irrigation and the excess has been allowed to drain away. The loss of moisture on oven drying (as above for soil moisture content) is expressed as a percentage of the weight of oven-dry soil remaining.

$$\frac{\text{weight of fresh sample} - \text{weight of dried sample}}{\text{weight of dried sample}} \times 100$$

TOTAL SOIL ORGANIC MATTER

The organic matter in a soil can be determined by igniting a sample at a moderate temperature and recording the loss on ignition. Provided that temperatures are kept below 350° to 400°C there will be little or no loss of carbonates (as carbon dioxide gas).

It is convenient to use the sample of soil taken for moisture content. After determining the moisture, the dish and sample are placed into a cool muffle furnace. The temperature is raised to 350°C (dull red heat) for several hours. The dish is then removed to a desiccator to cool and then weighed. The result is expressed as follows:

$$\frac{\text{weight of oven-dry sample} - \text{weight of ignited sample}}{\text{weight of oven-dry sample}} \times 100$$

= percentage loss on ignition.

In waters which contain fair quantities of suspended matter, the organic content can be determined on the residue obtained on filtering a sample.

SOIL CARBONATE CONTENT

The presence of carbonates is a valuable indication of chemical and physical conditions in the soil. Calcium present in soils is usually determined and reported as calcium carbonate. A suitable piece of apparatus for carrying out the determination of calcium carbonate is the Collins' Calcimeter. This consists of a water jacket, in which the various working parts are enclosed, and is provided with a measuring tube graduated from 0 to 50 in tenths of a ml and a levelling tube. The level is adjusted by means of a special air flask and bellows. Gas is generated in a flask outside the water jacket by tilting the flask and allowing dilute hydrochloric acid to run from a small tube on to the soil sample contained in the flask. The volume of gas released is determined by noting the change in the level in the measuring tube which was previously adjusted to zero. The temperature of the water and the atmospheric pressure are noted and the necessary corrections made to obtain results at normal temperature and pressure. Full details are supplied with the apparatus.

HYDROGEN ION CONCENTRATION (pH)

The pH of samples of water can be determined directly in the field using a portable meter, or in the laboratory using a pH meter (as described in Chapter 1).

Soil pH values can be determined in the field with a portable pH meter, by inserting the combined spear type glass and reference electrode directly into the soil profile. The soil should contain sufficient moisture to make a good contact. It is advisable to add a little water from a wash bottle as a standard procedure to even out differences of moisture content in different soils.

In the laboratory, fresh soil samples should be used where possible. The sample should be prepared by moistening it to a paste with de-ionized water and stirring well before taking a reading. In the results, it should be stated whether fresh soil or air-dried soil was used.

Values of pH are a useful guide to soil conditions. British soils can be broadly divided into alkaline (pH 6–8) and acid (pH 4–6) and characteristic vegetation is associated with these soil types.

MINERAL NUTRIENT AVAILABILITY IN WATERS AND SOILS

Water Soluble Salts

The soil solution contains varying amounts of soluble salts in the form of carbonates, bicarbonates, nitrates, chlorides and sulphates of the metallic cations (namely calcium, potassium, sodium and magnesium).

Natural waters contain varying amounts of these dissolved salts, some of which are carried from soil by run-off waters. Knowledge of the concentration of water soluble salts is useful when considering the suitability of the medium for plant growth, the osmotic effects on germination of seeds or the uptake of water by plants.

The numbers of individual anions and cations are determined by methods described in the section on plant analysis.

Conductivity Measurements

An approximate value for the total soluble salts in waters and soil suspensions can be obtained by measuring their electrical conductivity.

Measurements may be made in the field with a portable Dionic Water Tester (manufactured by Evershed and Vignoles, London, W.4). Waters can be tested directly but it is necessary to prepare a 1:5 suspension of soil in water for testing. The temperature of the solution is taken and the electrode distances adjusted so that the reading obtained is that which would have been recorded had the determination been carried out at 20°C.

In the laboratory a more refined piece of apparatus is used. Conductivity is measured by means of a Wheatstone bridge with an alternating current to avoid polarization of the electrodes (obtained by using a thermionic-valve oscillator and amplifier). A telephone receiver is used to determine the point of minimum sound or, alternatively, the point of balance is detected visually with a cathode ray tube. The conductivity cell consists of two platinum electrodes fixed in a constant position in relation to each other. A standard potassium chloride solution is prepared by dissolving 0·7456 g of solid in de-ionized water and diluting to 2 litre. The electrode is immersed in standard KCl and the variable resistance of the Wheatstone bridge adjusted until the point of balance is reached. The electrode is rinsed and the resistance of the soil extract or natural water determined.

The specific conductivity, in reciprocal ohms (or mhos), of the 1:5 soil suspension or natural water at 20°C is given by:

$$\frac{\text{Resistance of KCl (0·005N)}}{\text{Resistance of soil suspension}} \times \frac{1}{\text{Specific resistance of 0·005N}}$$
(KCl at 20°C=1540 ohms)

The results should be reported as specific conductivity at 20°C. The concentration of total soluble salts can be roughly related to these values but this depends largely upon the composition of the salts present.

Exchangeable Cations in Soils

Mineral and organic colloids in soils have negative valence charges that hold dissociable cations in equilibrium with the soil solution. Determination of the availability of these plant nutrients raises special problems which are beyond the scope of this book. However, it can be mentioned that a number of methods are used to estimate the availability of the cations in soil and these have been related to the responses of plants grown in these soils. These methods involve leaching the soil with concentrated salt solutions (such as ammonium nitrate, ammonium acetate) or with dilute acids (such as acetic acid) and determining the cations displaced from the exchange sites.

For example, calcium and potassium and possibly other cations can be leached from fresh or oven-dried soil with 0·5N ammonium nitrate. The leaching is more effective if it is added in several small quantities than if added all at once. A small quantity of oven-dried soil is weighed into a 100 ml conical flask, 30 ml of extractant added and shaken in a shaking machine for 2 h. It is then filtered into a second flask. The filter paper plus residue is returned to the first flask and a further 30 ml of extractant added and shaken as before for 1 h. This is filtered, as before, into the second 100 ml conical flask, and the residue washed with a further 30 ml of ammonium nitrate. The combined filtrates are transferred to a volumetric flask and made up to volume. The concentration of calcium and potassium in the extract are determined by the methods described elsewhere.

Each exchangeable cation is reported as mequiv per 100 g of oven-dried soil

$$\text{i.e.} \quad \frac{\text{p.p.m. cation}}{\text{equivalent weight in mg}} \text{ per 100 g dry soil}$$

(=mequiv per cent or mequiv 100 g)

Total Exchangeable Bases (Cations) and Exchangeable Hydrogen

The exchangeable hydrogen and the sum of the exchangeable bases of a soil indicate the suitability of the soil for the growth of plants, i.e. the base unsaturation is given by the exchangeable hydrogen content, the base supplying power by the total exchangeable base content and the sum of these values gives the total capacity of the soil for holding cations.

A convenient rapid method for use in non-calcareous soils is that developed by Brown[5].

Determination of exchangeable hydrogen—2·5 g of soil is placed in a 50 ml conical flask, 25 ml of neutral normal ammonium acetate is added, the flask is stoppered and allowed to stand for 1 h with shaking; pH is determined in the mixture. The mequiv of exchangeable hydrogen per 100 g of soil are read directly from a graph in which the pH of ammonium acetate leachates of a number of soils is plotted against the mequiv hydrogen obtained by titration. (See the curve used by Brown[5].)

Determination of total exchangeable bases—2·5 g soil and 25 ml of normal acetic acid are mixed and treated in the same manner as the mixture prepared for exchangeable hydrogen determination. The pH is determined and read from a graph of the pH of normal acetic acid soil mixtures plotted against base content found by analysis of ammonium acetate leachates of a number of soils.

EXPRESSION OF RESULTS BY WEIGHT OR VOLUME

Where soils with a widely differing organic matter content are being compared, it is necessary to express the results in terms of a unit volume of soil instead of dry weight. If equal weights of a soil with a high organic content are compared with a soil containing little organic matter, the former will occupy a much larger volume than the latter. This is important to remember when considering the volume of soil exploited by plant root systems.

PLANTS

COLLECTION OF MATERIAL FOR ANALYSIS

It is very important that samples are typical of the plant material which it is intended to represent; if they are not, the analytical results will be of no value.

The details of sampling in the field will depend upon the type of material and the purpose for which the sample is required. Individual plants, parts of plants, such as leaves, or a bulk of material may be collected. Precautions should be taken to avoid contaminating samples with soil which may contain larger amounts of the element which it is intended to determine, than are in the plant material. Samples are conveniently carried to the laboratory in labelled polythene bags.

PREPARATION OF SAMPLES

Traces of soil and particles of soot can be removed from plant leaves by washing with water containing a wetting agent[6]. Owing to the loss by solution of some of the more soluble inorganic constituents, such as potassium, washing must be done in a systematic manner and for a set period of time. Roots should be quickly washed free of soil.

The clean material is dried as rapidly as possible after collection in order to reduce chemical and biological changes to a minimum.

Green material should be spread out on shallow trays and killed quickly at 100°C, drying being then completed at 60–70°C in a forced draught oven.

The dried material is ground in a suitable mill and the resulting powder thoroughly mixed. A sub-sample of the ground material is stored in a labelled glass specimen tube for future analysis.

Grinding of Plant Samples

For most purposes it is sufficient to grind the material until it passes through a mesh with round holes 0·4 mm in diameter.

The Christy and Norris junior mill (C & N mill) is recommended for grinding oven-dried samples of plant material. In this mill, grinding is accomplished by a four-armed beater-cross which revolves freely and at high speed in a plain circular grinding chamber. At this high speed plant material, which is fed through the feed inlet, is shattered until it is sufficiently fine to pass through a small iron screen plate with holes 0·4 mm in diameter. When in operation, air is drawn through the mill. It is necessary to collect the sample in a large cellulose extraction thimble or a silk collecting sleeve, so as not to interrupt the air flow. The grinding chamber and beater are easily cleaned between samples with a 1 in. paint brush.

Ashing Plant Materials

In order to determine the inorganic constituents of plant tissues it is necessary, first of all, to remove all traces of organic matter. Carbon is conveniently destroyed by a process of wet digestion using a mixture of sulphuric, nitric and perchloric acids[2]. As a precaution samples of plant material should always be predigested in nitric acid prior to the addition of perchloric acid; this will preclude the danger of explosion and fire. Addition of a ternary mixture of 100 parts by volume of nitric acid, 10 parts by volume of sulphuric and 40 parts by volume of perchloric acid has advantages; the digestion mix can quickly be brought to a temperature of 180–200°C, with a resulting increase in efficiency of oxidation. The presence of sulphuric acid in the mixture overcomes the risk of explosion when the perchloric acid has dissociated into nascent chlorine and oxygen. The fumes given off must be efficiently removed through a water pump or by means of an efficient extractor fan.

Briefly, the procedure is as follows:

Up to 2 g of dried plant material is transferred to a 50 ml Kjeldahl flask or a small conical flask (the quantity used will depend upon the determinations to be carried out on the digest). To this is added 5 ml concentrated nitric acid, which is heated gently at first, then the temperature raised to 180–200°C to boil the acid and get rid of the fumes of oxides of nitrogen. This predigestion should take about 45 min. The flask is cooled a little, and 5 ml of ternary acid mixture added then heated to 180–200°C. Heating is continued until the acids are largely volatilized, and the residue is clear, white and just moist with sulphuric acid.

The residue is taken up in 1:3 hydrochloric acid (*ca* 2·5N acid) to bring into solution the mineral nutrients released on digestion. The solution is filtered to remove dehydrated silica and made up to a known volume with 1:3 HCl.

Aliquots of this solution can now be taken for analysis.

METHODS USED FOR DETERMINING THE MINERAL ELEMENTS PRESENT

A selection of the methods used, and the elements determined hereby inplant ash extracts (or soils and waters), is given in Table 14.

TABLE 14

Element to be determined	Method	Analytical techniques
Calcium	Removal of interfering phosphates by ion exchange resin[7]	Flame photometer
Potassium		Flame photometer
Sodium		Flame photometer
Calcium and Magnesium	Versenate determination[8]	Volumetric analysis
Phosphorus	Molybdate blue or vanadomolybdophosphoric yellow colour method[2]	Spectrophotometer or colorimeter
Nitrogen	Kjeldahl method followed by steam distillation[2, 9]	Volumetric analysis
Ammonia	Kjeldahl method followed by distillation in Conway units[11]	Volumetric analysis
Iron	o-Phenanthroline method[2, 9]	Colorimeter
Aluminium	Aluminon method[2, 9]	Spectrophotometer
Sulphate	Barium sulphate precipitation[2, 9]	Gravimetric analysis
Bicarbonate	Alkalinity determination[9]	Volumetric analysis
Nitrate	Kjeldahl method followed by distillation with Devarda's alloy[1]	Volumetric analysis

To illustrate the use of some important pieces of equipment some analyses will now be dealt with in more detail.

The Determination of Calcium in Plant Tissue

An important dry test used in qualitative chemical analysis is the introduction of a metallic salt into a non-luminous flame resulting in the production of a colour characteristic of the particular metal.

A commercially manufactured instrument known as a flame photometer utilizes this phenomenon to measure the relative concentrations of some alkali metals (calcium, sodium, potassium) in solutions. The use of such an instrument speeds up analysis without sacrificing the accuracy of standard chemical methods.

In general, the solution is atomized (sucked into a jet of air as fine droplets) and introduced into a non-luminous gas flame burning under carefully controlled conditions. The flame is then coloured by the metals present, and the intensity of the light emitted is measured by means of a photocell. The various regions of the light spectrum which are appropriate to the different elements are isolated by passing the light through an optical filter. The intensity of the light emitted with the sample (as recorded on the galvanometer) is compared with that emitted with a standard solution of the element being measured. Full details of the flame photometer are provided with the instrument.

Owing to severe interference from even small amounts of phosphate, the flame photometer cannot be used to determine directly the calcium in plant-ash extracts[7]. Firstly, it is necessary to remove the phosphates present in solution by means of a cation-exchange resin column (see Chapter 15). Suitable columns can be made from 7 mm diameter glass tubing previously tapered at one end having a length of about 35 cm. A number of these tubes can be mounted in a wooden rack held by means of Terry clips. The cation-exchange resin (Amberlite IR –120(H)) which is packed tightly into the glass tubing to a depth of about 5 cm, is held in place by two cotton wool plugs. The tubes should be capable of holding 10 ml of water above the resin and this should run through in not less than 20 min.

To prepare the columns for use, they should be washed with 5N nitric acid and several times with de-ionized water. A standard solution of calcium is prepared by weighing accurately 2·4971 g of calcium carbonate (previously dried at about 200°C) and dissolving it in 50 ml of N hydrochloric acid and making up to 1 litre. This solution contains 1 mg calcium per ml (1,000 p.p.m.). A number of solutions containing from 0 to 75 p.p.m. of calcium are prepared by diluting the standard solution prepared above. 10 ml of each solution is passed through the resin columns. After complete drainage, the columns are washed twice with 5 ml portions of water, all washings being rejected. The calcium which is held on the ion-exchange resin is removed with 5 N nitric acid until 10 ml of eluate

397

have been collected in a calibrated flask. Using the appropriate calcium filter in the flame photometer, the instrument is set at zero with the blank (containing the reagents but no calcium) and at 100 with that containing 75 p.p.m. of calcium. Duplicate readings for all the solutions are taken and then a calibration graph can be constructed.

Aliquots of the plant-ash extracts which must be less acid than 0·25N are transferred to the ion-exchange columns and treated in the same way as the calcium standard above. At the same time determinations on a blank and a standard containing 75 p.p.m. calcium can be carried out and these solutions used to set the flame photometer. The calcium concentration in the 5N nitric acid eluate can be determined by checking the readings obtained against the calibration curve.

The Determination of Total Nitrogen

Organic matter is oxidized by sulphuric acid in the presence of a suitable catalyst and nitrogen converted quantitatively to ammonia (Kjeldahl method). The ammonia is liberated by distillation in a Markham steam distillation apparatus[10], in the presence of caustic soda, and collected in boric acid. The ammonia is then titrated directly with standard hydrochloric acid using a mixed indicator.

The following method is that recommended by Humphries[9].

Digestion—About 50–100 mg of dry plant material should be weighed out and transferred to a small Kjeldahl flask. A small amount of catalyst (a mixture of 1 g copper sulphate, 8 g potassium sulphate, 1 g selenium dioxide) on the tip of a small spatula is added, and 1 ml of nitrogen-free sulphuric acid. This should be heated gently on a digestion stand until fumes of sulphuric acid are freely evolved (this operation must be carried out in a fume cupboard), then heated more strongly until the digest is apple green in colour. The digestion should be continued for half an hour longer. Blanks on the reagents alone should be run at the same time. During digestion care must be taken to avoid particles of undigested carbon sticking to the sides of the tube.

Distillation—A Markham distillation apparatus[10] is recommended (*Figure 166*). If the apparatus has not been used for some time it should be steamed out thoroughly for about 10 min. With the water boiling vigorously in flask D, clip A should be closed so that steam passes into the steam jacket (E). The digest is introduced into the apparatus through the side tube (C) and the digestion flask washed out twice with about 1 ml of distilled water each time. The ground glass stopper should now be replaced and excess of 40 per cent sodium hydroxide added to the funnel (C). When steam issues freely from the tube B at the bottom of the steam jacket (E) the lower clip (B) should be closed. The stopper in funnel C is lifted and the soda allowed to run into the digest. The ammonia liberated is distilled into 5 ml of 2 per cent boric acid contained in a 50 ml conical flask. The tip of the condenser should be immersed in the acid until after the first few drops have distilled, then raised above the surface of the boric acid. The distillation should be continued until 25 ml of distillate have collected. When the distillation is complete, the burner is removed and the liquid in F flushes automatically into E. Water is now poured into C and this washes through into the steam jacket. Clip B is opened and the fluid in E allowed to run to waste. The apparatus is now ready for another distillation.

Two drops of indicator, a mixture of 6 ml methyl red (0·16 per cent in 95 per cent alcohol); 12 ml Bromo-cresol green (0·04 per cent in water); 6 ml 95 per cent alcohol, should be added to the distillate and titrated with N/28 hydrochloric acid to a faint pink colour (pH 4·9). 1 ml N/28 HCl $\equiv$ 0·5 mg nitrogen.

If the blank exceeds 0·05 ml of acid one or more of the reagents contains an excessive amount of nitrogen or the distillation apparatus is contaminated.

REFERENCES

[1]Piper, C. S. (1942). *Soil and Plant Analysis*, 1st ed. Adelaide; University of Adelaide

[2]Jackson, M. L. (1958). *Soil Chemical Analysis*, 1st ed. Englewood Cliffs, N.J.; Prentice-Hall

[3]Cline, M. G. (1944). 'Principles of Soil Sampling.' *Soil Sci.* **58**, 275

[4]Reed, J. and Rigney, J. (1947). 'Soil Sampling from Fields of Uniform and Non-Uniform Appearance and Soil Type.' *J. Amer. agric. Soc.* **39**, 26

[5]Brown, I. C. (1943). 'A Rapid Method of Determining Exchangeable Hydrogen and Total Exchangeable Bases of Soils.' *Soil Sci.* **56**, 353

[6]Mason, A. C. (1952). 'Cleaning of Leaves Prior to Analysis.' *Ann. Rep. E. Malling Res. Stat.* **3**, 104

[7]Hemingway, R. G. (1956). 'The Determination of Calcium in Plant Material by Flame Photometry.' *Analyst*, **81**, 164

[8]Mackereth, F. J. H. (1957). *Water Analysis for Limnologists*. Freshwater Biol. Assn.; Westmorland

[9]Humphries, E. C. (1956). 'Mineral Components and Ash Analysis.' *Modern Methods of Plant Analysis*, Ed. K. Paech and M. V. Tracey, **1**, 468, Berlin; Springer-Verlag

[10]Markham, R. (1942). 'A Steam Distillation Apparatus Suitable for Micro-Kjeldahl Analysis.' *Biochem. J.* **36**, 790

CHAPTER 18

MEASUREMENTS OF ENZYME ACTIVITY IN PLANTS AND MICRO-ORGANISMS

The numerous biochemical reactions which make up the metabolism of a living cell are catalysed by an almost equally large number of organic catalysts known as *enzymes*. The present chapter presents a brief outline of some of the more important methods used to measure the activity of individual enzymes of bacteria, algae, fungi and flowering plants (the enzymology of other plants such as mosses and ferns has been almost completely neglected).

The details of any procedure will clearly depend on the particular enzyme and organism being studied. A single chapter such as this can merely aim to present observations of general importance; the reference works of Dixon and Webb[1] and Colowick and Kaplan[2] are recommended as guides to the detailed literature of particular enzymes.

MEASUREMENT OF ENZYME ACTIVITY IN INTACT CELLS

The activity of most enzymes cannot be measured directly in intact cells and the preparation of *cell-free extracts* is usually necessary. However, by careful selection of enzyme and organism, measurements in intact cells can be made; these are often quick and convenient, and can yield much useful information. Successful measurements of individual enzymes can only be made, however, if a number of requirements are met. Amongst the more important are the following:

(a) The substrate (i.e. the substance on which the enzyme acts) must be able to reach the enzyme quickly and easily; that is, the cell membrane must not present a permeability barrier to the substrate.

(b) If the substrate is metabolized by more than one enzyme, the activity of all others must be prevented so that only the relevant one can be measured (this is not critical if the reaction product is being measured).

(c) Confirmation that the substrate is being metabolized by the particular enzyme being investigated, necessitates measurements of product accumulation or altered co-factors in addition to substrate disappearance.

400

(d) Because of (c) above, the product (or, alternatively the changed co-factor) must not be further metabolized, and must accumulate to a level at which it can be detected.

(e) The actual measurement of activity frequently involves chemical analysis of the product (or co-factor or substrate), consequently the reagents used for analysis must be able to reach the product. That is, they must either enter the cell easily, or the product must accumulate outside the cell.

The ways in which the above requirements are met vary considerably and it is not possible to give a comprehensive account in the short space available. Instead, a few examples will be presented to illustrate some of the enzymes which can be measured conveniently in intact cells.

1. MEASUREMENT OF DEHYDROGENASE ACTIVITY WITH ARTIFICIAL HYDROGEN ACCEPTORS

Dehydrogenases catalyse the removal of hydrogen from a substrate and its transfer to a suitable hydrogen acceptor. In living cells most dehydrogenase reactions utilize one or other of the two pyridine nucleotides, nicotinamide adenine dinucleotide (NAD) and nicotinamide adenine dinucleotide phosphate (NADP) as the hydrogen acceptor. Although these natural co-enzymes can be used when dehydrogenases are measured in cell-free extracts they cannot be used with intact cells and instead, artificial acceptors are utilized.

A particularly useful artificial hydrogen acceptor is *tetrazolium chloride*. This is the salt of a weak base and the tetrazolium part of the molecule is reduced to an insoluble red *formazan*. Thus, dehydrogenase activity can be measured by following the appearance of a pink colour when suitable living cells are incubated in the presence of tetrazolium chloride and a suitable oxidizable substrate. Reduction of the tetrazolium chloride is not a measure of any single dehydrogenase but rather of all the dehydrogenases which participate in the complete oxidation of the substrate.

There are many other artificial hydrogen acceptors and particularly common ones belong to the group known as *redox dyes* (e.g. *methylene blue* and *benzylviologen*). These compounds readily undergo oxidation–reduction changes which are accompanied by a change in colour. Unlike tetrazolium chloride, the reduced dyes can also function as artificial hydrogen *donors* for the reverse of the dehydrogenase reaction. Such redox dyes have one serious disadvantage namely, that they are readily reoxidized in air. That is, the experiments must be performed under anaerobic conditions. Tetrazolium chloride does not suffer from this disadvantage since the formazan is stable in air.

Suitable Experimental Details

A convenient reaction mixture for measuring dehydrogenase activity in yeast cells includes: 2·0 ml of a 20 per cent yeast suspension in 0·01 M phosphate pH 7·0 and 1·0 ml of 0·5 per cent tetrazolium chloride. When this mixture is incubated at 35°C a deep pink colour is produced in about 5–10 minutes. Glucose can be added if necessary but at high temperatures the tetrazolium chloride can become reduced chemically in the presence of glucose. The experiment can be made quantitative by recording the time taken for a standard colour to be reached. Using this as a basis, the effects of temperature, pH, presence or absence of glucose, etc. can be investigated. When preparing the standard, the reaction can be stopped (when a suitable colour has developed) by adding a drop of saturated mercuric chloride to kill the cells.

Tetrazolium chloride can also be used to investigate (qualitatively) the activity of dehydrogenases in higher plant tissues. For example, when a germinating broad bean seed (showing radicle and plumule) is cut in half longitudinally and put in a dish with 0·5 per cent tetrazolium chloride, the location of the red colour indicates the position of greatest dehydrogenase activity.

2. THE ACTIVITY OF ENZYMES WHICH HAVE ACCOMPANYING GAS EXCHANGES

When the reaction under investigation is accompanied by either an uptake or an output of gas, measurements with intact cells are frequently convenient. Although measurement of gas changes overcomes many of the difficulties associated with enzyme measurements in intact cells, certain requirements still have to be met. Thus, although further metabolism of the product by non gas-exchanging reactions does not interfere with the measurements, one has to distinguish between the particular enzyme and the many other reactions (notably those of respiration) which also have accompanying gas exchanges.

Convenient enzymes for measurement by this method are *decarboxylases*. These catalyse the removal of carbon dioxide from a substrate and can therefore be assayed by following the evolution of carbon dioxide. Substrates such as glutamate, pyruvate and oxaloacetate can be decarboxylated under appropriate conditions. Measurement of activity of these enzymes in intact cells is, however, largely confined to bacterial suspensions.

Details of one decarboxylase are presented below.

Glutamic Decarboxylase

This enzyme catalyses the decarboxylation of glutamic acid to γ-aminobutyric acid and carbon dioxide. The activity of the enzyme can be measured by following the evolution of carbon dioxide when glutamic acid is added to the cells. Metabolism of glutamate by other reactions can be prevented by performing the experiment under acid conditions when the glutamate is metabolized completely by the decarboxylase reaction. Acid conditions are also generally used for the measurement of other decarboxylases.

Suitable experimental details using Escherichia coli—When 1·0 ml of a suitable suspension of *E. coli* is shaken in a Warburg flask (see p. 333) with 1·0 ml of M/20 phthalate buffer pH 4·6 and glutamic acid (e.g. 10 μmoles) the evolution of carbon dioxide due to glutamic decarboxylase activity can be measured directly. The uptake of oxygen is very small and can be ignored.

3. MEASUREMENT OF SURFACE ENZYMES

One of the obvious ways in which the problems of intact cells can be overcome is by selecting an enzyme located at the surface of the cell. However, it remains necessary to select a system in which the product is either metabolized slowly (relative to the rate of its formation) or not at all.

Two examples of surface enzymes and their measurements are as follows.

(a) *Invertase of Yeast*

Invertase catalyses the hydrolysis of sucrose to glucose and fructose. It is very active on the surfaces of yeast cells.

Sucrose is a non-reducing sugar whereas the products are reducing. The activity of the enzyme can therefore be measured by following the appearance of reducing sugars (e.g. by using the Fehling's test, p. 185). When 0·5 ml of 25 per cent yeast suspension is incubated with 4 ml of 1 per cent sucrose solution for 10 minutes at room temperature, the Fehling's test can be applied to the supernatant after separation of the cells by centrifugation.

(b) *Alkaline Phosphatase in Escherichia coli*

Phosphatases hydrolyse a wide range of organic phosphates to inorganic phosphate and the appropriate organic group. When the pH optimum of the enzyme is high (pH 7·5–8·0) it is termed alkaline phosphatase. It is a surface enzyme in *Escherichia coli* but both its formation and its activity are inhibited by orthophosphate. Thus it can only be measured in cells grown in a low-phosphate medium and from which the phosphate has disappeared before the experiment is performed. Its measurement is described here, not only because it is a surface enzyme but because a very convenient assay technique has been perfected.

Although the "normal" substrates in living cells are organic phosphates such as glucose phosphate and glyceraldehyde phosphate; alkaline phosphatase can be measured much more conveniently by using p-nitrophenylphosphate as substrate. Not only is the product p-nitrophenol non-metabolizable (and as such does not disappear) but it is also coloured. Since the substrate is colourless the production of a yellow colour is a measure of enzyme activity. If a colorimeter is not available the experiment can be made quantitative by measuring the time taken to reach a standard colour. A suitable reaction mixture contains 5·0 ml of 0·5 ml tris buffer pH 7·9, 1·0 ml of a *dilute* cell suspension and 2·0 ml of water. 1·0 ml of 0·05 M p-nitrophenylphosphate is added to begin the reaction and after 5–10 minutes incubation at 37°C the appearance of a deep yellow colour indicates alkaline phosphatase activity.

MEASUREMENT OF ENZYME ACTIVITY BY INCREASING THE PERMEABILITY OF CELLS

When the cells are almost impermeable (to the substrate, co-factors, or the reagents used in the assay) one usually has to prepare cell free extracts. However, there are a few enzymes which can be measured when the permeability barrier of the cells is destroyed.

At present, such methods have been established for only two groups of organisms, *bacteria* and *algae*.

(a) *Bacteria*

Pre-incubation of bacterial cells with a solvent such as *toluene* or *butanol* increases the permeability of the cells and allows activity of many enzymes to be measured. This not only avoids the necessity of preparing cell free extracts but also requires fewer cells for a convenient assay.

The details of one suitable experiment are as follows:

β-galactosidase in Escherichia coli—The enzyme catalyses the hydrolysis of *β*-galactosides (e.g. lactose) and is only formed when the organism is grown in medium supplied with a suitable *inducer*, such as lactose.

As for alkaline phosphatase (above) a convenient assay of the enzyme depends on a careful selection of a suitable substrate. Thus, with *O*-nitrophenyl–*β*-galactoside as substrate the *O*-nitrophenol produced by enzyme activity is non-metabolizable and is also coloured. Hence, the appearance of a yellow colour is a measure of enzyme activity. Unlike alkaline phosphatase, however, the cells have to be pre-treated with toluene (2–3 ml of cell suspension shaken with 2 drops of redistilled toluene for 15 minutes at 37°C) to make them permeable. A suitable reaction mixture contains 5·0 ml of 0·02 M sodium phosphate buffer pH 7·6, 1·0 ml of a *dilute* cell suspension (pre-treated with toluene) 1·0 ml of 0·05 M *O*-nitrophenyl–β-galactoside and 1·0 ml of water. Incubation temperature is 37°C.

(b) *Algae*

Until recently, experiments in which cell permeability was increased were confined to bacteria. However, it has been found that freezing and re-thawing of cells of the green alga *Chlorella* allows an enzyme to be measured. The freezing and thawing are gentle (merely placing in a deep-freeze at −15°C for 1–24 hours and then thawed for use) and is not comparable to the violent freezing and thawing used to break cells (see p. 409).

Although increasing the permeability of algae cells by freezing may be useful for the measurement of several enzymes, so far only one has been investigated. The details are presented below.

Measurement of isocitrate lyase activity in Chlorella[3]—Isocitrate lyase is a critical enzyme of the glyoxylate cycle[4] and catalyses the breakdown of isocitrate to glyoxylate and succinate. Operation of the glyoxylate cycle allows an organism to grow with acetate as a sole carbon source. Isocitrate lyase can be detected in acetate-grown cells of *Chlorella* but not in cells grown with carbon dioxide or glucose as a carbon source.

A suitable reaction mixture for measurement of the enzyme contains, in a total volume of 3·2 ml; 200 μmoles of phosphate buffer pH 7·5, 15 μmoles $MgSO_4$, 6 μmoles reduced glutathione, 24 μmoles isocitrate and 1·0 ml of thawed cell suspension. The mixture is incubated for 30–60 minutes and glyoxylate then measured colorimetrically.

Measurement of glyoxylate depends on its conversion to the phenylhydrazone. This is achieved by pipetting 0·5 ml of the above reaction mixture into 0·2 ml of 15 per cent $^w/_v$ trichloroacetic acid and then adding 0·4 ml of 0·1 per cent $^w/_v$ dinitrophenyl-hydrazine in 2 N hydrochloric acid. When 1·6 ml of 2·5 N sodium hydroxide is added 15 minutes later an orange colour indicates the amount of glyoxylate formed and is therefore a measure of isocitrate lyase activity.

MEASUREMENT OF ENZYME ACTIVITIES IN CELL-FREE EXTRACTS

As previously mentioned, only a few enzymes can be measured in intact cells. Generally the cells have to be broken and a cell-free extract prepared. Studies with cell-free extracts are also desirable even for the enzymes measured indirectly in intact cells, since critical measurements of many enzyme properties can only be made with such extracts.

METHODS OF PREPARING CELL-FREE EXTRACTS

The review of Hugo[5] is recommended for methods applicable to micro-organisms. The choice of method for any particular organism is largely empirical and it cannot be assumed that a method which is suitable for one will be so for another. This section merely describes some of the methods most commonly used and the organisms for which they are most suitable.

For most systems there are two general comments. Firstly, *conditions are to be kept as cold as possible*. Most enzymes become unstable immediately the extracts are made and, unless the extraction is made at low temperatures (0–4°C), activity of the enzyme may diminish rapidly. Secondly, the extraction is made in the buffer in which activity can be measured. Thus, the first general step is to harvest the organism, wash it with ice-cold buffer of suitable pH and molarity and resuspend in the buffer before breakage of the cells. A large amount of material is usually needed for cell-free extract preparation. Hence micro-organisms are generally concentrated during harvesting and are suspended in a volume of buffer much smaller than the original volume of culture.

(a) *Grinding with Pestle and Mortar*

This simple method is useful for making extracts of multicellular organisms such as those of higher plants and filamentous fungi. The mass of plant material is ground in an ice-cold mortar with a suitable volume of ice-cold buffer and usually with an abrasive (e.g. sand).

Grinding is also useful (although now generally superseded by other methods) for micro-organisms, and many of the classical studies on extracts from bacteria and yeast used such a method. Sand is rarely used, however, and is usually replaced by either alumina or glass powder. The former is more suitable because the preparation of powdered glass of uniform size is difficult. Micro-organisms are best ground as a paste rather than as a more dilute suspension.

(b) *Blenders and Homogenizers*

Although method (a) is convenient and simple, its efficiency is relatively low. More efficient grinding can be achieved by using a variety of mechanical blenders or homogenizers. The Waring blender is a particularly useful instrument and is of widespread use in the preparation of extracts from higher plants. Essentially it consists of a container (either glass or stainless steel) with a set of rotating blades fixed to a spindle through the base. The electric motor is housed in the base and efficient mixing and pulping of the tissue is achieved after only 2–3 minutes of high-speed rotation of the blades.

In another type of homogenizer overhead rotating blades are lowered into the container and the electric motor is housed above the blending assembly and not in the base.

Although the above blenders and homogenizers are particularly useful for higher plants, they also function efficiently for filamentous fungi. However, some of these latter organisms can be broken more efficiently in a Virtis high-speed homogenizer.

Mechanical grinding by homogenizers also increases the efficiency of breakage of micro-organisms. As with hand grinding, the abrasive (alumina or glass powder) must be included.

Further elaborations of the basic homogenizer principle may extend the range of organisms efficiently extracted with these pieces of equipment. In the Silverson, for example, the materials are drawn by suction into the working head and there mixed by rapid rotation of the blades. In addition to this, the material is expelled from the working head and during this expulsion it is subjected to considerable shearing forces.

For multicellular organisms such as higher plants and filamentous fungi, preliminary hand-grinding is sometimes advantageous. If liquid nitrogen is used an unglazed porcelain (*not glass*) pestle and mortar is recommended. This achieves large-scale breakage of the tissue and allows a more homogeneous blending and centrifugation at later stages.

(c) *Vibratory Methods*

Extraction by these methods is achieved by shaking of the tissue with a suitable breaking agent such as ballotini beads (i.e. minute glass beads). The most common instrument is that designed by Mickle[6]. It consists of a pair of horizontally mounted spring steel bars which are caused to vibrate in an alternating electric field. One end of each bar is fixed while the other, which projects from the apparatus, carries a cylindrical glass vessel containing the cell suspension and glass beads. The apparatus must be cooled since the time required for efficient disruption can be lengthy. Thus *Escherichia coli* suffered 80 per cent disintegration after 25 minutes, and *Staphylococcus aureus* after 45–50 minutes.

This method is also useful for removal of flagella from the bacterium *Salmonella*. In addition, it has been used to prepare extracts of micro-algae but its efficiency is relatively low.

(d) *Ultrasonic Disintegrators*

Like the previous method, ultrasonic disintegration is most efficient for micro-organisms. These are broken when a suspension is subjected to ultrasonic energy which is thought to produce an implosion of the minute gas bubbles in the liquid (cavitation). This produces localized pressure changes of a high magnitude and breaks the cells. Such a method is widely used for suspensions of bacteria but has not been found too efficient for other micro-organisms, although it is used for some algae. Some bacteria (e.g. *Escherichia coli*) frequently require less than a minute of ultrasonic energy, others however (e.g. *Mycobacteria*) require more than seven minutes. The efficiency can frequently be increased by using a smaller volume of suspension. Increasing the density of cell suspension above a certain value decreases the efficiency.

(e) *French Pressure Cell*[7]

Breakage of cells by this method is achieved by forcing a suspension of micro-organisms (it is not efficient with larger multicellular organisms) under high pressure through a very small orifice, the size of which is regulated with a needle-valve.

The apparatus consists of a heavy stainless steel cylinder with a hollow core. The suspension of micro-organisms is poured into this core (with the orifice closed) and a tightly fitting piston, fitted with a rubber or leather washer, forced down by means of a hydraulic press. Because the temperature rises as the cells are forced through the slightly open orifice, the initial suspension must be cold. The entire operation is best performed at low temperatures and the broken suspension collected in a tube immersed in ice.

The method is very efficient for micro-algae (a 70–80 per cent breakage of *Chlorella* cells is common after a single passage through the press), and also breaks (although less efficiently) yeast and various bacteria. It is most convenient for use with volumes from 15–30 ml but is not efficient for volumes above 100–150 ml. A continuous French press is now being manufactured which will function with 5–10 litres of suspension.

(f) *Hughes Press*

This method was first described by Hughes[8] and, although it is primarily used for bacteria, it also breaks cells of other micro-organisms, although possibly less efficiently. Its greatest advantage is that over the short time usually taken (1–5 seconds) the suspension remains frozen. The frozen suspension (mixed with suitable abrasives) is contained in a steel cylinder. The increased pressure from a hydraulic ram and the shearing action of the abrasives disrupt the cells and the crushed material is forced out of the cylinder into a reservoir.

(g) *Alternating Freeze–Thaw Technique*

It was pointed out previously that freezing and thawing of the green alga *Chlorella* apparently increased the permeability of the cells and allowed (at least) one enzyme to be measured. Alternating rapid freezing and thawing is also a means of breaking cells and apart from animal tissues, has been most widely used for bacteria. The usual technique is to freeze the suspension in dry ice or liquid nitrogen, then thaw it and to repeat this process several times. After centrifugation the supernatant then contains many active enzymes.

(h) *Chemical and Enzymatic Destruction of Cell Walls*

A number of methods are known whereby the surface layers of cells can be destroyed and enzymes can then be identified in the supernatant after centrifugation. Apart from a single report[9] of the use of cellulase in higher plants, all other methods have been used for micro-organisms, chiefly bacteria.

Autolysis has been used for yeast and bacterial cells and depends on enzymes, contained within the cells themselves, destroying cellular organization. Autolysis frequently continues for several days and preservatives such as toluene, ether, thymol or chloroform are used to prevent infection by foreign organisms.

The addition of *specific enzymes* has also been used to destroy cell walls. The most common is *lysozyme* (extracted from egg white) which destroys the walls of bacteria. The remaining protoplasts bounded by the cell membrane can then be lysed (burst) when placed in a hypotonic solution. The use of lysozyme is specific for bacteria since it depends on characteristic chemical properties of their cell walls.

Bacteriophages are viruses which infect bacteria and cause lysis of the bacterial cell; several enzymes have been measured in extracts prepared in this way.

Acetone powders are prepared by treating cells (bacteria have been used most widely, although yeasts have also been examined) with acetone (other dehydrating agents are less commonly used) and then drying rapidly under a vacuum. Extraction of the powder with water or a suitable buffer yields a preparation containing several enzymes.

SUMMARY OF USEFUL METHODS OF PREPARING CELL-FREE EXTRACTS OF VARIOUS ORGANISMS

(1) *Higher Plants:* hand-grinding with a suitable abrasive, and blending by various mechanical means.

(2) *Algae:* The French press appears to be most efficient method, although Mickle shaking with glass beads and ultrasonic disintegration are also useful.

(3) *Filamentous Fungi:* Homogenizers, of various kinds, appear to be most efficient, although many of the methods for unicellular organisms are probably efficient after preliminary grinding of the material[10].

(4) *Yeasts:* Mickle shaking with ballotini beads, French and Hughes' presses, autolysis and possibly blending with suitable abrasive.

(5) *Bacteria:* Ultrasonic disintegration, French press, Hughes press, Mickle shaking with glass beads, alternate freezing/thawing, possibly blending with suitable abrasive, enzymatic and vival lysis, preparation and extraction of acetone powders.

REMOVAL OF CELL DEBRIS AND ISOLATION OF THE RELEVANT FRACTION

The resultant preparation from the above extracting procedures is heterogenous and contains intact cells, broken portions of cell wall and membrane, organelles such as nuclei, mitochondria, ribosomes and chloroplasts (together with broken portions of the larger organelles) and the soluble protein. Before the enzyme activity can be measured the fraction in which it is located must be separated, usually by centrifugation, from residual material.

For most purposes an initial centrifugation (all procedures described below are to be performed at 0°–4°C and refrigerated centrifuges must therefore be used) at about 20,000–30,000 g effects a preliminary separation into the soluble enzymes (the "soluble" fraction also contains ribosomes) and those associated with the "particulate" fraction. Apart from the specialized enzyme systems associated with some organelles (see next section) the majority of enzymes are found in the "soluble" fraction.

Although this soluble fraction contains many different enzymes, the conditions of extraction and assay (e.g.pH and molarity of buffer, substrate, co-factors, etc.) make possible a specific measurement of an individual enzyme. However, the same reasons which argue for the use of cell-free extracts rather than intact cells when attempting critical measurement of some enzyme properties, also argue for *purification* of the particular enzyme from the crude extract. That is, critical measurements (particularly of the kinetics of activity) depend on separation of the appropriate enzyme from many of the others in the crude extract.

As each purification procedure is usually specific for a single enzyme, little of a general nature can be described here. The volumes of Colowick and Kaplan[2] are recommended for many of these details.

Preparation of Fractions Containing Subcellular Organelles

The separation into a"soluble"and a"particulate"fraction is only approximate and further separation of the various subcellular components can only be achieved by more differential centrifugation.

Localization of enzyme activities in cells of bacteria is largely unknown. Thus, the following remarks apply to other organisms, in particular to higher plants. Further details of isolation of subcellular organelles from higher plant cells can be found in the recent review of Hallaway[11].

The various components are separated chiefly by differential centrifugation; particles sedimented by brief centrifugation at 50–200 g are called "debris", those at 500–1,200 g (15–20 minutes) nuclei and plastids, those at 12,000–30,000 g (30 minutes) are "mitochondria" and those at 100,000–120,000 g (90 minutes) the ribosomes.

Preparation of organelle-fractions containing active enzymes often requires modification of the above extraction techniques. Thus extraction of intact nuclei is best achieved by using gentle grinding conditions followed by centrifugation in sucrose solutions of different densities containing calcium chloride. Also, isolated chloroplasts can fix radioactive carbon dioxide only when extracted in buffered saline (0·35 M sodium chloride) or buffered sucrose. Similarly the preparation of active intact mitochondria can only be made in buffered sucrose (a final sucrose concentration of 0·2–0·4 M) and when the pH is maintained between restricted limits (pH 7·2–7·5).

Isolation of a fraction homogeneous for one organelle is difficult in many micro-algae because each algal cell frequently has a single large chloroplast. During extraction it is broken into pieces of different sizes, and these contaminate many of the subcellular fractions.

SOME GENERAL REMARKS ON THE MEASUREMENT OF ENZYME ACTIVITY IN CELL-FREE EXTRACTS

Methods of measuring each individual enzyme are specific and must therefore be obtained from the relevant literature. Although the details may vary, the basic rationale of many of the procedures is the same and some points of general importance are summarized here.

(a) *Composition of Reaction Mixture*

The actual compounds used in the reaction mixture will vary considerably but essentially all mixtures have the following type of composition:

(i) Substrate usually in a final concentration of 0·01–0·1 M (possible limits are much wider).

(ii) Extract in sufficient amount (the volume will depend on the protein content of the extract) to give a measurable activity during the incubation period.

(iii) Co-enzymes and co-factors. These are a variety of compounds necessary for efficient functioning of the enzyme, and all must be added when a purified extract is being used. Although many of them need not be added to a crude extract, it is usually advisable to use the most complete reaction mixture when first attempting to assay an enzyme. The concentrations of most of the co-factors are usually low $(10^{-4}–10^{-5}$ M) but when the compound actually participates in the overall reaction (e.g. the co-enzymes NAD and NADP in dehydrogenase–reductase reactions) substrate concentrations of $10^{-1}–10^{-2}$ M are desirable.

(iv) A suitable volume of reaction mixture is then made up with the buffer in which the extract was made. The buffer concentration varies considerably, although 0·05–0·1 M is common. After the mixture is made up it should always be confirmed that none of its components have altered the pH.

(b) *Incubation Temperature and Time*

The best indication of a suitable temperature is that afforded by the optimum temperature for growth of the organism. However, direct tests can easily be made to find a suitable temperature for the particular enzyme. In general, measurements with algae and higher plant extracts are made at 20–30°C, and those with fungal and bacterial extracts at 30–37°C.

In general, as short a reaction time as possible is desirable (although, of course, a measurable amount of reaction must have taken place). Long periods merely encourage side-reactions and even contamination by bacteria. A time-course (enzyme activity plotted against time) is usually needed to confirm that up to the time at which measurements are made, the reaction proceeds at a linear rate.

(c) Methods of Enzyme Assay

The actual technique used to measure the activity of an enzyme will be highly specific. For all, however, it is desirable to measure something other than (or in addition to) substrate disappearance. Of the many methods available only three general points will be made:

(i) *Colorimetric methods of analysis*—Methods of assay in which reagents react with either the substrate or product to produce a coloured compound (or, of course, in which either the substrate or product itself is coloured) are very convenient, although a colorimeter (see pp. 48–52) is needed for quantitative studies. Colorimetric methods have two main advantages. Firstly, the reaction can be measured with small amounts of material and secondly, they are convenient for performing large numbers of assays. A wide range of colorimetric methods for the assay of numerous compounds is presented by Snell and Snell[12].

(ii) *Use of radioactive substrate*—This also allows small amounts of material to be measured. However, its convenience depends on the ease with which radioactivity of the substrate can be distinguished from that in the product. This is frequently difficult to achieve.

(iii) *Use of linked reactions*—When there is no convenient way of measuring (chemically) the products of a reaction, it is sometimes possible to allow a product to act as substrate for a second enzymatic reaction and to use this latter reaction as a measure of the amount of substrate present. A critical requirement of this approach is that the second reaction should be limited solely by the substrate level (that is, by the amount of product produced by the first reaction). This is best achieved by adding an excess amount of the second enzyme and its co-factors. Thus, it is desirable to have the second enzyme as a commercially manufactured preparation.

The measurement of *hexokinase* activity is an example of this approach. Hexokinase catalyses this reaction:

$$\text{Glucose} + \text{ATP} \rightleftharpoons \text{Glucose-6-phosphate} + \text{ADP}$$

The glucose–6–phosphate can be measured by linking it to the following reaction catalysed by glucose–6–phosphate dehydrogenase:

Glucose–6–phosphate $+$ NADP $\rightleftharpoons$ 6–phosphogluconate $+$ NADPH

when the amount of NADP reduced (measured by increase in absorption at 340 mμ) is a measure of the glucose–6–phosphate level.

(d) *Controls*

(*i*) *Requirements for enzyme activity*—Systematic omission of the various components from the complete reaction mixture elucidate the requirements for maximum activity.

(*ii*) *Demonstration of an enzymatic reaction*—This is most conveniently obtained by using an extract which has been boiled for a few minutes. This heating destroys enzyme activity, so that any reaction in the "boiled enzyme control" is chemical.

(*iii*) *Interference with the assay technique*—It must be shown that none of the components of the reaction mixture interfere with the reaction on which the assay is based.

(*iv*) *Comparison of activities in different extracts*—These cannot be made directly since they may differ in amounts of enzyme merely because of different efficiencies of cell breakage. A comparison can be made, however, if the specific activity of the enzyme is calculated; this is the *activity per unit protein* in the extract. When activities are measured after incubation for a given time, comparisons are valid only when the activity is linear up to that time and when it is proportional to the amount of enzyme (extract) present. A convenient method of measuring the protein content of extracts is that of Lowry[13].

CONCLUSION

Two final comments are perhaps necessary; firstly, to repeat that attempts to measure any particular enzyme can be made only after consulting literature concerned with that enzyme, secondly, whereas measurements of many enzyme activities are conveniently measured when the technique becomes familiar, early failures are usual. Continued practice and slight modifications generally overcome these initial difficulties.

COMMON BUFFERS FOR USE IN ENZYME MEASUREMENTS
(adapted from Ref. 14)

1. *Mixed Phosphate Buffer*

Phosphate buffers of different pH can be prepared by mixing different proportions of KH_2PO_4 (acidic) and K_2HPO_4 (basic) together. The sodium salts can be used as alternatives.

The table below shows the preparation of 0·1 M phosphate buffers of pH 5·8–8·0 (outside this range the buffering capacity decreases markedly).

pH	ml 0·2 M K$_2$HPO$_4$	ml 0·2 M KH$_2$PO$_4$	
5·8	8·0	92·0	Dilute to 200 ml with H$_2$O
6·0	12·3	87·7	,, ,, ,, ,, ,, ,,
6·2	18·5	81·5	,, ,, ,, ,, ,, ,,
6·4	26·5	73·5	,, ,, ,, ,, ,, ,,
6·6	37·5	62·5	,, ,, ,, ,, ,, ,,
6·8	49·0	51·0	,, ,, ,, ,, ,, ,,
7·0	61·0	39·0	,, ,, ,, ,, ,, ,,
7·2	72·0	28·0	,, ,, ,, ,, ,, ,,
7·4	81·0	19·0	,, ,, ,, ,, ,, ,,
7·6	87·0	13·0	,, ,, ,, ,, ,, ,,
7·8	91·5	8·5	,, ,, ,, ,, ,, ,,
8·0	94·7	5·3	,, ,, ,, ,, ,, ,,

2. "Tris" Buffer

This buffer is prepared by mixing different proportions of hydrochloric acid and "tris" (2-amino-2-(hydroxy-methyl)-propane-1:3-diol). The pH range over which it functions (pH 7·2–9·1) is higher than the phosphate buffer.

Preparation of 0·05 M "tris" buffer:

pH		ml 0·2 M "Tris"	ml 0·1 N HCl	
23°C	37°C			
9·10	8·95	25	5·0	Dilute to 100 ml with H$_2$O
8·74	8·60	25	10·0	,, ,, ,, ,, ,, ,,
8·50	8·37	25	15·0	,, ,, ,, ,, ,, ,,
8·32	8·18	25	20·0	,, ,, ,, ,, ,, ,,
8·14	8·00	25	25·0	,, ,, ,, ,, ,, ,,
7·96	7·82	25	30·0	,, ,, ,, ,, ,, ,,
7·77	7·63	25	35·0	,, ,, ,, ,, ,, ,,
7·54	7·40	25	40·0	,, ,, ,, ,, ,, ,,
7·36	7·22	25	42·5	,, ,, ,, ,, ,, ,,
7·20	7·05	25	45·0	,, ,, ,, ,, ,, ,,

The components of a buffer solution can normally be calculated by using a modification of Henderson's equation (taken from Wallwork[15]).

(A)
$$pH = pK + \log \left(\frac{\text{concn base}}{\text{concn acid}} \right)$$

if this equation is expanded:

(B) antilog $(pK - pH)$ = ratio of the concn of base: acid.

For example: 0·2 M sodium phophate buffer pH 7·5 $(pK=6·8)$ (base $-$ Na$_2$HPO$_4$ mol.wt$=141·97$; 28·394 $g/1,000$ ml water$=0·2$ M soln) (acid $-$ NaH$_2$PO$_4$.2H$_2$O mol.wt$=156·03$; 31·206 $g/1,000$ ml water$=0·2$ M soln).

From A above

$$7·5 = 6·8 + \log \left(\frac{\text{concn base}}{\text{concn acid}} \right)$$

From B above   antilog 0·7 = ratio base:acid
$$= \text{ratio } 5:1.$$

Thus $^5/_6$ of 28·394 g = base = 23·65 g

$^1/_6$ of 31·206 g = acid = 5·205 g

by mixing 23·65 g of Na$_2$HPO$_4$ and 5·205 g of NaH$_2$PO$_4$ 2.H$_2$O and making up to 1,000 ml, a 0·2 M sodium phosphate buffer solution of pH 7·5 is obtained.

ACKNOWLEDGEMENTS

Most of the experiments described in this chapter are part of the undergraduate teaching course in the Botany Department, University College, London. I am particularly grateful to Prof. L. Fowden, Mr. P. J. Syrett and Mr. H. Tristram for having introduced the experiments to me and for agreeing to their publication here. I also wish to thank Mr. Syrett for reading the manuscript and for making a number of suggestions.

REFERENCES

[1]Dixon, M. and Webb, E. C. (1964). *Enzymes*, 2nd ed. London; Longmans
[2]Colowick, S. P. and Kaplan, N. O. (Eds.) (1955–1963). *Methods in Enzymology*, Vols. I–VI, 1st ed. London; Academic Press
[3]Syrett, P. J., Merrett, M. J. and Bocks, S. M. (1963). 'Enzymes of the Glyoxylate Cycle in *Chlorella vulgaris*.' *J. exp. Bot.* **14**, 249–264
[4]Kornberg, M. L. and Elsden, S. R. (1961). 'The Metabolism of C$_2$ Compounds in Micro-organisms.' *Advance Enzymol.* **23**, 401
[5]Hugo, W. B. (1954). 'The Preparation of Cell-free Enzymes from Micro-organisms.' *Bacteriol. Rev.* **18**, 87–105
[6]Mickle, H. (1948). 'A Tissue Disintegrator.' *J. R. micr. Soc.* **68**, 10–12
[7]Milner, H. W., Lawrence, N. S. and French, C. S. (1950). 'Colloidal Dispersion of Chloroplast Material.' *Science*, **111**, 633–634
[8]Hughes, D. E. (1951). 'A Press for Disrupting Bacteria and Other Micro-organisms.' *Brit. J. exp. Path.* **32**, 97–109

[9]Cocking, E. C. (1960). 'A Method for the Isolation of Plant Protoplasts and Vacuoles.' *Nature, London*, **187**, 962–963

[10]Stine, G. S., Strickland, W. N. and Barratt, R. W. (1964). 'Nine Methods for Disrupting Mycelia of Neurospora crassa.' *Canad. J. Microbiol.* **10**, 29–35

[11]Hallaway, M. (1965). 'The Localization of Biochemical Activities in the Cells of Hugher Plants.' *Biol. Rev.* **40**, 188–230

[12]Snell, F. D. and Snell, C. T. (1948–1961). *Colorimetric Methods of Analysis*, Vol. I–IV, 3rd ed. U.S.A.; Van Nostrand

[13]Lowry, O. H., Rosebrough, N. J., Farr, A. L. and Randal, R. J. (1951). 'Protein Measurement with the Folin Phenol Reagent.' *J. Biol. Chem.* **193**, 265–275

[14]Dawson, R. M. C., Elliott, D. C., Elliott, W. H. and Jones, K. M. (Eds.) (1959). *Data for Biochemical Research*, 1st ed. Oxford; Oxford University Press

[15]Wallwork, S. C. (1956). *Physical Chemistry for Students of Pharmacy and Biology*, 1st ed. London; Longmans

SUPPLY UNITS

BACTERIA

National Collection of Dairy Organisms, National Institute for Research in Dairying, Shinfield, Reading, Berks., U.K.

Pathogenic Bacteria (plant)
Ministry of Agriculture Plant Pathology Laboratory, Harpenden, Herts., U.K.

Pathogenic Bacteria (plant and mammalian)
National Collection of Type Cultures, Central Public Health Laboratory, Colindale Avenue, London, N.W.9.
National Type Collection of Industrial Bacteria, Torry Research Station, Aberdeen, Scotland.

FUNGI

Commonwealth Mycology Institute, Ferry Lane, Kew, Richmond, Surrey, U.K.

Pathogenic to Plants and Animals
The Director of Medical Mycology, London School of Hygiene and Tropical Medicine, Keppel Street, Gower Street, London, W.C.1.

Wood Rotting Fungi
Forestry Production and Research Laboratory, Princes Risborough, Aylesbury, Bucks., U.K.

YEASTS

Non Pathogenic
Brewing Industrial Research Foundation, Nutfield, Redhill, Surrey, U.K.

ALGAE

Fresh Water Algae and Protozoa
Type collection of algae and protozoa, The Botanical School, Downing Street, Cambridge, U.K.
Freshwater Biological Association, Ferry House, Far Sawrey, Ambleside, Westmorland, U.K.

Marine Algae
Biological Supply Agency, Rhydfelin, Aberystwyth, Wales.
(Specify fresh or preserved.)

Marine Biological Association, Citadel Hill, Plymouth, Devon, U.K.

Port Erin Biological Station, Isle of Man.

BRYOPHYTA

Mosses and Liverworts

University of London, Botanical Supply Unit, Elm Lodge, Englefield Green, Surrey, U.K.

Chelsea Physic Gardens, Royal Hospital Road, London, S.W.3. (All plants must be collected. No charge. Plants grown to order.)

Freshwater Biological Association. (Preserved or fresh.)

University Gardens

Bedford College, King's College, University College London. London University, Edinburgh University, Glasgow University. Belfast University, Oxford University, Cambridge University.

PTERIDOPHYTA

Biological Supply Unit.

Chelsea Physic Gardens.

Freshwater Biological Supply Association.

Biological Supply Agency.

(Biological Supply Agency, Wales, for *Lycopodium* and *Selaginella*.)

GYMNOSPERMEAE AND ANGIOSPERMEAE

Chelsea Physic Gardens (not Pinus)

Biological Supply Unit.

(Male Gingko (no cones available) from Chelsea Physic Gardens.)

Seeds and bulbs

Biological Supply Unit.

Chelsea Physic Gardens.

Carter—various branches in London.

EXAMINATION QUESTIONS

These questions are quoted by kind permission of The City and Guilds of London Institute in conjunction with The Institute of Science Technology and by The University of London.

G.C.E. (A) General Certificate of Education Advanced Level and Scholarship questions.

C. & G. (C) Science Laboratory Technicians' Certificate questions.

C. & G. (A) Science Laboratory Technicians' Advanced Certificate questions.

CHAPTER 1

1. What provisions should be made in connection with the installation, use and maintenance of a highly sensitive balance to be used for accurate weighing in research work? C. & G. (A).

2. What are the essential parts of ONE type of microscope with which you are familiar? Describe how you would maintain the instrument. C. & G. (C).

3. Name a simple type of vacuum pump and describe its action. C. & G. (C).

4. *a* What is meant by (i) pH *and* (ii) buffer solutions?
   b Describe (i) a colorimetric *and* (ii) an electrometric method for determining the pH of a solution. C. & G. (A).

5. Describe the cleaning of glassware for biological use. C. & G. (C).

6. Prepare a standard (approx. N/10) solution of potassium dichromate and use it to standardize the sodium thiosulphate provided. C. & G. (C).

7. Discuss the precautions necessary in the use of radioactive isotopes in experimental work in botany. Give an account of their use.

CHAPTER 2

1. Explain the terms 'fixing', 'hardening' and 'preserving' as applied to plant material. Discuss the applications of reagents commonly used for these purposes. C. & G. (A).

2. *a* Explain the meaning and purpose of the following processes used in histology:
   <blockquote>
   (i) fixation
   (ii) dehydration
   (iii) regressive staining }
   (iv) mordanting } Chapter 4
   </blockquote>
   b What are artefacts? C. & G. (C).

3. *a* Describe, with the aid of a diagram, the construction and working of a simple "rocker" microtome.

   b Give briefly ONE explanation for each of the following difficulties which may arise when using a rocker microtome for cutting sections in wax:

      (i) curving of the ribbons

      (ii) failure of the sections to adhere together to form a ribbon

      (iii) tissue falls out of the wax section. C. & G. (C).

4. Explain what is meant by EACH of the following terms:

    (a) fixation

    (b) preservation

    (c) vital staining } Chapter 4. C. & G. (A).

    (d) double staining }

CHAPTER 3

1. You are provided with a piece of sunflower stem preserved in 70 per cent alcohol. Using a hand razor, cut 12 transverse sections from the material and preserve in a corked specimen tube in 70 per cent alcohol.

    Make a temporary, stained preparation of ONE of the sections, staining with aniline hydrochloride (or sulphate) and mounting in dilute glycerol. Leave your preparation suitably labelled for inspection by the examiner. C. & G. (C).

2. *a* Describe the construction and operation of a simple 'rocker' microtome.

   b Describe how to hone and strop a microtome knife and how to determine if it is suitable for use. C. & G. (A).

3. Describe the construction, maintenance and uses of EACH of the following:

    (a) A base sledge microtome.

    (b) A freezing microtome. C. & G. (A).

CHAPTER 4

1. Make a Gram stained preparation of a smear of the micro-organisms from culture A. Counter stain with neutral red.

    Examine your preparation microscopically and give a report illustrated with a diagram. C. & G. (A).

2. *a* Give an account of a modern histological or cytological technique used in Botany of which you have practical experience.

   b Discuss some important applications of the technique you describe. C. & G. (A).

3. *a* Make a Feulgen preparation of onion root tip by the smear technique.
   b Make permanent double-stained preparations of transverse and longitudinal sections of specimen C. C. & G. (A).
4. *a* Make a smear preparation of the pollen mother cells of specimen B to show chromosomes.
   b Make a permanent double-stained preparation of a transverse section of specimen C. C. & G. (A).

CHAPTER 5

1. Give a detailed account of how to make:
   (a) A strip film preparation from fossil material.
   (b) A permanent smear preparation of young bean roots to show chromosomes (Chapter 4).
   (c) A permanent whole mount preparation of *Volvox* (Chapter 4) C. & G. (A).
2. Describe how you would macerate a timber sample and prepare it for mounting under a microscope.
3. Give an account of the preparation of fossil plant material for microscope laboratory examination. C. & G. (A).

CHAPTER 6

1. Demonstrate the presence of starch and protein in slices of potato C.
   Leave your demonstrations for inspection and give a brief account of your method. C. & G. (C).
2. Make micro-slide preparations to demonstrate:
   (a) Oil in sections of specimen K.
   (b) Cellulose in transverse sections of specimen L.
   (c) Inulin in transverse sections of specimen M.
   (d) Fibres in transverse sections of specimen N.
   Give a brief account of your method in each case and leave your preparations suitably mounted for inspection. C. & G. (A).

CHAPTER 7

1. *a* Describe TWO distinct methods of sterilizing soil.
   b Describe how to prepare and propagate geranium cuttings. C. & G. (C).
2. Write a short account of *each* of the following:
   (a) The preparation of potting composts.
   (b) The drying and storage of seeds in the laboratory.
   (c) The technique of artificial pollination. C. & G. (A).

3. Describe how:
   (a) To fill an aquarium tank with water so as to prevent disturbing the gravel at the bottom of the tank.
   (b) To hone a razor (Chapter 3).
   (c) To clean microscope slides which are smeared with balsam. C. & G. (C).
4. Describe how you would bring about the germination of (a) fern gametophytes and (b) broad beans, and how you would maintain their growth. C. & G. (A).

CHAPTER 8

1. Describe how to prepare and mount freshly picked flowers as herbarium specimens. C. & G. (C).
2. Describe:
   (a) Methods of drying and mounting herbarium specimens.
   (b) A method of preserving the green colour of a plant specimen which is to be used for making of a wet museum mount. C. & G. (A).
3. Describe methods for the preservation and display of plant specimens. C. & G. (A).

CHAPTER 9

1. List ALL the precautions necessary to ensure a satisfactory sterilization in (a) the autoclave and (b) the hot air oven. C. & G. (C).
2. *a* List the methods available for sterilizing solids and liquids.
   b What methods would you use for sterilizing the following:
   (i) Talcum powder,
   (ii) Glucose solution,
   (iii) Nutrient broth in small screw-capped bottles,
   (iv) Slopes of coagulated serum?
   Give reasons for your selection. C. & G. (C).
3. *a* Describe methods which are available for the sterilization of (i) apparatus *and* (ii) culture media.
   b Describe methods available for the culture of anaerobic micro-organisms (Chapter 10). C. & G. (A).
4. Describe the methods of dispensing liquid and solid media. What are the advantages and disadvantages of using screw-capped bottles and plugged flasks for the storage of media.
5. Give an account of the essential features of a small, sterile room. C. & G. (A).

CHAPTER 10

1. Describe, with the aid of diagrams, ONE method of preserving micro-organisms by freeze drying. Give a list of the methods available for the preservation of stock cultures of micro-organisms. C. & G. (A).

2. Give a concise account of the general methods for the isolation and pure culture of micro-organisms. C. & G. (A).

3. *a* With the aid of diagrams, describe a named counting chamber or haemacytometer.

   b How would you calculate the number of fungal spores/ml present in an aqueous suspension?

4. Describe carefully what is meant by, and how you would prepare *each* of the following:

   (a) plain agar slopes
   (b) plain agar plates
   (c) a buffered liquid medium
   (d) sub-cultures of a named micro-organism
   (e) a pure culture of a named micro-organism.

CHAPTER 11

1. Describe, with details of the apparatus required, how to set up an experiment to show the effect of unilateral light on the growth of a plant stem. C. & G. (C).

2. How would you determine (a) the fresh weight and (b) the dry weight of a seedling? Comment on the changes in the fresh weight and dry weight of a seed during germination. G.C.E. (A).

3. Describe carefully any experiment which you have yourself carried out with a Klinostat.

   Explain what you attempted to find out and how the apparatus was set up. State the results you obtained and the conclusions you made from them. G.C.E. (A).

CHAPTER 12

1. Outline the process of photosynthesis.

   Describe a demonstration of this phenomenon designed to show the presence of ONE of the chemical products. C. & G. (C).

2. Describe how to set up an apparatus suitable for the quantitative estimation of carbon dioxide given off by respiring peas.

   Include in your account details of any necessary reagents for the experiment. C. & G. (C).

3. Describe experiments to demonstrate that starch is a product of photosynthesis. C. & G. (C).

4. Describe in detail, how you would carry out experiments to demonstrate that green germinating seeds can respire (a) aerobically and (b) anaerobically. G.C.E. (A).

5. Describe in detail how you would carry out experiments to demonstrate that (a) light and (b) carbon dioxide are essential for photosynthesis. G.C.E. (A).

CHAPTER 13

1. Give a detailed account of the assembly of the apparatus and reagents necessary to demonstrate EACH of the following:
   (a) Transpiration,
   (b) Root pressure. C. & G. (C).

2. Compare under optimal illumination the rates of transpiration from the upper and lower surfaces of (a) an old leaf and (b) a young leaf of the plant provided. Use the cobalt chloride paper strip method.
   Give a brief account of your method and record and comment on your results. C. & G. (A).

3. Explain clearly what is meant by 'osmosis', 'turgor' and 'plasmolysis'. G.C.E. (A).

4. How does an increase in the rate of air movement over the leaves of a plant lead to an increased rate of water absorption by its roots? G.C.E. (A).

5. Draw and describe a simple potometer. How would you attempt to compare the rate of transpiration of a leafy shoot with the rate of evaporation from a free water surface? G.C.E. (A).

CHAPTER 14

1. With the aid of diagrams, describe the construction and use of:
   (a) A Warburg constant volume manometer.
   (b) A Barcroft differential manometer. C. & G. (A).

2. Describe fully how:
   (a) To prepare a mixture of known volumes of oxygen and carbon dioxide.
   (b) To determine the dry weights of plant material (Chapter 11).
   (c) To measure the total surface area of a leaf (Chapter 11). C. & G. (A).

CHAPTER 15

1. Describe the apparatus and techniques involved in the separation of a mixture of amino acids by paper or column chromatography. C. & G. (A).

CHAPTER 16

1. Describe the method of softening water by ionic exchange. C. & G. (C).
2. Give a description of the apparatus used and the precautions which must be taken when:
   (a) Purifying a flammable liquid by distillation.
   (b) Purifying a liquid by distillation under reduced pressure.
3. Give an account of the use of a fractionating column and, with the aid of diagrams, describe an assembly of apparatus using one.
4. Describe, with the aid of fully labelled diagrams, the construction of and *one* use for:
   either (a) a fractional distillation apparatus
   or (b) a Soxhlet extraction apparatus. C. & G. (A).

CHAPTER 17

1. Describe, giving full experimental details, how to determine quantitatively for a sample of fresh plant tissue such as leaves EACH of the following:
   (a) The percentage dry weight,
   (b) The percentage organic content,
   (c) The percentage mineral ash content. C. & G. (A).
2. Given a sample of lake water, describe in detail how you would determine EACH of the following:
   (a) total suspended solids
   (b) total dissolved solids
   (c) total dissolved organic matter
   (d) pH by an electrometric method. C. & G. (A).

CHAPTER 18

1. What is an enzyme? What problems have to be overcome when attempting to measure the activity of a single enzyme in intact cells? Quote one example of such activity.
2. Describe, fully, two methods of obtaining cell-free extracts of micro-organisms. How would you remove the cell debris and prepare an initial separation of the enzyme fractions?
3. Outline some of the general considerations you would apply when attempting to measure the activity of an enzyme in a cell-free extract. What type of control reactions can be operated?
4. How would you prepare one litre of a 0·01 M sodium phosphate buffer of pH 7·0? Use Henderson's formula and leave your calculations for examination. (Na_2HPO_4 mol.wt = 141·97; $NaH_2PO_4.2H_2O$ mol.wt = 156·03, pK value 6·8).

INDEX

INDEX